Canadian Feathers

Canadian Feathers:

A Loon-atics Guide to Anting, Mimicry and Dump-nesting

Pat E Bumstead

Simply Wild Publications Inc
100 Lake Lucerne Close SE
Calgary, Alberta T2J 3H8

www.simplywildpub.com

First Edition Printed in Canada 2001

Bumstead, Pat, 1952-
Canadian Feathers

ISBN 0-9689278-0-7

1. Birds--Canada--Guidebooks. 1. Title
QL685.B85 2001 598.0971 C2001-911077-4

Editor: Pam Pritchard
Illustrator: Norman Worsley

Front Cover Design: Jeremy A. S. Drought

Cover Photo: Common Loon by Brian Wolitski www.bwolitskiwildlifephoto.com

Attention Schools and Organizations:

Quantity discounts are available on bulk purchases of this book for educational purposes. Special books or book excerpts can be created to fit specific needs. For information, please contact Simply Wild Publications, 100 Lake Lucerne Close SE, Calgary, Alberta, T2J 3H8
Phone 1-877-278-5999 Fax (403) 279-3304
E-mail: simplywildpub@home.com
Website: www.simplywildpub.com

Printed In Canada on acid free paper by Friesens

Contents

Appendices

Wildlife Habitats

Mixed Woodlands
Deciduous and coniferous forests with shrubs, clearings and open canopy

Coniferous Forests
Evergreen forests of spruce and pine, with closed canopy

Grasslands and Prairies
Open grassy areas of native prairie grasslands and agricultural lands

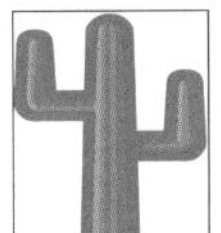

Deserts and Scrublands
Areas of minimal rainfall, minimal vegetation and extreme temperatures

Marshes and Sloughs
Wetlands of reeds, grasses and shallow, standing water

Mountains and Cliffs
High rocky areas often above the tree line

Seashore and Open Ocean
Mudflats, coast lines, open sea and ocean islands

Lakes and Rivers
Inland freshwater areas from shallow ponds to very deep water bodies

Arctic Tundra
Areas of severe cold and windswept, flat tundra

List of Illustrations

Preface

This book is dedicated to the Wilson's Phalarope. A few years ago I got my first look at this beautiful little shorebird. My field guide helped me identify it, but didn't tell me why it was spinning circles in the water.

Much later, after referring to a multitude of books and encyclopedias, I discovered the reason (*to stir up insects from the bottom of the pond*). I also discovered that these birds have long practiced female liberation, as it's the females who choose the males, and leave them to brood and raise the chicks. Now THIS was interesting!

During my quest, it occurred to me that it would be nice to find bird tidbits like this in a single volume, and Canadian Feathers was born. After many years of working in the conservation education field, I knew people were always eager to learn more, but often didn't know where to look. It is my hope that Canadian Feathers will ease that process.

This book doesn't pretend to be a field guide for bird identification. Rather, it is a volume to follow the many excellent field guides out there. After a rewarding day of birding, curl up in your favorite chair and learn more about the lives of the birds you've just seen.

Or, read it cover to cover and astound your friends with a never ending supply of Canadian bird trivia—a sure way to tell who your true friends are!

As with all good ideas, this one grew from being a book for bird watchers, to an excellent resource for teachers, libraries, home schoolers, and anyone with an interest in the wildlife of Canada.

While the phalarope was my inspiration, he didn't actually prove to be much help in the preparation of the book. Dwight Knapik, with his encyclopedic knowledge of birds of the world, was my sounding board and technical advisor. Norman Worsley provided the wonderful bird illustrations scattered throughout the book. Pam Pritchard took on the massive job of editing and proofing, and Jennifer Tizzard kept me working whenever I started to flag.

I hope you enjoy reading this book as much as I enjoyed writing it, and that your new found knowledge of Canadian birds enriches your life as it has mine.

Pat Bumstead
Calgary, Alberta
2001

Introduction

Birds, with their marvelous capability of flight, do not recognize international borders. With a few exceptions, most of the birds seen in Canada make yearly journeys to other countries. Many go south, but a few travel east or west. Canada is their summer home, and it is here they breed and raise their families.

One birder I spoke to in the deserts of the southwestern United States was lamenting the fact she had never seen any of these birds in their brilliant breeding plumage. It is our privilege to be the host country for this annual renewal of life; our wild areas are home to many thousands of nests and young birds.

This book hopes to foster an appreciation of how these delicate creatures live, and their dependence on our healthy ecosystems. It also hopes to simplify the quest for knowledge on Canadian birds by presenting a complete, single-source reference on all species seen on land or from our coasts.

Of the 426 species represented here, the majority nest in Canada, but the book also includes pelagic wanderers who nest in the Pacific, or on other oceanic islands. 'Accidental visitors' who occasionally stray far from their normal range have not been included.

Information is arranged in alphabetical order by their common family names. Each family page describes general characteristics including description, behaviour, diet, reproduction and status. Species accounts include habitat, size, range, Canadian nesting sites and a host of interesting facts. Sidebars include information on the origin of names, legends and unique family behaviours. Scattered throughout are black and white illustrations, Did You Know boxes, and trivia questions to test your knowledge. An hour-glass with time running out indicates those on Canada's endangered species list, as compiled by the Committee on the Status of Endangered Wildlife in Canada (COSEWIC).

The book includes a glossary and appendices for those readers seeking additional information. An extensive index makes it easy to locate individual species, as well as some common traits and shared features.

It is my sincere hope that you find this book useful and enlightening. Birds are a vital part of nature, and their future is in our hands.

World Species 13
Canadian Species 3

The Albatross Family - Diomedeidae

Characteristics

Albatross are the largest of the seabirds, with wingspans up to 3.6 m (12 ft) in the larger species, lengths up to 3 m (4 ft), and weights of 8–9 kg (15–20 lbs). Plumage is mainly white or sooty brown with black markings, and varies from species to species. Sexes look alike. Bills are stout and strongly hooked with a sheath of horny plates, **tubular nostrils** and **salt-excreting glands**. These birds have large heads, stout bodies and extremely long and narrow wings.

Their short legs are set in the middle of the body, so they stand upright and walk fairly well. To take flight they must run on water or land, or drop off a cliff. With webbed feet, they are good swimmers on the surface but cannot dive. Two species, the wandering and royal albatross, have the largest wingspan of any living bird, and can reach 50 kmh (30 mph) in level flight.

Behaviour

These birds are capable of long, sustained flight for months over the ocean, and are seldom seen from shore. They do not come to land except to breed on remote oceanic islands. Capable of remaining airborne on motionless wings for many hours, they soar endlessly on the winds, sometimes following ships to feed on the garbage thrown overboard. Their specialized **salt-excreting glands** allow them to drink sea water and expel the salt, and all their food is obtained from the sea.

Diet

Squid, cuttlefish, fish, sea urchins and other small marine animals make up their diet.

Reproduction

Courting birds spend a great deal of time soaring back and forth around large colonies, and engage in bowing, bill clapping, fencing and dancing displays around the nest. While albatross mate for life, this ceremony helps re-establish the pair bond. A single white egg is laid in a ground nest, and the larger male takes the first **incubation** shift, which may last for several weeks. **Incubation** is over two months, carried out by both sexes in turn.

The newly hatched chick is covered in long down, and fed **regurgitated** food and oil from the stomachs of its parents. Young albatross discharge stomach oil as a defensive measure. They **fledge** between four and nine months, depending on the size of the species. Chicks of the larger albatross species take nearly a year to **fledge**, and thus they breed only every other year. Some species take seven to nine years to reach breeding age.

Family Status

Albatross are found in every ocean but the North Atlantic, and species are limited to one hemisphere by the windless **doldrums** of the equator. The three species here are found only in the northern hemisphere.

One species, the short-tailed albatross, is near extinction. Almost wiped out by the plume trade in the 1800's, a volcanic eruption struck their breeding grounds a hundred years later. It was thought they had vanished, but a few young birds that had been out at sea returned to breed. Protected by law in 1957, they are slowly clawing their way back, with approximately 1,000 birds alive in 1999.

 **Black-footed Albatross**

Size: 59–63 cm (27"–29"), wingspan to 2.1 m (7 ft)
Range: Alaska, Pacific coast of Canada and USA

- weigh 3–4 kg (7–9 lbs)
- may follow ships for several hours, feeding on garbage on moonlit nights
- nest on Midway Island in the south Pacific and the Hawaiian Islands
- do not breed until they are nine years old
- lifespan up to 27 years

The word albatross has been traced to the Portuguese word for seafowl, and these animals were once a staple diet for islanders in the Pacific, as well as whalers and sailors.

♦

During the late 19th century they were slaughtered by the thousands for plumes for hats, and feathers for stuffing mattresses and pillows.

 **Laysan Albatross**

Size: 77–80 cm (31"–32"), wingspan to 2.1 m (7 ft)
Range: Alaska, Pacific coast of Canada and USA

- weigh 2–3 kg (5–8 lbs)
- feed on squid at night when they come to the surface
- travel great distances from nesting grounds; one banded bird was recovered 23 days later more than 3,200 km (2,000 mi) away
- do not breed until seven years of age
- large egg laid is 10% of females' body weight
- breed in the Hawaiian Islands
- lifespan up to 40 years

Laysan Albatross

 **Short-tailed Albatross**

Size: 73–83 cm (30"–37"), wingspan to 2.4 m (8 ft)
Range: Alaska, Pacific coast of Canada and USA; Japan, China

- largest albatross species in the North Pacific
- also called Steller's albatross

- once travelled to the coast of British Columbia to **moult**, and their remains are often found in archaeological sites there
- breed only on Torishima Island, off Japan

World Species 22
Canadian Species 13

The Auk Family - Alcidae

Characteristics

Auks are short-winged, marine diving birds of the northern hemisphere, ranging in size from 17–75 cm (7"–30"). Their colouration is largely black and white, and they resemble the penguins of the southern hemisphere in both habits and colouring. Their dense waterproof **plumage** helps protect them from cool ocean temperatures. Sexes look the same outside of breeding season. Several species have ornamental head plumes. Bills are often brightly coloured and differ among the species: short and stout; long and slender; or compressed and sculptured.

Chunky bodies with large heads and short tails, legs and necks, are propelled with rapid, vigorous motions of the wings, powered by strong **pectoral muscles**. While flight in the air is awkward, they use their wings to propel them underwater, and are excellent swimmers and divers. Their feet are used for steering.

Their legs are attached near the rear of the body. To assume an upright posture while standing, they rest their compact body on their rumps, with their feet extended out in front. The feet are webbed and each of the three toes bears strong claws.

Behaviour

Highly **gregarious**, these birds spend most of their time on the open seas, and come ashore only to breed, returning to where they were hatched.

Diet

Their diet consists of small fish, marine crustaceans and mollusks obtained by swimming and diving in the ocean. Auks are wholly dependent on the sea for their food.

Reproduction

These birds breed in mixed colonies of thousands on cliff ledges, in rock crevices, caves or burrows. The one or two large bluish or greenish eggs with dark markings are pear-shaped, so they roll in a circle instead of off the ledge. **Incubation** lasts 24–40 days, and is shared by both sexes. Young leave the nest 28–46 days after hatching, and are fed by their parents for up to seven weeks.

Family Status

Auks occupy a special niche in the nearshore and offshore polar and **temperate** seas. The family consists of auklets, dovekies, guillemots, murres, murrelets, puffins and razorbills. One species, the marbled murrelet, is currently listed as endangered in Canada.

The great auk was a large flightless bird standing more than 60 cm (2 ft) high. They were killed by sailors for food, by fishermen for bait, and by commercial hunters for their feathers. Their population was estimated in the millions throughout Europe and North America, but their flightless capacity made them easy prey for man and as a result, they were exterminated by 1844.

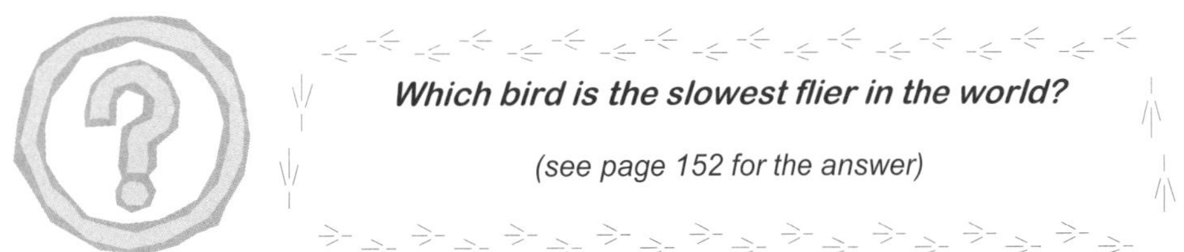

Which bird is the slowest flier in the world?

(see page 152 for the answer)

Cassin's Auklet

Size: 20–22 cm (8"–9")
Range: Alaska, Pacific coast of Canada and USA

- nocturnal and seldom seen during the day while nesting
- dig their own burrow with their sharp claws, taking up to 60 days to do so
- young fed by **regurgitation,** with contact in the dark burrow being made by sound
- one of the most abundant and widely distributed members of the Auk family

Nest on the northern British Columbia coast.

Rhinoceros Auklet

Size: 35–37 cm (14"–15")
Range: Alaska, Pacific coast of Canada and USA

- the largest auklet species
- in breeding season, a small horn appears at the base of the bill, hence the name
- spend their entire lives at sea, except for spring breeding when they come ashore at night
- eggs are laid in a mass of sticks and stems at the end of a 6–16 m (8–20 ft) self-dug burrow.
- parents fly out to sea at night to feed, then remain in the burrow during daylight hours

Nest on the coastline of British Columbia.

> In spite of their resemblance to penguins, the auk family is not related to these birds of the southern hemisphere. They are, however, related to gulls and shorebirds.

Dovekie

Size: 20–22 cm (8"–9")
Range: Atlantic coast of Canada; Greenland

- dive for food from the surface, using their wings to propel them underwater
- can sustain dives for 33–68 seconds
- nesting colonies number millions of birds
- the only auk species in the Atlantic
- important food item for Arctic foxes, gulls, gyrfalcons and people
- name means 'dove-like diver'

Nest along the coasts of the Arctic Ocean.

 **Black Guillemot**

Size: 30–35 cm (12"–14"), wingspan to 57 cm (23")
Range: Alaska, northern and Atlantic Canada; Greenland, Russia, Europe

- known for their bright red feet, and the brilliant red on the inside of their mouths
- summer **plumage** is black with extensive white patches, winter **plumage** is white with black wing patches
- flight is strong and swift, usually close to the water in wide circles
- population is declining due to global warming; melting sea ice has increased the distance the birds must fly for food and reduced the number of nesting sites available
- lifespan up to 13 years

Nest on the Atlantic coast of the Maritimes and along the Arctic Ocean.

 **Pigeon Guillemot**

Size: 30–35 cm (12"–14")
Range: Alaska, northern Canada, Pacific coast of Canada & USA; Japan, Russia

- perform a water dance where pairs gather on the water for mutual display of calling and showing red mouth linings; lines are formed on the water until they all dive and chase each other under the surface
- nest in small colonies of just a few pairs
- most widespread member of the family
- also known as 'sea pigeons'

Nest on the coast of British Columbia.

 **Common Murre** Nest on the coast of Newfoundland and the Arctic Ocean.

Size: 40–42 cm (16"–17"), wingspan to 75 cm (30")

 **Thick-billed Murre** Nest along the coast of the Arctic Ocean.

Size: 42–47 cm (17"–19")
Range: Alaska, northeastern Canada, Pacific coast of North America; Europe

- so heavy bodied they cannot take off from the water without running along the surface
- have been caught in trawler nets 210 m (690 ft) below the surface
- nest as high as 460 m (1,500 ft) above the water; young chicks flutter down to the sea 18–25 days after hatching, but do not fly until 40–46 days
- nesting in colonies of thousands, each bird can identify its own eggs by their individual pattern of colour and markings
- called 'northern turr' in Newfoundland
- the world murre population is estimated in the millions, with thick-billed outnumbering common by three to one

 **Ancient Murrelet**

Size: 24–25 cm (9"–10")
Range: Alaska, Pacific coast of Canada, USA to Mexico; Asia

- name comes from the grey feathers on the head in breeding season
- active at night and sleep during the day
- live on open seas in the winter
- within two or three days after hatching, parents call the chicks down to the water at night, where they are fed by their parents until they can fend for themselves

Nest along the coast of northern British Columbia.

 **Marbled Murrelet**

Size: 22–27 cm (9"–11")
Range: Alaska, Pacific coast of Canada and USA; Russia, Japan

- name refers to irregular spots and bars of summer **plumage**
- do not breed until they are five years of age
- before the breeding season, they **moult** their black and white feathers to a dull brown, which camouflages them while **incubating**
- both parents **incubate**, changing shifts daily at sunrise
- only member of the auk family that sometimes nest in trees

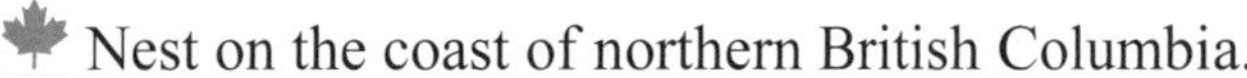
Nest on the coast of northern British Columbia.

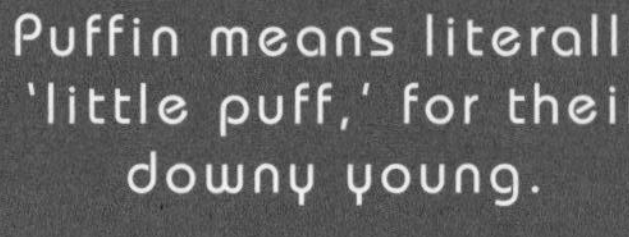

 **Common Puffin**

Size: 27–33 cm (11"–13"), wingspan to 60 cm (24")
Range: Atlantic coast of Canada; Europe, United Kingdom, Russia, Iceland

- bill in breeding season is bright reddish orange with a yellow-bordered blue patch; these horny plates are shed in the summer, leaving a smaller, duller bill
- have a distinctive triangular bill which is red with a bluish grey base
- bright red-orange feet in breeding season turn black in summer
- poor flyers but good swimmers, propelling themselves through water with their wings
- also known as 'sea parrots'
- young leave the nest without their parents seven weeks after hatching
- provincial bird of Newfoundland
- considered a delicacy in England in the Middle Ages, they were sold at '3 puffins for a penny', as they have very little flesh and three birds were needed to make a meal
- population has declined considerably since 1900 due to pollution and persecution

Nest along the coast and islands of Newfoundland and the Arctic Ocean.

 **Horned Puffin**

Size: 32–37 cm (13"–15")
Range: Alaska, Pacific coast of Canada; Russia

- name comes from the small horn of fleshy tissue above the eyes, which is shed after breeding season
- dive with body rising clear of the water before plunging under
- non-**incubating** birds fly to sea during the day and return with bills full of food to feed their young and partner
- breeding adults have white face and brightly coloured bill of red and yellow

Nest on the coast of northern British Columbia.

Horned Puffin

Puffins do not breed until 4 or 5 years of age, and the pair stay together for life.

 **Tufted Puffin**

Size: 35–37 cm (14"–15")
Range: Alaska, Pacific coast of Canada & USA; Russia

- name comes from tufted eyebrow plumes which are shed in the summer
- bill is layered with seven brightly coloured plates in breeding season which are individually shed in the summer; winter beak is one third smaller and black
- largest member of the puffin family
- white facial feathers are replaced by black in the summer, and bright orange feet change to grey
- breeding adults have a white face, tufted eyebrow plumes and bright red and yellow bill

Nest on the coast of northern British Columbia.

 **Razorbill**

Size: 40–45 cm (16"–18"), wingspan to 67 cm (27")
Range: Atlantic coast of Canada and USA; Greenland, Iceland, Scandinavia

- named for the flattened shape of their bill, which has a sharp cutting edge
- can dive to great depths, and have been caught in fishermen's nets 18 m (60 ft) below the surface
- nest as high as 300 m (1,000 ft) above the ocean
- about two weeks after hatching, the young leap from the cliffs into the sea at night
- called 'tinkers' in Newfoundland
- closest living relative to the extinct great auk

Nest along the coast of Newfoundland and the Arctic Ocean.

World Species 7
Canadian Species 2

The Avocet & Stilt Family - Recurvirostridae

Characteristics

Avocets and stilts are 27–50 cm (11"–20") wading birds related to sandpipers. **Plumage** is a striking white and black, and both sexes look the same outside of breeding season. They have small heads; long necks; and long **upcurved bills**. These birds are strong fliers, with long pointed wings and short square tails.

Their extremely long legs make them proportionately the longest-legged wading bird in the world, with the possible exception of the flamingos. Full or partially webbed toes ensure they are excellent swimmers, and they readily dive.

Behaviour

Highly **gregarious**, these birds travel in flocks and are always found near water in shallow ponds or muddy seacoasts. They often utter loud yapping or yelping cries.

Diet

Small **aquatic** animals and insects are picked from the water surface and the surface of the submerged mud. Food is located by swinging their long, sensitive bill from side to side through the water.

Reproduction

These birds nest in small colonies. Shallow ground depressions lined with plant stems are located on small islands or boggy shorelines of freshwater lakes and marshes. Both species help build the nest. If rising water threatens the eggs, they will build a deep pile with a shallow depression in the top. **Clutches** are three to five buff green, peg-top shaped eggs with dark markings. Like many other birds, the adults feign wing or leg injuries to distract predators away from the nest. **Incubation** of 22–29 days is shared by both sexes. Chicks are **precocial,** and never fed by the parents, as they are able to fend for themselves a few hours after hatching. First flight is achieved at 27–28 days of age.

Chicks are often **brooded** to keep them warm and dry. These birds have a very strong **brooding** instinct, which has been observed in chicks as young as two days old.

Family Status

Found worldwide in tropical and **temperate** zones, there are even two species of *Recurvirostridae* found in the high Andes and Himalayas. During **migration**, a few American avocets occasionally stray to the Atlantic coast of North America. In the 19th century there was a small breeding population there, but they were hunted to near-extinction. Since given protection, the population is once again increasing along the eastern seaboard.

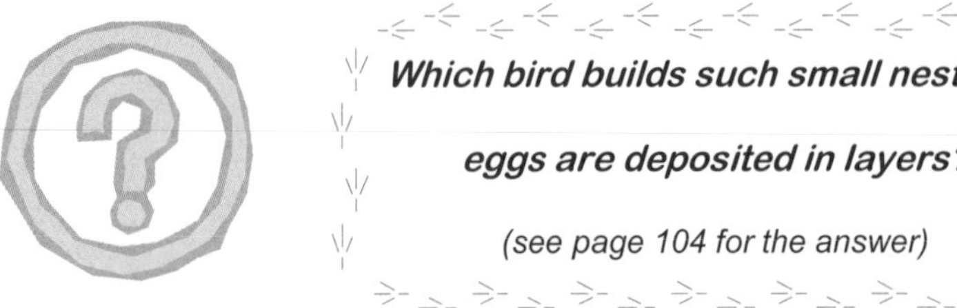

American Avocet

Size: 42–45 cm (17"–18"), wingspan to 95 cm (38")
Range: Central and western Canada and USA

- long bill, 5–10 cm (3"–5"), is sensitive enough to feel food items without seeing them
- both sexes have bright blue legs
- when disturbed, all birds will join in communal defense against predators
- often feed in flocks, a long line of birds advancing abreast
- develop chestnut coloured head and neck during breeding season
- after breeding, the male stretches one wing across the female's back, then they run a few steps with their bills crossed like swords

Nest in southern Alberta, Saskatchewan and Manitoba.

Avocet is from the Latin word meaning 'small, graceful bird.'

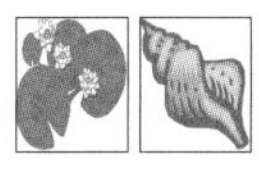

Black-necked Stilt

Size: 32–37 cm (13"–15")
Range: Western Canada and USA to Gulf Coast

- newly hatched young already have the long red legs of the species
- parents make as many as 100 trips per day from the water to the nest, keeping their feathers wet so evaporation cools both the adult and young
- nicknamed 'lawyer birds' because of their continual vocalizations, and because they are sharp eyed and often sound loud alarms when predators approach
- aggressive in breeding season, often flying low over an intruder while uttering loud alarm calls
- nearly hunted to extinction in the 19th century for the **plume trade**

Expanding their breeding range north into Alberta and Saskatchewan.

World Species 91
Canadian Species 10

The Blackbird Family - Icteridae

Characteristics
Blackbirds are medium sized, 15–32 cm (6"–13"), songbirds with glossy, metallic black as the predominant family colour, although some also have **plumages** with brown, buff, orange, red or yellow. Males are larger and more highly coloured than the females. Their **conical** bill is sharply pointed. Specialized jaw muscles and a cutting ridge in the roof of the mouth act like a can-opener to shell acorns and nuts. Like all perching birds, their feet are small and weak.

Behaviour
All members of the family are showy, noisy and easily observed birds. Highly **gregarious**, all species form large flocks outside of the breeding season. They are strong, direct fliers with pointed wings. The **temperate** species **migrate** south in the autumn.

Diet
Their diet consists of seeds, nuts, grains, berries, insects, spiders and snails. The grackle is the most **omnivorous**, also taking amphibians, small fish, eggs and young birds.

Blackbirds obtain much of their food by **gaping**—inserting their bill into a potential food source and then forcibly opening it. They '**gape**' into rotting wood, curled leaves, flowers, clumps of grass and soil, exposing food not available on the surface.

Reproduction
With the exception of the orioles and the brown-headed cowbird, most members of this family nest in cup nests of grass, twigs and pine needles, sometimes held together with mud or lashed to standing reeds. Nests are located on the ground, in reed beds, shrubs or small trees. Orioles build pouch nests which swing from a tree branch. Three to seven green, blue or pinkish eggs with dark markings are laid, and **incubated** 11–14 days by the female. The young leave the nest 9–20 days after hatching.

Cowbirds are **brood parasites,** always laying their eggs in the nests of other birds and relying on the host to raise them. The female watches a smaller bird build a nest, and when she leaves to feed, the cowbird lays her own eggs. She may then jab into the host eggs with her beak, and once they are speared, fly away with them, making many trips to get rid of them all.

Family Status
The family consists of blackbirds, grackles, orioles, meadowlarks, cowbirds and bobolinks, as well as the tropical species. They are found only in the **New World**. In the southern USA, winter flocks of red-winged blackbirds, yellow-headed blackbirds, common grackles and brown-headed cowbirds have been estimated to number 50 million birds.

The vinous-tinted blackbird, which once lived on Lord Howe Island in the Tasman Sea, has been extinct since 1920. Rats introduced to the island by a shipwreck preyed on the eggs and young birds, eventually wiping out the population.

Brewer's Blackbird

Size: 17–22 cm (7"–9"), wingspan to 35 cm (14")
Range: Western Canada and USA

- males have iridescent purple and green hues to their **plumage**
- jerk their head back and forth as they walk, giving them a strutting appearance
- of all blackbirds, these are the least daunted by humans
- nests may be located from ground level to as high as 45 m (150 ft) in a tree
- communal nesters

Nest in BC, Alberta and south central Saskatchewan to Ontario.

Red-winged Blackbird

Size: 17–22 cm (7"–9"), wingspan to 35 cm (14")
Range: Canada, USA to Central America and Caribbean

- red and yellow shoulder patches of the males are grown in the second year, and can be flashed or hidden at will
- males' bright red shoulders and song are used to defend **territory**
- one of the earliest spring **migrators**, with the males returning before the females
- communal nesters, often nesting alongside other blackbird species
- male has a harem of three to eight females nesting in his **territory**; he helps feed all young after they leave the nest
- most widespread member of blackbird family, nesting from Alaska to Central America
- thought to be the most numerous bird in North America
- lifespan up to 14 years

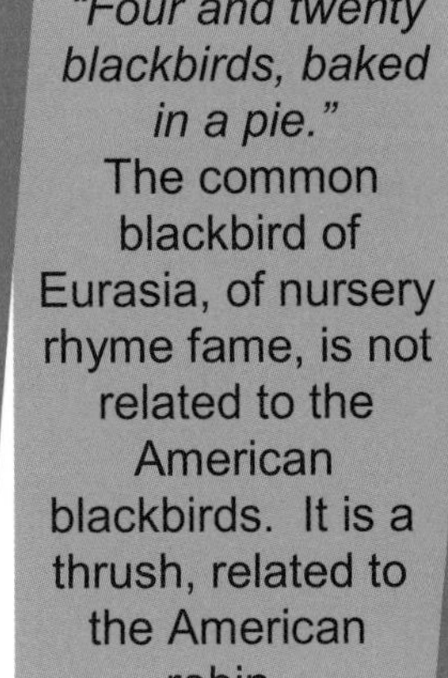

Nest Canada wide.

Rusty Blackbird

Size: 20–25 cm (8"–10"), wingspan to 37 cm (15")
Range: Alaska, Canada, USA

- named for the brown edges of their new feathers in the fall
- adults and juveniles have yellow eyes
- often wade in shallow water to feed on **aquatic** prey
- most northerly member of the blackbird family, breeding within the Arctic Circle
- nests are built a few metres above water in a tree or shrub
- **monagamous** solitary nesters; may nest in loose colonies
- is the fastest declining bird species; over a 25 year period their numbers have decreased by 80%

Nest Canada wide except for the Great Plains.

 **Yellow-headed Blackbird**

Size: 20–28 cm (8"–10")
Range: Western and central Canada, USA

Yellow-headed Blackbird

- flocks of males precede females in spring **migration**
- found from sea level to 1,500 m (5,000 ft) in the Rockies
- communal nesters, often sharing the marsh with other species
- nest built by female only is a deep, basket-like cup of water-soaked grasses and reeds with a partial canopy at the top; forms a tight nest when the grasses dry
- nests are only built in habitat over standing water
- the male has a harem of three to eight females nesting in his **territory**; he helps feed all young after they leave the nest

 Nest in western Canada and southern Manitoba.

 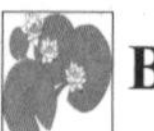 **Bobolink**

Size: 17–20 cm (7"–8"), wingspan to 30 cm (12")
Range: Southern Canada, USA to South America

- name comes from their burbling song, delivered in flight as the male floats down from a perch
- **migration** flight is 8,000 km (5,000 mi) from Canada to Argentina
- male has up to four females on his **territory**; he helps raise the young of the first mate, then the others in succession of mating
- nest in loose colonies in open hayfields
- females carry eggshells away from the nest once the eggs have hatched

Nest in southern Canada from British Columbia to Maritimes.

 **Brown-headed Cowbird**

Size: 17–20 cm (7"–8")
Range: Southern Canada, USA, Mexico

- up to 40 eggs per year laid in the nests of other, smaller songbirds; then care of the young is left to the host birds; eggs often hatch before the hosts' eggs so they get more food
- **parasitizes** more than 140 bird species; in some areas entire species of songbirds have vanished because of this **brood parasite**
- once followed roaming buffalo herds, and their nomadic lifestyle meant they could not tend nests of their own
- deforestation is enlarging their range, to the detriment of other birds
- have over 40 different calls, which take them over two years to learn

> With all young cowbirds raised in the nests of other species, it remains a mystery how they are able to recognize their own kind.

Breed across southern Canada.

Common Grackle

Size: 28–34 cm (11"–13")
Range: Canada, USA

> Grackle comes from the Latin '*graculus*,' meaning jackdaw.

- **plumage** is black with iridescent purple and green hues
- adults have yellow eyes
- classed as a songbird because they have all the vocal equipment needed, but their song is actually a raucous squawk
- lifespan up to 16 years

Nest from Alberta to Maritimes.

Meadowlark

Size: 20–25 cm (8"–10"), wingspan to 42 cm (17")
Eastern species: Eastern Canada, USA to South America — Nest from Ontario to Maritimes.

Western species: Western Canada and USA — Nest from British Columbia to Ontario.

- bright yellow breast is marked by a black crescent at the throat
- young birds have white hair-like growths on the roof of their mouth that point towards their throat for easy feeding
- males are **polygamous**, sometimes maintaining several nests on the same **territory**
- found up to 3,050 m (10,000 ft) in the mountains
- nests are located at the foot of grassy clumps, and the female weaves the tops of the blades together to make a dome; often two **clutches** per year
- state bird of Kansas, Montana, Nebraska, North Dakota, Oregon and Wyoming

Baltimore/Bullock's Oriole

Size: 17–20 cm (7"–8"), wingspan to 30 cm (12")
Nest throughout southern Canada.

Orchard Oriole

Size: 15–17 cm (6"–7"), wingspan to 25 cm (10")
Nest in southern Manitoba and Ontario.

Range: Canada, USA to South America

- adults are a vivid orange or yellow with black markings
- males arrive back in the spring prior to females
- yearling males often resemble females, possibly to reduce agression from adult males
- male helps feed young
- Baltimore oriole is the state bird of Maryland
- flight speed 40 kmh (25 mph)

> Oriole nests are among the most complex of all nests. The female constructs a hanging pouch, woven together from grasses, hair and string, fastened to a tree branch by the rim, some 2–9 m (6–30 ft) up. The inside is lined with feathers and down.
>
> ♦
>
> Contrary to popular opinion, Baltimore orioles were not named after a baseball club, but rather after early settlers in Maryland.

World Species 278
Canadian Species 33

The Bunting and Sparrow Family - Emberizidae

Characteristics
This is a large family of small songbirds ranging in size from 11–22 cm (4"–5"). **Plumage** is usually a dull brown, with distinct head markings. The exceptions are the towhees, buntings and juncos, who are more grey, black and white. Males and females differ slightly in **plumage**, but are the same size. Their stout, **conical** bills are adapted for crushing and taking husks off seeds, with a cutting edge angled at the base. Many species have a bony hump in the roof of the mouth, against which seeds can be crushed.

Behaviour
In the **migratory** species, males arrive before the females in the spring, and defend their **territory** against other males. Open country species perform song flights, rising a few yards above the ground and then slowly circling back to earth, singing throughout the flight. After pairing, a characteristic form of sexual behaviour involves chasing and a headlong, twisting pursuit of the female by the male, ending with both birds tumbling to the ground in a mass of feathers.

While they are **territorial** in the nesting season, these birds are highly **gregarious** during other times of the year, and often join mixed flocks.

Diet
Primarily ground feeders, their diet consists mainly of seeds and grains, although insects, spiders, and berries are also taken. Newly hatched young are fed exclusively on insects because of their high protein content.

Reproduction
Two to nine greyish green eggs with dark markings are laid in cup nests of grasses, twigs, moss and rootlets, lined with feathers, hair and finer grass. Females generally build the nest and **incubate** the young, although there are some exceptions. **Incubation** lasts 10–15 days, and the young leave the nest 7–15 days after hatching. Males sometimes feed the female while she sits, but always join in feeding the young.

Family Status
This family contains sparrows, towhees, juncos, longspurs, and snow and lark buntings.

Ancient peoples believed the sparrow sprang from horsehair and mud. To the Chinese, they foretell good luck; in Hindu mythology they are symbols of fruitfulness and fertility; and in ancient Rome they were considered sacred to the god Venus.

The Guadeloupe rufous-sided towhee has been extinct since 1897. Found only on one island off the coast of California, it was exterminated by man, and the goats and feral cats which he introduced to the island.

Two species are listed as endangered in Canada.

Lark Bunting

Size: 12–17 cm (5"–7")
Range: Southeastern Canada, western and central USA

- birds at the rear of a large flock flutter continually to the front, making it look like an enormous wheel rolling across the prairies
- males perform a conspicuous hovering flight song, rising up and down
- some males are **polygamous,** attracting up to seven females at a time while others attract none
- population numbers and breeding range fluctuate considerably from year to year
- state bird of Colorado

Nest in southern Alberta, Saskatchewan and Manitoba.

The name bunting here is misleading, as true buntings are found only in Eurasia and Africa. These birds were named by early settlers for their resemblance to familiar birds back home.

Snow Bunting

Size: 12–17 cm (5"–7"), wingspan to 32 cm (13")
Range: Alaska, Canada, northern USA; Europe and Russia

- winter **plumage** of white with brown markings mimics areas of broken snow cover
- love to bathe in snow and can stand temperatures of - 40ºC (-58ºF), burrowing in the snow to keep warm
- flocks turn and whirl in unison, making it harder for predators to get individual birds
- found further north than any other songbird, and winter south to the limits of the snowline
- have a long hind toenail, thought to aid walking as they spend a great deal of time on the ground
- name comes from their **migration** to southern Canada in advance of the first heavy snows
- two **clutches** per year

Nest on the Arctic tundra.

Dickcissel

Size: 15–17 cm (6"–7"), wingspan to 27 cm (11")
Range: Southern Canada, USA, Mexico to South America and West Indies

- name comes from birds' incessant calls on nesting grounds
- **migrating** flocks can contain up to 500,000 birds
- nest is built on the ground, hidden in clumps of vegetation or under small shrubs
- two **clutches** per year
- flight speed 40 kmh (25 mph)

Nest in southern Saskatchewan and Manitoba.

Dark-eyed Junco

Size: 13–15 cm (5"–6"), wingspan to 25 cm (10")
Range: Canada, USA, Mexico

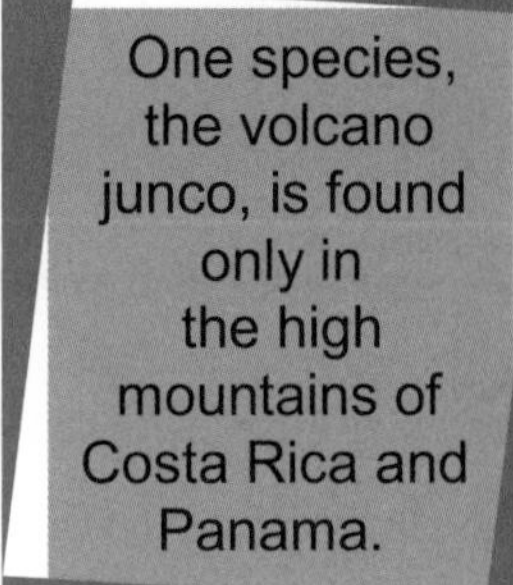

- upper and lower parts of the bill can be moved sideways to manipulate and crack seeds
- most widespread of all juncos, found north to the tree limit
- their many geographical races were once considered separate species
- two **clutches** per year
- lifespan up to 10 years

Nest throughout Canada.

Chestnut-collared Longspur

Size: 12–16 cm (5"–6")
Range: Southwestern Canada, western USA to Mexico

- male performs flight song while flying gradually upward, circles, then descends with rapid wing beats
- summer in northern prairies where grass is sparse and less than 20 cm (8") tall
- male defends a **territory** of 0.4–0.8 ha (1–2 acres) by singing from any convenient perch
- young are independent before one month old
- habitat is disappearing due to planted crops

Nest in southern Alberta and Saskatchewan.

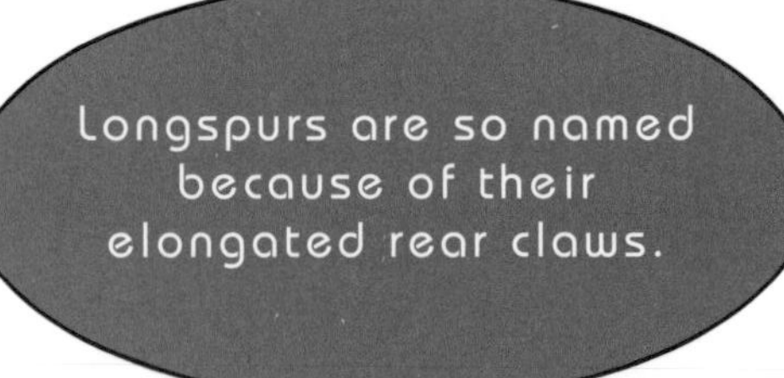

Lapland Longspur

Size: 15–17 cm (6"–7"), wingspan to 30 cm (12")
Range: Alaska, Canada, central and western USA; Siberia, Greenland

- walk or run over fields where weeds project above the snow
- possess a long hind toenail which may aid in walking
- feed themselves by scraping away ice and snow to get grain buried underneath
- winter in southern Canada
- usually in flocks with other longspurs, snow buntings and horned larks
- male has **courtship** flight display, singing constantly
- named in the 18th century for their range in Lapland (Siberia)
- the only longspur species found in both hemispheres

Nest on Arctic tundra.

 McCown's Longspur

Size: 12–17 cm (5"–7")
Range: Southwestern Canada, western USA to Mexico

- male and female pair show unusual attachment for each other, keeping close together and usually walking side by side
- females are persistent **incubators**, abandoning the nest only when nearly stepped on
- dislike moisture so much they may abandon their normal range during wet seasons
- two **clutches** per year
- named in 1851, after the Captain in the US Army who discovered them on the high prairies of west Texas

Nest in southern Alberta and Saskatchewan.

Food is abundant on their nesting grounds because of the long daylight hours. Young longspurs, fed 24 hours a day, grow rapidly and take their first flights at an early 10–12 days old.

  Smith's Longspur

Size: 12–17 cm (5"–7")
Range: Alaska, NWT, mid western Canada and USA

- have a low, clicking call like the sound of winding a cheap watch
- one of the least known North American birds, rare and elusive
- have swift, erratic, zigzag flight
- breed at the treeline
- do not have a flight song, but mark their **territory** by singing from the top of a tree or hummock

Nest on the Arctic tundra.

Different tail markings of the longspur species

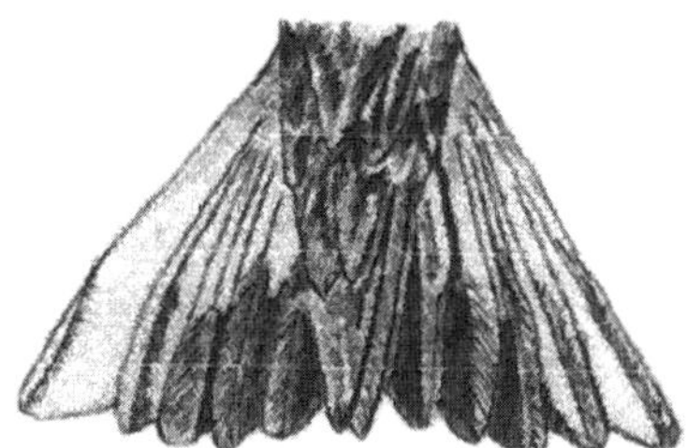

Chestnut-collared Longspur

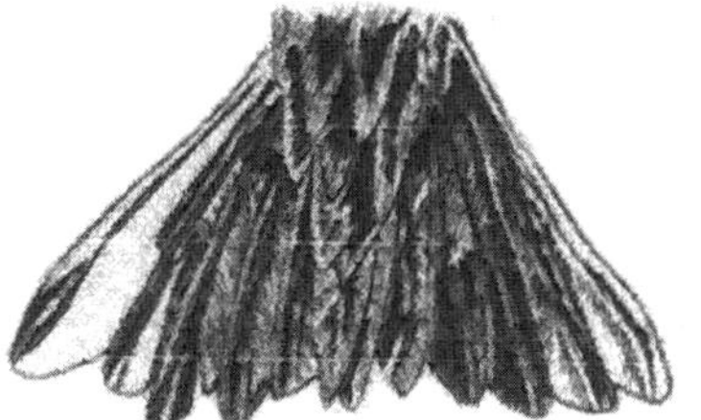

Lapland Longspur

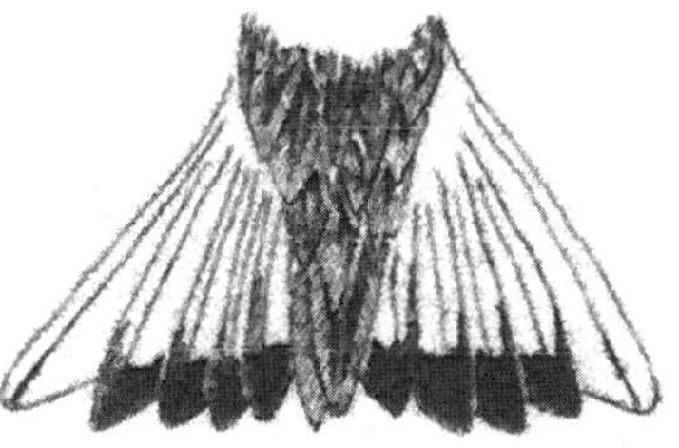

McCown's Longspur

Sparrows of the Prairies and Grasslands

Prairie sparrows are small, brown birds ranging in size from 10–15 cm (4"–6"). Their nests are built either in a slight cavity on the ground, or in sagebrush, cat tails, cactus or small shrubs.

Baird's Sparrow - Canada, USA to Mexico

- male has **territory** up to 0.8 ha (2 acres), defended by singing from low perches
- reluctant to fly and often run through the grass like a mouse

Nest in southern Alberta and Saskatchewan.

Brewer's Sparrow - Yukon, western Canada and USA to Mexico

- can survive weeks without water, getting their moisture requirements from their food
- males sing in chorus at dawn and twilight
- once the most abundant sparrow in Death Valley, USA
- as many as 47 nests can be found in 40 ha (100 acres) in Washington state

Nest in southern British Columbia and Alberta.

Clay-coloured Sparrow - Canada, USA to Mexico

- **migrate** by day or night, moving in waves of 25–100 birds
- male has **territory** of less than 1,022 sq. m (11,000 sq. ft), and collects food from outside this area
- one of the few prairie birds that sing into the heat of July

Nest in Alberta, Saskatchewan and southern Manitoba and Ontario.

Field Sparrow - Canada, USA to Mexico

- **migrate** mostly at night in small flocks
- male defends **territory** by patrolling from bush to bush and singing from perch

Nest in southern Ontario and Quebec.

Grasshopper Sparrow - sw Canada, USA to El Salvador, West Indies and South America

- named for their song which sounds like the buzzing of grasshoppers
- male claims up to 1.2 ha (3 acre) **territory** by singing all day; females also sing
- prefer to run instead of flying if in danger; Latin name means "*sand runner*"

Nest in southern Alberta and Saskatchewan.

Sparrows of the Prairies and Grasslands *(continued)*

Henslow's Sparrow - Eastern Canada and USA

- male maintains a **territory** up to 0.8 ha (2 acres)
- males sing night and day, and incessantly in the rain
- some males fight for **territory** like tiny roosters

Nest in southern Ontario.

Lark Sparrow - Canada, USA to Mexico

- male **courts** female by strutting around on the ground with wings trailing and tail spread
- one of the finest singers in the sparrow family, hence the name
- flight speed to 45 kmh (28 mph)

Nest in southern Alberta, Saskatchewan and Manitoba.

Le Conte's Sparrow - Canada, USA

- one of the smallest sparrows at just 11 cm (4.5")
- often scurry through the grass instead of flying

Nest in Alberta, central Saskatchewan through to Ontario.

Nelson's Sharp-tailed Sparrow - Canada, Atlantic Coast to Florida

- walk rather than hop when feeding
- males do not hold **territories**, and mate with more than one female
- more carnivorous than other sparrows, eating insects, spiders and small snails

Nest in Alberta, southern Saskatchewan and Manitoba.

Savannah Sparrow - Alaska, Yukon, Canada, USA to El Salvador

- **migrate** at night
- often sing all day long
- prefer to run through the grass instead of flying
- both parents share **incubation** duties
- named after Savannah, Georgia where it was first identified
- flight speed to 67 kmh (42 mph)

Nest across Canada.

One subspecies of the savannah, the **Ipswich sparrow**, is found only on Sable Island off the coast of Nova Scotia, and is on Canada's endangered species list.

Sparrows of the Prairies and Grasslands *(continued)*

Swamp Sparrow - Canada, USA to Mexico

- do much of their feeding by wading in the water, picking seeds and insects off the surface
- **fledglings** sometimes fall into the water where they are eaten by frogs, fish and turtles
- nest always has a side opening

Nest from Alberta to Manitoba.

Vesper Sparrow - Canada, USA to Mexico

- named for their almost continual evening singing
- frequently take dust baths in the ruts in gravel roads
- also found in the Rocky Mountains up to 3,700 m (12,000 ft)
- flight speed 27 kmh (17 mph)

Nest in Alberta, Saskatchewan and southern Canada through to the Maritimes.

Sparrows of the Woodlands and Coniferous Forests

Woodland sparrows, at 12–22 cm (5"–9"), are slightly larger than their prairie cousins. Nests are built in a variety of locations, from ground level to low shrubs to high in the trees.

Chipping Sparrow - Alaska, Canada, USA to Nicaragua

- once called 'horse birds' for their habit of collecting horse hair to line their nest
- one of the smallest and tamest sparrows
- one of the most common victims of the **parasitic** egg-laying habits of the brown-headed cowbird
- found up to 3,350 m (11,000 ft) in the Rocky Mountains
- flight speed to 32 kmh (20 mph)
- lifespan up to 13 years

Nest across Canada.

Fox Sparrow - Alaska, Canada, western USA

- named for the reddish fox-like colour of their **plumage**
- **migrate** at night
- one of the finest singers in the sparrow family
- often scratch in the dirt, kicking backward so vigorously as to dig a hole

Nest in British Columbia and northern Canada.

Sparrows of the Woodlands and Coniferous Forests *(continued)*

Golden-crowned Sparrow - Alaska, Yukon, western Canada and USA to Mexico

- flocks return to the same place each summer to breed
- males sing continually in June; to miners laboring along Alaskan gold trails it sounded like *"I'm so weary"* and they called these birds 'weary willies'
- spend most of their time on the ground
- flight speed up to 32 kmh (20 mph)

Nest in British Columbia and Yukon.

Harris' Sparrow - Western Canada and USA

- among the last **migrant** songbirds to leave in the fall
- breed in mossy bogs and scrub forest
- vigorously scratch in leaves and soil for seeds, berries, insects, spiders and snails

Nest in Northwest Territories, Nunavut, northern Manitoba.

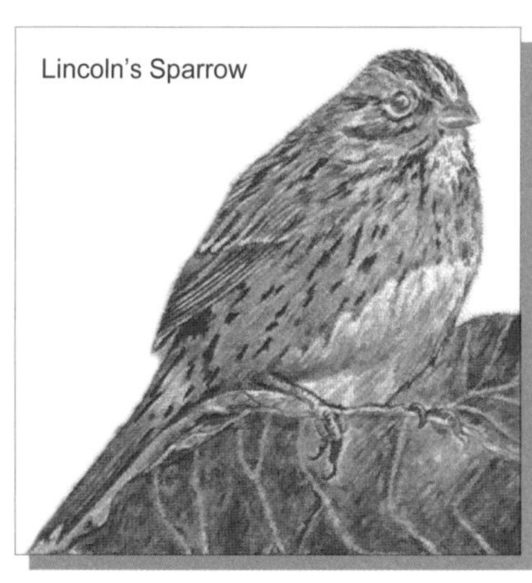
Lincoln's Sparrow

Lincoln's Sparrow - Alaska, Canada, USA to Central America

- male holds **territory** of 0.4 ha (1 acre)
- nest in bogs, wetlands and thickets
- seldom seen because of their extreme shyness

Nest across Canada.

Song Sparrow - Alaska, Canada, USA to Mexico.

- song is variable from one male to another, and females also sing
- young birds learn to sing by listening to other males
- male holds **territory** of less than 0.4 ha (1 acre)
- one of the best known North American songbirds, often dwelling near people
- found up to 2,000 m (6,500 ft) in the Rocky Mountains during the summer
- flight speed 48 kmh (30 mph)
- lifespan up to 10 years

Nest across Canada.

The word sparrow means 'flutterer', and was originally applied to any small bird.

Tree Sparrow, American - Alaska, NWT, Canada, USA

- can withstand temperatures of -28°C (-18°F), but need an adequate food supply
- flocks estimated to consume 875 tons of weed seeds annually in Iowa
- male defends **territory** of more than 1 ha (2.5 acres) within which all food is collected
- travel up to 4,800 km (3,000 mi) on their **migration** north in the spring
- travel in winter flocks of 30–40 birds
- lifespan up to 9 years

Nest in northern Canada.

White-crowned Sparrow - Alaska, Canada, USA to Mexico and Cuba

- feed on the ground, vigorously scratching with both feet
- will often burst into song under the light of the moon
- the most studied sparrow in North America
- has local name of Canada bird, as one of their songs sounds like "*Oh sweet Canada Canada Canada*"
- flight speed 30 kmh (19 mph)
- lifespan up to 13 years

Nest in British Columbia and across northern Canada.

White-throated Sparrow - Yukon, Canada, USA

- males sing throughout the day, females occasionally sing
- summer across Canada up to the tree limit; one of the most common sparrow species
- lifespan up to 9 years

Nest in northwestern Canada, Ontario to the Maritimes.

 Rufous-sided Towhee

Size: 17–23 cm (7"–9")
Range: Southern Canada, USA to Central America

- sometimes split into two species - Eastern spotted towhee, and spotted towhee in the west
- name 'towhee' comes from their call; also called 'chewinks' for their call
- because of their ground foraging habits, they are sometimes called 'ground robins'
- two **clutches** per year
- lifespan up to 12 years

Nest in southern British Columbia, Alberta and Saskatchewan, or southern Manitoba, Ontario and Quebec.

World Species 65
Canadian Species 7

The Chickadee Family - Paridae

Characteristics

Chickadees are plump, active, woodland birds of the **temperate** regions ranging in size from 7–15 cm (3"–6"). Their soft, thick **plumage** is grays & browns, with black throats and black caps. Some species have conspicuous crests. Males and females look alike. They have short, stout, **conical** bills and their nostrils are partially covered with bristles. Their strong legs and feet are specially suited to their **arboreal** life.

Behaviour

Highly acrobatic and **gregarious**, they move around in trees on the top, bottom or sides of branches. They often hang upside down to pick insects from the underside of leaves and twigs. Prey is held underfoot and hammered with the bill, or beaten on branches before eating. Feeding flocks use high pitched whistles to keep in touch. They are among the most adaptable of small birds, and popular with people because they often allow close approach and will sometimes eat from a human hand. People also like them because they are small and cute, do not cause any serious nuisance, and eat insects. Their common name comes from their frequent *"chick-a-dee-dee"* calls.

As non-**migratory** species, these birds have several adaptations for surviving the winter. Their plumage is much denser than other birds of similar size. On colder days, they fluff their feathers to increase the layer of insulation, reducing heat loss by 20%. At night, they reduce energy expenditure by dropping their body temperature to -10ºC (14°F), and roost together in small groups in tree cavities, sharing body heat. They also burrow down into the snow for its insulating warmth and protection from cold winds.

Two species, the boreal chickadee and Siberian tit, survive northern temperatures of -45ºC (-50ºF). As these birds only forage in daylight, during certain times of the year their feeding time is reduced to three or four hours, with 21 hours of darkness and fasting.

Diet

Their diet consists of caterpillars, insects, larvae and spiders, as well as seeds of conifers, berries and other wild fruit. Seeds are **cached** in various locations for periods of shortage, which is why chickadees do not stay long at back yard feeders. They constantly pick up a seed and then fly away to **cache** it. Although they are primarily insect eaters, they survive on seeds and berries during the winter months.

Reproduction

These birds are mainly cavity nesters, using abandoned tree cavities 2–64 m (3–80 ft) from the ground. The female lines the nest with plant fibers, hair, feathers and insect cocoons. Four to thirteen white eggs with dark markings are laid, and **incubated** 11–13 days. While she is **incubating** the eggs, the male brings her food, and continues to help her feed the young birds when they have hatched. The chicks fly 14–18 days after hatching.

Family Status

This family is found throughout the world, with the greatest number of species in the northern hemisphere.

Boreal Chickadee

Range: Tree limit in Alaska, Canada to northern USA

- have a buffy brown breast and sides
- in some winters, small numbers wander hundreds of miles south of their usual range
- spend most of their time in the interior of dense conifers
- store food in trees for the winter, at a height that will be above the snow

Nest across Canada except for the Great Plains.

> Weight for weight, black-capped chickadees eat more food, use more oxygen and generate more heat than any other vertebrate.

Black-capped Chickadee

Range: Alaska, Canada, USA

- if disturbed while sitting on the nest, they utter a snake-like hiss
- both parents share **incubation** duties
- native Americans called them *'tsikilili'* and considered them a bringer of news; if a chickadee perched on your house it was thought that company would soon arrive
- called 'willow tits' in England
- state bird of Maine and Massachusetts
- provincial bird of New Brunswick
- lifespan up to 12 years

Black-capped Chickadee

Nest across Canada.

Chestnut-backed Chickadee

Range: Southern Alaska along the coast to California, inland to western North America

- the only chickadee that lives on the Pacific coast
- share their range with the black-capped, but these birds prefer to feed on the top half of conifers, while black-capped feed on the lower half

Nest along the coast of British Columbia.

Mountain Chickadee

Range: Alaska, British Columbia, Alberta to Arizona, New Mexico and Texas

- live up to 3,050 m (10,000 ft) in the Rocky Mountains but descend to lowlands in winter

Nest in British Columbia and western Alberta.

Siberian Tit

Range: Alaska, Yukon, Europe, northern Asia

- also known as 'grey-headed chickadee'
- have been seen eating fat from frozen caribou carcasses at -29°C (-20° F)
- an **Old World** species that has crossed the Bering Sea
- most northerly member of the chickadee family

Nest in the Yukon.

Tufted Titmouse

Range: Southeastern Canada, USA

- largest member of the Paridae family
- pairs mate for life, separate during the winter into mixed flocks of birds, join again in spring
- line their nest with hair plucked from living mammals, including people, and snakeskin
- both sexes sing
- two **clutches** per year
- lifespan up to 12 years

Nest in southern Ontario.

Did You Know...

*Birds have the best colour vision of all vertebrates. Some species even see ultra-violet light, which means they are able to pick up highlights and tones in **plumage** unseen by people.*

*Raptors, whose survival depends on hunting, have eyesite two to three times better than humans. Each image they see is magnified because of the internal structure of the eye, which is built like a telescope. Frontally placed eyes give them **depth perception** essential to a successful hunt.*

*Songbirds, on the other hand, have eyes placed on the sides of their head. This allows them better **peripheral vision** so they can watch for predators while feeding.*

Some species are even more specialized. The American woodcock has eyes placed on the top of their head, so they can watch for danger while feeding, which is done by probing into the ground with their bill. American bitterns have eyes placed very close to the base of the bill, which allows them to see straight ahead when they're in their defensive freezing posture.

World Species 30
Canadian Species 4

The Cormorant Family - Phalacrocoracidae

Characteristics

Cormorants are long-necked, long-billed, water birds found in most parts of the world on sea coasts, large lakes and rivers. They range in size from 62–100 cm (25"–40"), with wingspans up to 1.5 m (60"). Most species are black, and their feathers sometimes have a greenish or bluish metallic sheen. Both sexes look the same. Their eyes and facial skin are often brightly coloured, and the bill is long, strong and hooked at the tip. All species have a small throat pouch for holding fish. Wings are short and rounded, and the tail is long, stiff and rounded as well. Large feet set far back on the body have fully webbed toes, and their legs are short and strong. When standing, they assume an upright position and their back appears hunched.

Behaviour

Strong fliers and swimmers, cormorants use their feet to propel them when diving underwater, and their wedge-shaped tail for steering. They are capable of diving to 37 m (48 ft). By squeezing air out of their **plumage**, they sink slowly below the surface of the water. As their feathers are not completely waterproof, they stand with their wings outstretched after fishing, drying them in the sun. The North American species are **migratory**, while the birds found in tropical locales are not.

Diet

They are primarily fish eaters, with crustaceans, eels and amphibians also taken. They dive in pursuit of prey, and the fish is brought to the surface before being swallowed. Often persecuted by fishermen, these birds in fact take smaller fish of no economic importance. Eighty percent of their diet is actually cunners and sculpins, which are direct enemies of commercially useful fish.

Reproduction

Cormorants are **gregarious** birds, breeding in large colonies on rocky shores, cliff ledges or in trees. The circular nests are bulky structures of sticks, marine plants, rubbish and seaweed. Two to seven bluish white eggs are laid, and **incubated** 22–31 days by both sexes. The eggs hatch in the order they are laid. Young cormorants are **altricial**, hatched naked and helpless, and do not attain adult **plumage** until their third year.

Family Status

Cormorants have been exploited by man for centuries for their fishing skills. In the Orient, they were fitted with a ring around their neck to prevent them from swallowing, then secured by a cord to the boat. When they resurfaced from a dive, the fisherman would run his hands up the bird's neck, and the fish would be deposited in the boat.

In South America, the guanay cormorant is called the most valuable wild bird in the world, due to the value of its excrement, or guano, for commercial fertilizers. Millions of birds in their nesting colonies provide tons of guano annually, which is harvested and sold.

Steller's spectacled cormorant has been extinct since 1850. Once found on islands in the Bering Sea, these birds were nearly flightless. Weighing 5–6 kg (12–14 lbs), they were hunted to extinction for their meat. They are one of the rarest museum specimens in the world, with only six stuffed birds and two skeletons remaining.

Brandt's Cormorant

Size: 85–90 cm (34–36"), wingspan to 1.2 m (49")
Range: Pacific coast from Alaska to Mexico

- throat pouch becomes bright blue in breeding season
- often gather in compact flocks over feeding grounds with only their head, neck and part of their back showing above the water
- males fight fiercely over **territories** no bigger than their nest site

Nest in waters along Vancouver Island.

Cormorant comes from '*cormoran*,' which means pertaining to the sea.

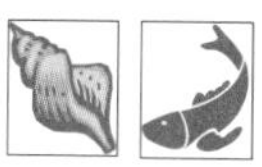

Double-crested Cormorant

Size: 72–90 cm (29"–36"), wingspan 1.3 m (54")
Range: Southern Canada, central USA; coastal North America to Florida and California

- dive to 7.5 m (25 ft) in pursuit of fish, and stay submerged 30–70 seconds
- employ communal fishing techniques, where the birds herd fish into a fan shaped formation
- old nests are often rebuilt and may be used up to four years
- the only cormorant likely to be seen on inland waterways
- population dropped from 1969–1971 due to high levels of pesticides in fish

Nest across Canada.

Great Cormorant

Size: 80–100 cm (32"–40"), wingspan 1.5 m (60")
Range: Atlantic coast of Canada and USA; Greenland, Iceland to the Mediterranean

- can stay submerged for 20–70 seconds
- in breeding season, they have turquoise blue eyes
- adults do not reproduce until three to five years of age
- in hot weather, the adults bring water in their **gular pouch** and **crop** to pour over the chicks

Nest along the Gulf of St Lawrence and the east coast.

Pelagic Cormorant

Size: 62–72 cm (25" –29"), wingspan 1 m (40")
Range: Pacific coast from Alaska to Mexico; Bering Sea to Japan

- have been caught in fishermen's nets at 54 m (180 ft) below the surface
- can take flight from the water surface, and from an underwater dive
- nest may be used in successive seasons until it is 1.5–1.8 m (5–6 ft) high

Nest on coast of British Columbia.

World Species 15
Canadian Species 2

The Crane Family - Gruidae

Characteristics

Cranes are tall, stately, long-necked, wading birds living on wide marshlands, wet plains and prairies. They stand 0.6–1.5 m (2–5 ft), with a wingspan of 2.1–2.4 m (7–8 ft), and are the tallest flying birds. **Plumage** is largely greyish blue or white. Sexes look alike, but the males are slightly larger. The sturdy bill is long and straight, and the head is partially naked of feathers. They have a specially modified windpipe which produces trumpet-like sounds that can be heard for several miles. Wings are long and wide, with inner **secondary feathers** that hang over the short tail when resting. Their long, powerful legs have four sharp, clawed toes on each foot.

Behaviour

Cranes mate for life, and are known as the dancers of the bird world for their graceful **courtship** displays. Pairs will leap 1.8–2.5 m (6–8 ft) into the air, swing sideways and bow before each other, uttering loud cries and bugles. Young cranes often dance in what is believed to be sheer exuberance, and mated pairs dance to reinforce the pair bond. **Migrating**, 'V' shaped flocks often fly at great heights, up to 9,100 m (30,000 ft). In flight, their long neck is stretched out and the stilt-like legs trail behind.

Graceful **terrestrial** birds, they stalk sedately about in marshes and on plains searching for food.

Diet

Cranes eat a variety of animal and vegetable matter: mice, eggs, young birds, insects, snakes and grain.

Reproduction

Nests are mounds of marsh plants built by both sexes in shallow water with a slight depression in the centre, and surrounded by tall vegetation. **Clutches** normally contain two greenish white eggs, which are **incubated** 28–35 days by both sexes. Chicks are covered with brownish or grey down and can swim and walk when a few hours old, but do not fly until 60–90 days after hatching. Once the chicks have hatched, they will remain with their parents through the next breeding season, **migrating** with them to their wintering grounds. Young birds often form flocks of their own, and do not breed until they are three to five years old.

Family Status

The Japanese regard cranes as symbols of longevity that live for 1,000 years. While this is an exaggeration, cranes are very long lived birds, with one Siberian white crane living to 61 years old.

Cranes are a very old family, with fossil records dating back 40–60 million years. Found in Asia, Europe, North America and Africa, populations are decreasing everywhere due to loss of marshland habitat and hunting. One species, the whooping crane, is on Canada's endangered species list.

Which bird is completely encased in feathers from its beak to its toes?

(see page 127 for the answer)

Sandhill Crane

Size: 85–120 cm (34"–48"), wingspan to 2.1 m (84")
Range: Alaska, Canada, USA to Mexico and Cuba

- during a summer, these birds will consume 400 to 500 grasshoppers, crickets and earthworms daily
- nest is made by both sexes of whole plants pulled up by the roots
- flight speed to 56 kmh (35 mph)
- lifespan up to 20 years

Nest in northern Canada from Alberta to Ontario.

Crane comes from the Anglo Saxon '*cran,*' meaning to cry out.

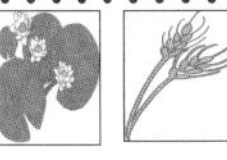

Whooping Crane

Size: 122–140 cm (49"–56"), wingspan to 2.2 m (90")
Range: Northwest Territories, Alberta to Texas

- tallest and heaviest North American wading bird, averaging 6–7 kg (14–16 lbs)
- windpipe is 1.5 m (5 ft) long and buried in the hollow keel of the breastbone
- one bird in Texas reportedly ate 800 grasshoppers in 75 minutes
- nest is 1.2–1.5 m (4–5 ft) across
- female **incubates** the eggs at night, and the male sits during the day
- eliminated from their historical nesting range because of drained marshes and planted crops
- nearly extinct by 1941 due to habitat loss and hunting; the population was down to 21 birds
- population critically endangered with approximately 400 birds (1999)

Whooping Crane

Nest only in Wood Buffalo National Park, Alberta.

When depicted in English heraldry, cranes are always holding a stone in one foot, an image that became symbolic of vigilance. This rose from a legend telling how one bird stood guard at night and if danger threatened, he dropped the rock to warn the others.

World Species 6
Canadian Species 1

The Creeper Family - Certhiidae

Characteristics

Creepers are small, 12–15 cm (5"–6") tree dwelling, perching birds found in old growth mixed and coniferous forests. **Plumages** are generally brown with some white barring or spots. Both sexes look the same. Their name comes from their behaviour of creeping about on trunks and branches, searching for food in the bark cavities with their long, **downcurved** bills. Their long, sharp, curved claws grip the bark surface, and the stiff tail is used as a third support.

Behaviour

These small **arboreal** birds are always active. Feeding behaviour is a spiraling movement up the tree trunk, then a drop to the ground at the base of the next tree before climbing again. Thin, hissing sounds are used to keep in contact with others in foraging groups, or between pairs in the spring. These high pitched calls are sometimes beyond the hearing of humans. When frightened, creepers freeze and flatten against the tree trunk, which makes them virtually invisible.

A non-**migratory** species, creepers maintain the same range year round.

Diet

Their strong bill is specially adapted for feeding on hidden insects, larvae and other small creatures. Many **invertebrates** winter in cracks and crevices in the bark, and their specialized bill allows creepers access where birds with smaller, stubby bills are unsuccessful.

Reproduction

Creepers are cavity nesters, nesting in rotting tree cavities or under a strip of bark on a dead tree. The nest is made of grass, moss and conifer needles, woven together with spider silk. Five to eight translucent white eggs with dark markings are laid. **Incubation** lasts 14–15 days, and the young leave the nest 13–14 days after hatching.

Family Status

Creepers are widely distributed throughout Europe and Asia, and particularly in the Himalayan mountains. They are found in all **temperate** forests of the northern hemisphere. The brown creeper is the only member of the family in North America and the United Kingdom, where they are called 'tree creepers'.

Brown Creeper

Size: 12–15 cm (5"–6")
Range: Alaska, Canada, USA, Central America

- strong, stiff tail feathers lend support in climbing, and these central tail feathers are so important they are **moulted** separately from the others
- common in Canada but often overlooked because of their colour and size
- lifespan up to 5 years

 Nest across central Canada.

World Species 103
Canadian Species 8

The Crow, Jay & Magpie Family - Corvidae

Characteristics

Corvids are the largest perching birds in the world, ranging from 25–67 cm (10"–27"). Crows and ravens have black feathers with a metallic blue or green gloss. Nutcrackers, jays and magpies have brighter colouring, in which grey, green, white or blue are prominent. The sexes are similar in **plumage**, and there are no seasonal changes. Noisy, **gregarious** birds, they have long, stout bills and strong legs, feet and wings. Large external nostrils are partially concealed and shielded by small bristly feathers. The family represents one of the most advanced stages of avian evolution, showing a highly developed intelligence and complex social organization.

Behaviour

These birds have the highest ratio of brain size to body weight of any family of birds. American crows can be taught to string beads, count up to four, and are good at solving puzzles and performing astonishing feats of memory. All members of this family are skillful mimics of other birds, mammals, and humans, and appear to have a language of their own. Although they are classed as songbirds, they have no true song, only harsh loud squawks and calls.

Some members of this family are known to ride the back of large hoofed mammals such as elk, picking off ticks embedded in their fur. Extremely curious birds, they are well known camp robbers, stealing any food they can find from campers and hikers. They often use their strong feet to hold their food while eating. Jays have been known to store 3,000 acorns a month, thereby helping to propagate oak trees. Food **caching** is prevalent in this family, and they are all quick to exploit any opportunity to seize unexpected food items. Crows learned to drop mollusks from the air to break them open by watching gulls. Gulls dropped them repeatedly on sand and mud, but the crows were quick to learn to use rocks and other hard surfaces.

Diet

Corvids are **omnivorous** scavengers who eat virtually anything—insects, mollusks, seeds, fruit, nuts, carrion, mice, eggs and fish.

Reproduction

These birds mate for life. **Courtship** is marked by **allopreening** and feeding, behaviour which is also used to maintain pair bonds. Nests are bulky masses of twigs and stems located from ground level to 46 m (150 ft) up, and vary in size according to the species. From two to thirteen greyish green eggs with dark markings are laid, and **incubation** starts with the first egg. As the young hatch in the order they were laid, there is a considerable size difference among the **clutch**. The smallest and youngest chicks will die if there is not enough food for all. Young are **altricial,** born naked and helpless. Females generally do all the **incubating**, but males feed the female as she is **brooding**, and both parents help feed the newly hatched chicks. The young leave the nest at 17–28 days, but do not fly until 28–42 days after hatching. Some species nest in loose colonies and some are solitary nesters.

Family Status

Corvids are found throughout Europe, Africa, Asia and the Americas. Most corvid species are non-**migratory**, or make only local movements in times of food shortages.

American Crow

Size: 42–53 cm (17"–21"), wingspan to 1 m (40")
Range: Canada, USA

- immature crows have blue eyes, while adults have brown ones
- have at least 23 different calls
- Latin name means "*raven with a small nose*"
- carry clams, scallops, mussels and sea urchins high into the air, then drop them on rocks or highways to crack them open
- gather in large flocks in the fall and winter—up to 200,000 birds
- do not breed until their second year
- flight speed to 52 kmh (32 mph)
- lifespan up to 14 years

Nest from north central British Columbia to Newfoundland.

> Crows have been the subject of superstition and legend in every country.
>
> ◆
>
> They were considered sacred by many native American tribes.
>
> ◆
>
> The term 'scarecrow' originated from farmers hanging dead crows on a fence or making straw figures to keep these birds from their crops.

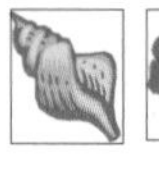

Northwestern Crow

Size: 40–42 cm (16"–17")
Range: Alaska, British Columbia to Washington

- well known as a beachcomber and scavenger, eating food washed in by the tides
- mated pairs form very strong attachments to each other
- drop food from great heights onto rocks or roads to break shells open
- found only along seacoasts and in coastal towns

Nest along British Columbia coast.

Blue Jay

Size: 27–32 cm (11"–12"), wingspan to 44 cm (17")
Range: Western Canada and USA, east of the Rocky Mountains

- known to guard and feed older, tired blue jays, even leading them to water
- **caches** nuts and seeds in the ground, many of which sprout into new trees
- the pair build a false nest of twigs before building the true one where the female lays the eggs
- male feeds female during breeding season **courtship**
- provincial bird of Prince Edward Island
- lifespan up to 15 years

Blue Jay

Nest from central Alberta to Newfoundland.

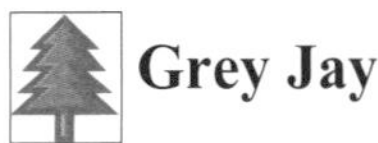

Grey Jay

Size: 25–32 cm (10"–13"), wingspan to 42 cm (17")
Range: Alaska, Canada, western USA

- are able to lower their body temperature and enter a state of controlled **hypothermia** to conserve body heat during the winter
- do not **cache** food in the ground as heavy snow may cover it; instead they glue seeds and nuts to conifer needles using their sticky saliva
- very bold; known for stealing food from campers, hunters and hikers, and for following the noise of a gunshot to a carcass
- nest built by both sexes in late winter (February - March)
- sometimes called 'Canada jay', also known as 'whiskey-jacks', from the Cree word '*wiskedjac'*
- lifespan up to 10 years

Nest from Yukon to Newfoundland except for the Great Plains.

All members of the Corvid family are famous for their habit of **'anting'**.

Landing on an ant hill, they walk about and stir up the ants so the insects swarm all over their body.

Irritated ants secrete formic acid, which is a powerful insecticide. This kills the pests in the bird's feathers. No harm appears to come to the bird from this practice.

Steller's Jay

Size: 30–32 cm (12"–13")
Range: Canada and USA west of Rocky Mountains, to Mexico

- **plumage** is dark blue and black
- range up to 3,350 m (11,000 ft) in the Rocky Mountains
- provincial bird of British Columbia

Nest in British Columbia and southwestern Alberta.

Black-billed Magpie

Size: 44–55 cm (17"–22") incl. tail 22–30 cm (9"–12"), wingspan to 60 cm (24")
Range: Alaska, western Canada and USA; Europe, Asia

- readily identified by white and dark **plumage**; dark colours are actually iridescent green
- tail is slightly more than one half the length of the entire bird
- will alight on the backs of large mammals such as deer, to pick ticks from their fur
- known for raiding the nests of other birds, and eating young birds and eggs
- the nest building process is part of **courtship**; the male brings the female twigs and she arranges them
- nests are composed of a domed mass of sticks with side entrances, held together with mud

Nest from southern Yukon to western Manitoba.

There is an old legend that says the magpie was the only bird to refuse to enter the ark, preferring instead to sit on a perch on the roof, from which it could jabber about the discomfort of those caught in the flood.

Clark's Nutcracker

Size: 30–32 cm (12"–13")
Range: Western Canada and USA

- have elastic pouches under their tongues to store up to 70 seeds at once
- highly **gregarious** flocks show a complex social organization
- use their bills like a crowbar to pry seeds from cones, then **cache** them in over 1,000 locations each winter; can process up to 30,000 seeds per season
- show remarkable ability to locate seed **cache**, even if it's buried under snow
- will dig through 20 cm (8") of snow to retrieve seeds
- found up to 4,000 m (13,000 ft) in Rocky Mountains
- named for William Clark of Lewis & Clark expedition

Nest in southern British Columbia and southwestern Alberta.

The word raven comes from the Anglo Saxon '*hraefn,*' referring to its cry.

Common Raven

Size: 55–67 cm (21"–27"), wingspan to 1.4 m (56")
Range: Alaska, Canada, USA to Central America; Iceland, Europe, Asia, Africa

- largest perching bird in the world, and largest member of the crow family
- black **plumage** has an iridescent purple hue
- soar at great heights like hawks or eagles, often performing acrobatic rolls in flight where pairs dive to earth or turn over in a series of somersaults
- nest is built of dead branches broken off by the bills of both sexes, enclosing a deep cup in the centre; up to 1 m (3 ft) across and 1.2 m (4 ft) high
- Alexander the Great was said to have been led across the desert by two ravens
- in Britain, legend maintains that England will not fall as long as ravens live in the Tower of London, and the birds are protected at that site
- provincial bird of the Yukon
- flight speed to 56 kmh (35 mph)
- lifespan up to 29 years

Nest from high Arctic islands to Newfoundland, but are expanding their range southward.

One name for a group of ravens is an 'unkindness,' as it was once thought that the parent birds pushed their young out of the nest to feed on dew until they reached a certain age.

World Species 127
Canadian Species 2

The Cuckoo Family - Cuculidae

Characteristics

Cuckoos are long, slim, medium sized birds, 27–32 cm (11"–12") with long tails. Their grey or brown **plumage** is loose-webbed, and stiff and wiry in some species. Sexes look alike. The longish bill is slightly **decurved,** and stout. Legs are short in **arboreal** species and long in those that live on the ground. They have two toes pointing forward and two pointing backward.

Behaviour

Shy, retiring birds, cuckoos are difficult to see in the woodlands, and more likely to be heard than seen. They all have loud, unmusical voices and call when flying, sitting on the nest, or at night. Most species are found in the tropics, and those in **temperate** climates **migrate** to warmer areas in the winter.

Diet

Cuckoos eat insects, including hairy caterpillars which other birds don't like, lizards, small snakes, snails, and spiders. Their fondness for tent caterpillars makes them economically valuable to man.

Reproduction

Many **Old World** species are solely **brood parasites**, laying their eggs in the nests of other birds. Their eggs are thicker shelled, and sometimes have partially developed embryos when laid so they hatch sooner. If the cuckoo young is bigger than the host young, they will easily evict eggs and hatchlings from the nest. If the host young are the same size, cuckoo chicks make the same noise as the host, thereby confusing the female into thinking they are all hers.

North American cuckoos usually build their own loosely constructed nest of twigs lined with leaves, grass, moss and catkins, located up to 3.6 m (12 ft) above the ground in small trees. Two to four bluish green eggs are laid, and **incubated** by both sexes for 14 days, starting with the first egg. The young are born blind and helpless, and climb agilely around in the nesting bush at 7–14 days. Chicks are studded with stout quills that finally open into feathers just before they **fledge**.The immature **plumage** of the young is very much like that of the adult. The two North American species occasionally lay eggs in each others' nests.

Family Status

This family also includes roadrunners, ani and coucals, and is found in Europe, Asia, Africa, Australia and the Americas. In some areas, cuckoos are called 'rain crows' because their calls were once thought to predict rain. They are most numerous in years of heavy tent caterpillar infestations.

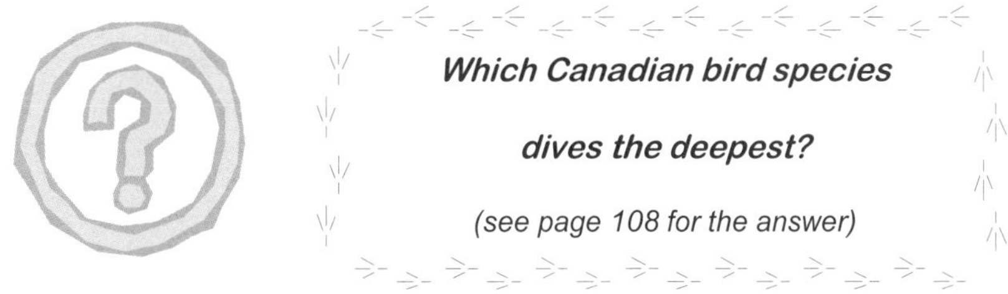

Black-billed Cuckoo

Size: 27–32 cm (11"–12"), wingspan to 42 cm (17")
Range: Central and eastern Canada and USA to South America

- one of the few birds to eat hairy caterpillars
- nestlings will feign death if disturbed
- sometimes **parasitize** nests of yellow-billed cuckoo and other bird species

Nest from central Alberta to the Maritimes.

Named for their '*cuck-oo*' call, the two note call of the European species has been invoked in many songs as well as cuckoo clocks.

Yellow-billed Cuckoo

Size: 27–32 cm (11"–12"), wingspan to 42 cm (17")
Range: Southern Canada, USA to South America

- up to 325 caterpillars found in the stomach of one bird
- sometimes lays eggs in the nest of the black-billed cuckoo
- also called 'rain crow', 'rain dove' and 'storm crow' for their habit of making unusual sounds just prior to summer storms
- flight speed to 35 kmh (22 mph)

Nest in southeastern Ontario and adjacent Quebec, with a small population in New Brunswick.

World Species 4
Canadian Species 1

The Dipper Family - Cinclidae

Characteristics

Dippers are the only truly **aquatic** songbirds. Plain, chunky birds of 17–21 cm (7"–8"), they have an extremely active disposition. Their soft, shiny **plumage** is predominantly grey or brown, and they have a thick undercoat of down. Sexes are alike. Dippers are closely related to both wrens and thrushes, and have some characteristics of each. They have slender, straight bills, short wings and tails, and stout claws for gripping the river bed in strong currents.

Dippers possess a large **preen gland**, 10% larger than other songbirds, which provides oil to keep their feathers waterproof. Moveable flaps over the nostrils keep out water, and their well developed **nictitating membrane** protects the eyes from sprays of water.

Behaviour

Dippers are named for their habit of bobbing their body rapidly up and down, some 40–60 times per minute. Although they swim poorly on the surface using their non-webbed feet, they are strong swimmers underwater, using their wings for propulsion. They can 'fly' to a depth of 6 m (20 ft) to reach the bottom to feed, and stay under the surface for 25 seconds. Dippers also walk along the bottom of streams, and readily plunge into water from the bank, boulder, or ice flow. They are generally solitary, and have a **territory** of 0.8–1.6 km (1/2–1 mi) of stream length, defended by song. Their ringing songs may be heard even in the dead of winter, and both sexes sing.

Diet

Feeding in freshwater streams, dippers eat the larvae of **aquatic** insects, mollusks, crustaceans, snails and small fish.

Reproduction

Nests are built on rock faces, under banks or against tree trunks with the entrance normally over water. The grass nests fit into the roofed cavity, and then the outer shell is built of mosses, which are dipped into the water before use. Three to six white eggs are laid, and **incubated** 15–17 days by the female. Both parents feed the young, and they sometimes have two **clutches** per year. The young fly 24–25 days after hatching.

Family Status

Dippers are confined to hilly and mountain regions of the Alps, Andes, Rockies and Himalayas. In Europe, they are known as 'water ouzels'.

 **American Dipper**

Size: 17–21 cm (7"–8")
Range: Alaska, western Canada and USA, Central America

- live at elevations of 600–3,500 m (2,000–11,500 ft)
- do not **migrate**, but may move down to lower mountain elevations if streams freeze
- sing throughout the year, with their song audible over rushing water

Nest in the mountains of British Columbia and Alberta.

World Species 295
Canadian Species 3

The Dove Family - Columbidae

Characteristics

Doves, or pigeons as they are also known, are plump birds with broad shoulders, short necks, small heads and short, slender bills with a fleshy area at the base. They range in size from 27–40 cm (11"–16"). Their soft, thick **plumage** is highly varied, and most have some metallic or iridescent glossy feathers. The sexes look alike. Long-shafted feathers are so loosely attached to the skin that they drop out easily, giving protection against being caught in the grasp of predators. Although wing sizes vary considerably among the species, they are all very strong fliers. Their legs are short with four toes on sturdy feet.

Behaviour

Most species are highly **gregarious**, and can be found perching in trees, along cliff ledges or walking on the ground with a mincing gate and bobbing head. They have the unusual ability to immerse their bill in water and suck it up, unlike most birds that must tip their heads back to drink. The most common vocalization is a cooing sound, which is produced while inflating the neck. Other sounds include hisses, grunts and whistles.

Diet

Most are ground feeders, eating a large variety of seeds, berries, nuts, buds, leaves, snails, worms and caterpillars. Some tropical species live largely on fruit. Food is stored in a **crop**, and doves have large, muscular **gizzards** that process their food. These birds can often be seen on the ground picking up small bits of gravel to help grind the food.

Reproduction

Nests are platforms of twigs, stems and roots located from ground level to 12 m (40 ft) up in trees, or on cliffs, bridges and buildings. One to four white eggs are laid, and **incubated** by both sexes for 17–19 days. Young are fed by both parents for the first few days on ‘pigeon’s milk’, a curd-like material rich in fat and protein that is secreted by special cells lining the crop. This liquid is scooped up when the young insert their bills deep into the parent’s mouth. Because of this specialized method of feeding, young grow rapidly and some can fly at two weeks. All species have two or three **clutches** per year.

Family Status

This family is found throughout the world except for the polar regions and some oceanic islands.

The ancient Romans used rock doves as messengers. News of Napoleon’s defeat at Waterloo reached England by carrier pigeon four days before ships and horses brought the news. In both World Wars, pigeons were used to carry messages across enemy lines. Doves are trained to return to their home lofts by taking them gradually farther away and releasing them. They are guided by the sun as a compass for direction, then use an internal time sense to correct their course to compensate for the sun’s movement.

The dodo, a large flightless dove hunted to extinction in 1680, is possibly the most well known extinct species in the world. Ten other dove species are now extinct, including the passenger pigeon of North America. Their massive flocks once darkened the sky, but within a very short span of time, man had hunted them to extinction. The last one on earth died at the Cincinnati Zoo in 1914.

Mourning Dove

Size: 27–32 cm (11"–13"), wingspan to 47 cm (19")
Range: Alaska, Canada, USA to Central America and Bahamas

- named for its sad, plaintive call, these are the most common native doves in North America
- mate for life
- male selects a **territory** in the spring and defends it by flying at and pecking other males
- nest often built on top of those of other birds
- the stomach of one bird held over 13,000 weed seeds
- flight speed to 72 kmh (45 mph)

Nest across southern and central Canada.

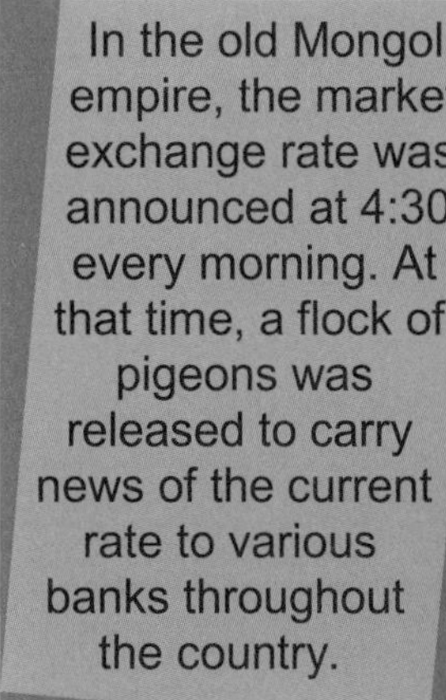

In the old Mongol empire, the market exchange rate was announced at 4:30 every morning. At that time, a flock of pigeons was released to carry news of the current rate to various banks throughout the country.

Rock Dove

Size: 32–35 cm (13"–14")
Range: Worldwide except for polar regions and Australia

- also called 'carrier pigeon', 'homing pigeon' or 'common pigeon'
- named for its preference of nesting on rocky places
- one of the swiftest birds in flight, up to 150 kmh (94 mph)
- nest up to an altitude of 1,500 m (5,000 ft) in Asia
- have multiple **clutches** per year
- believed to be the first domesticated bird, as the ancient Egyptians in 3,000 BC raised them for their meat and message carrying capabilities
- introduced to North America from Europe in 1606 at Port Royal, Nova Scotia
- lifespan up to 16 years

Nest across southern and central Canada.

Band-tailed Pigeon

Size: 35–40 cm (14"–16")
Range: Southwestern Canada, western USA to Central America

- also called 'wild pigeon'
- flocks fond of perching for long periods in the tops of tall trees
- regularly visit mineral springs, attracted by the calcium
- vulnerable to hunting because of their easy visibility, and habitat in Central American highlands where the human population is very dense
- have recovered from near extinction due to overhunting in North America

Band-tailed Pigeon

Nest in southwestern British Columbia.

World Species 148
Canadian Species 26

The Duck Family - Anatidae

Characteristics

Ducks are **aquatic**, swimming birds with webbed feet, short legs and tails, and longish necks. They range in size from 32–67 cm (13"–27"). Colouring differs between males and females, with the males being more brightly coloured. Their dense **plumage** is underlaid with a layer of soft down. Feathers are kept waterproof by anointing them with oil from a gland on their rump. Narrow, pointed wings mean they are swift, strong fliers. The wide, flat bill has fine serrations along the edge, and a soft membranous covering with a hooked tip. Species found in **temperate** or polar regions have a special adaptation for keeping the feet warm on ice. The arteries and veins are close together so warm, outward-flowing blood warms the cooler blood returning from the feet.

Behaviour

Highly **gregarious**, ducks gather in large flocks throughout the year except for breeding season, when they separate into pairs. Once a year, most species undergo an **eclipse moult,** where they lose all their flight feathers and are unable to fly for a few weeks. Males **moult** while the females are **incubating**, and the females **moult** when the young have **fledged**. Once the new, healthy **flight feathers** have grown in, they are able to leave the area and more effectively avoid predators. All species are **migratory.** Vocalizations are simple grunts, hoots, honks and coos produced by the males, but the quack is almost always the female.

Diet

Ducks feed on a wide variety of **aquatic** plants and animals, with some species also eating grain.

Reproduction

Courtship displays are genetically fixed and unique to each species, serving to prevent cross-breeding in large mixed flocks. Females often incite males to fight by swimming between two opponents.

Ducks cannot carry items in their bills, so nesting material is anything within reach at the nest sight. Material is pulled in with the bill and placed at their feet, forming a pile as the bird rotates. Down feathers are plucked from the female's breast to line the nest, and pulled over the eggs when she leaves to feed.

One egg is laid per day, usually early in the morning. **Delayed incubation** does not start until the last egg is laid, ensuring all eggs hatch at the same time, after about six hours. The female remains on the nest the first day after hatching, so the young can **imprint** on her appearance and voice. The day after hatching, the mother leads the **precocial** young to the water, where they swim and peck at food items. The hens guard and **brood** the young, but do not feed them. Males take no part in nest building, **incubation** or raising of young. Ducklings are covered with a soft down for about two weeks, then juvenile **plumage** feathers gradually develop.

Family Status

Ducks were among the first birds domesticated for their eggs and meat, and are found on every continent except Antarctica. Six species have become extinct since 1874, including the Labrador duck of the Atlantic coast. The last one was shot in 1875.

Ducks are divided into three separate sub-families, based on their behaviour and feeding habits.
(see following pages)

World Species 20
Canadian Species 15

Diving Ducks - subfamily Aythyini

Characteristics

These ducks dive for their food, aided in their swimming and diving by large feet and short legs. Their legs are located further to the rear of the body than those of other duck species, and they are awkward on land. They seldom visit crop fields like the dabbling ducks. Their smaller, more pointed wings make for swift flight, but these birds require a running start across the water while flapping to take to the air. Males of only a few species go through the **eclipse moult.**

This subfamily is further divided into sea ducks living on the ocean, and bay ducks who spend most of their time on inland waters.

Behaviour

Diving ducks are usually silent, and far less noisy than other species. Most species breed in the north, and **migrate** in large, compact flocks to their coastal wintering grounds.

Diet

Inland species dive for vegetation, leaves, roots, seeds and **aquatic** insects. Those that live primarily on the ocean feed on mollusks, crustaceans and small fish. Mollusks are eaten whole and the shell is broken into fine pieces by the bird's **gizzard.**

Reproduction

Courtship displays involve the male jerking the head back on the tail while kicking up a spurt of water, bowing while producing dove-like coos, and wagging the head from side to side.

Nesting habits are variable, with some birds nesting in tree cavities, some in cattail marshes and some on the tundra in small colonies. Egg colour varies from pinkish white to buffy green or cream. Three to nineteen eggs are laid, and **incubated** by the female for 23–32 days. Young leave the nest 24–36 hours after hatching, and fly 35–77 days after hatching.

The chicks of those species nesting in tree cavities leave the nest soon after hatching by jumping to the ground, protected from the fall by their downy covering. They bounce when they land, then follow the female to water.

Family Status

This is a very widespread family, covering much of the northern hemisphere during the summer months. Several species are suffering from loss of habitat as the prairie marshes are drained, and one species, the Harlequin duck, is on Canada's endangered species list.

What bird species is estimated to be the most numerous in the world?

(see page 158 for the answer)

Bufflehead Duck

Size: 32–40 cm (13"–16"), wingspan to 60 cm (24")
Range: Alaska, Canada, USA

- so named because their large, shaggy head shape resembled that of the buffalo
- smallest sea duck species
- birds pair up during spring **migration** north
- unlike other diving ducks, buffleheads can take off from the water without running along the surface
- nest in tree cavities up to 6 m (20 ft) above the ground, always near water
- flight speed 77 kmh (48 mph)

Nest Canada wide.

Canvasback Duck

Size: 47–60 cm (19"–24"), wingspan to 90 cm (36")
Range: Alaska, Canada, USA to Central America and Cuba

- **migrate** at high altitudes with great speed
- use their bill to strain seeds from the mud on the bottom of ponds, and also ingest poisonous lead shot
- with a flight speed of 115 kmh (72 mph), they are one of the fastest ducks in flight
- lifespan up to 19 years

Nest in Yukon, Alberta and southern Saskatchewan and Manitoba.

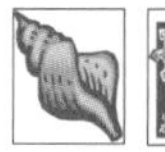

Common Eider Duck

Size: 57–67 cm (23"–27"), wingspan to 1 m (42")
Range: Alaska, coastal Canada; Greenland, Asia, Russia

- biggest North American duck
- adaptations to life in the Arctic include a dense coat of down, a thick layer of fat, and feathers covering almost all of the beak; can endure temperatures of -45°C (-50°F)
- can dive to 18 m (60 ft)
- seldom fly over land, travelling immense distances around land masses to reach their breeding grounds on the tundra
- use their wings to swim underwater, and if alarmed, they come out of the water flying
- nest in small colonies where they are not persecuted by man

Nest on coasts of the Maritimes and the Arctic Ocean.

Eider ducks possess a soft down undercoat whose insulating properties are unsurpassed by any man-made fibers. The down is collected during and after **incubation** for use in producing eiderdowns and padded clothing.

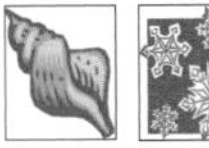 

King Eider Duck

Size: 47–62 cm (19"–25"), wingspan to 1 m (40")
Range: Northern and Atlantic Canada; Greenland, Europe, Russia

- named for the male's bright orange knob above the bill, and the pearly grey crown
- full adult **plumage** is not attained until their third year
- can dive to 55 m (180 ft)
- nests are scattered over the tundra on the mainland, well back from the coast

Nest on the coasts of the Arctic Ocean.

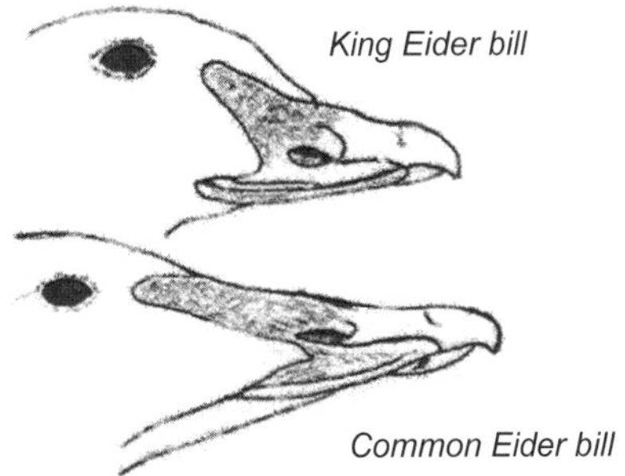

Harlequin Duck

Size: 37–52 cm (15"–21"), wingspan to 70 cm (28")
Range: Alaska, western and Atlantic Canada; Greenland, Russia

- name refers to the varied colours of the male that suggest an actor or harlequin made up to play a role
- dive underwater using both their feet and wings
- will walk on the bottom of streams looking for food

Nest in the Yukon and British Columbia, as well as northern Quebec and Labrador.

Long-tailed Duck

Size: 37–57 cm (15"–23"), wingspan to 77 cm (31")
Range: Northern and coastal Canada, Great Lakes; Europe, Russia

- male has two distinct **plumages** per year; dark with white highlights and white with dark highlights
- formerly called 'oldsquaw duck'
- utters a melodious call like that of a baying hound which can be heard for a mile; noisy and **garrulous** at all times
- can dive to 61 m (200 ft)
- nest on the tundra among Arctic terns which drive away predators by flying at them
- flight speed 117 kmh (73 mph)

Nest in the Yukon and Northwest Territories and Nunavut.

Redhead

Size: 45–55 cm (18"–22"), wingspan to 87 cm (35")
Range: Alaska, western Canada, USA to Jamaica

- fly rapidly in V-shaped flocks during **migration**
- dive to 3 m (10 ft) below the surface
- nest is attached to upright reed stems in marshes
- **dump nesters**, often laying their eggs in the nest of other ducks
- flight speed to 88 kmh (55 mph)

Nest in Alberta, Saskatchewan and southern Manitoba.

Ring-necked Duck

Size: 37–45 cm (15"–18"), wingspan to 75 cm (30")
Range: Canada, USA to Central America and Bahamas

- fly in small flocks of open formation
- can dive to 12 m (40 ft)
- highly susceptible to poisoning from lead shot picked up with their food
- lifespan up to 10 years

Nest Canada wide.

Goldeneyes are named for their bright yellow irises.

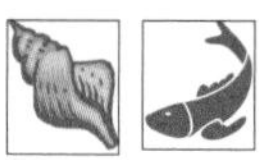

Barrow's Goldeneye

Size: 40–50 cm (16"–20"), wingspan 75 cm (30")
Range: Alaska, western Canada, USA; Iceland, Greenland

- fly close to the surface of the water before getting up enough speed to rise into the air
- vibrant whistling of the wings in flight can be heard over long distances
- love to play in the rapids of fast flowing streams
- nest in tree cavities up to 15 m (50 ft) off the ground, always near water

Nest in British Columbia and the Yukon.

Common Goldeneye

Size: 40–50 cm (16"–20"), wingspan to 80 cm (32")
Range: Alaska, Canada, USA; Europe, Russia, Mongolia

- swift, strong fliers attaining speeds up to 80 kmh (50 mph)
- dive to 6 m (20 ft) and may remain underwater for up to 21 seconds
- **courtship** starts in February on their wintering grounds
- nest in tree cavities up to 18 m (60 ft) above the ground, always near water
- lifespan up to 17 years

Nest Canada wide.

Common Goldeneyes

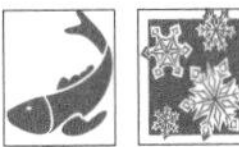

Greater Scaup

Size: 40–50 cm (16"–20"), wingspan to 85 cm (34")
Range: Alaska, Canada, USA; Europe, Asia, Russia

- may gather in flocks numbering 50,000 birds in their wintering grounds
- dive to 6 m (20 ft) and can remain submerged up to 60 seconds
- sometimes nest in small colonies on islands
- eggs laid in matted plants concealed in grasses on the tundra
- **dump nester**, often laying eggs in the nests of other birds
- the only scaup species found in both the **Old** and **New World**

Nest in Yukon, Northwest Territories, Nunavut and northeastern Canada.

Lesser Scaup

Size: 37–47 cm (15"–19"), wingspan to 82 cm (33")
Range: Alaska, Canada, USA to South America and West Indies

- dive to 6 m (20 ft)
- feed off pond bottoms, so are highly susceptible to lead poisoning from eating lead pellets
- lifespan up to 20 years

Nest Canada wide.

Black Scoter

Size: 42–52 cm (17"–21"), wingspan to 87 cm (35")
Range: Alaska, coastal Canada and USA; Eurasia

- the male is the only all black duck in North America
- bill has a large yellow knob at the base
- wings whistle in flight
- do not breed until their third year
- rarest and least known of North American scoters
- dive to 30 m (100 ft)

Nest in northern Quebec and Labrador.

Scoters are named for their habit of 'scooting' through foaming wave crests.

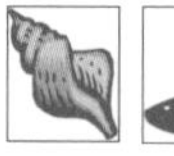  

Surf Scoter

Size: 42–52 cm (17"–21"), wingspan to 90 cm (36")
Range: Alaska, Canada, USA

- swim using their feet and the inner half of their wings, with the flight feathers folded back
- dive to 9 m (30 ft), and can stay submerged for up to 32 seconds
- to dive, they spring clear of the water and lunge forward and down in a high arc
- the only scoter species confined to the **New World**

Nest in Yukon, Northwest Territories and northern Canada.

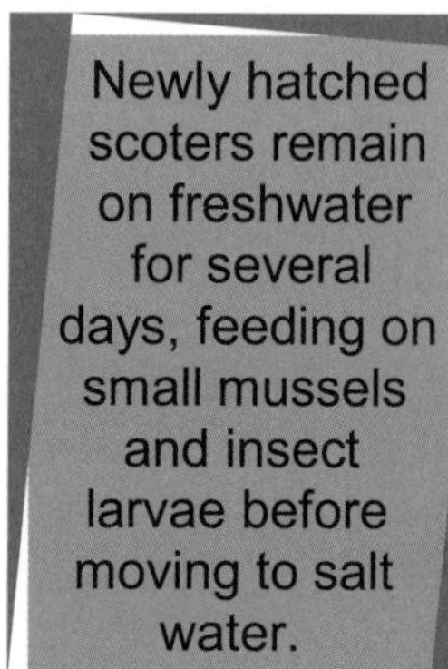

White-winged Scoter

Size: 47–60 cm (19"–24"), wingspan to 1 m (40")
Range: Alaska, Canada, USA; Eurasia

- largest scoter species
- dive to 12 m (40 ft), and stay submerged for 57 seconds
- do not come on land except for nesting season
- feed chiefly on mollusks which they collect from mussel beds
- feeding on shellfish is sometimes hazardous, as clams can close on the tongue of the bird and hang on
- **migrate** in long, irregular lines just offshore and a few metres above the water
- most abundant and widespread scoter numbering over one million birds in North America

Nest in Yukon, Northwest Territories and northern British Columbia through Manitoba.

World Species 39
Canadian Species 10

Dabbling Ducks - subfamily Anatini

Characteristics

Dabbling, or surface feeding, ducks have much smaller feet than diving ducks. Their short legs are placed toward the sides of the body and they walk with a distinctive waddle. With larger wings relative to their body size than other ducks, they can spring from the surface to fly without running along the water. They fly slower than other ducks, and drop with more precision into smaller ponds and marshes.

Behaviour

These ducks feed in shallow water by tipping up the body and tail and reaching below the surface, or by putting their head and neck under the surface. Only the bill and neck are submerged, they do not swim underwater.

Diet

Their diet consists of **aquatic** vegetation on or just below the surface, and they can be found in the smallest ponds or even puddles. In the fall, they move into fields and woodlands to eat grains, berries and nuts.

Reproduction

Most of these ducks use a shallow depression in the ground as a nest. Five to fifteen greenish or pinkish white eggs are laid, and **incubated** 21–33 days by the female. The young leave the nest 24–36 hours after hatching, but do not fly until they are 35–63 days old.

Wood ducks are the only native species of perching duck in North America, characterized by well developed claws, long tails and very iridescent wings. They nest in tree cavities previously used by other birds. They do not build their own hole, or enlarge them in any way. When the young are just 24 hours old, they climb out of the hole, jump from the tree and bounce on the ground. The mother then leads them to water.

Family Status

Because many of these ducks pick up food from the bottom of the ponds, they are highly susceptible to poisoning from ingesting lead shot with their food. During hunting season, thousands of pounds of lead shot from shotgun shells are deposited in marshes and ponds. Many dabbling duck populations are declining. Habitat loss is also a great threat, as wetlands are drained for farming.

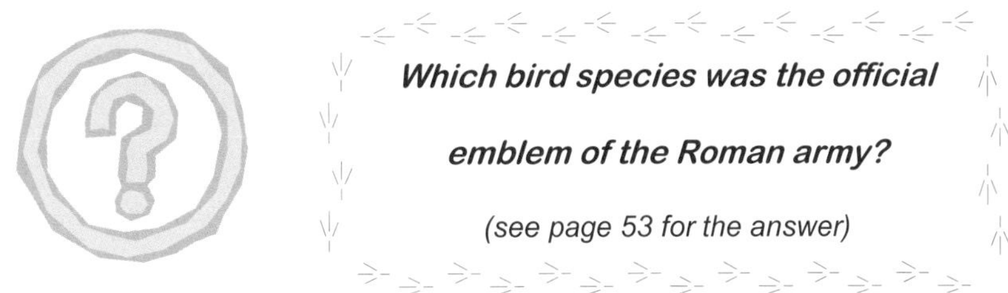

American Black Duck

Size: 52–62 cm (21"–25")
Range: Eastern Canada, USA to Bermuda

- one of the wariest, quickest, most alert of all ducks
- start into flight with a powerful spring from land or water, rising 2–3 m (8–10 ft) into the air before flying away
- flight speed 42 kmh (26 mph)

Nest from Ontario to the Maritimes.

Marsh or dabbling ducks rely on the touch receptors in their beaks to find food under the water, where it may be difficult to see.

If a food item cannot be reached by stretching the neck or tipping the whole body, it is unattainable.

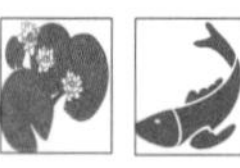

Gadwall Duck

Size: 47–57 cm (19"–23")
Range: Alaska, Canada, USA to Central America;
Iceland, Europe, Asia, Russia

- prefer to nest in small groups with others of their species
- flight speed 46 kmh (29 mph)

Nest in southern Alberta, Saskatchewan and Manitoba.

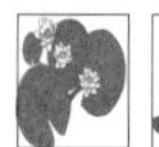 

Mallard Duck

Size: 50–70 cm (20"–28"), wingspan to 1 m (40")
Range: Alaska, Canada, USA to West Indies; Eurasia

- ancestor of all domestic ducks; first domesticated in China 2,000 years ago for their meat
- the most common duck species in the world
- 28,000 bullrush seeds were counted in the stomach of one bird
- flight speed 96 kmh (60 mph)
- lifespan up to 29 years

Nest Canada wide.

The word duck comes from the Anglo Saxon word for diver.

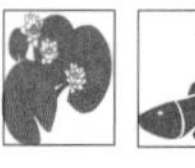 

Northern Pintail Duck

Size: 50–72 cm (20"–29")
Range: Alaska, Canada, USA to Hawaii & Central America; Russia, Scandinavia

- named for their long, tapering tail feathers
- each fall, more than one million pintails winter at a wildlife refuge in California
- most widely distributed North American duck species
- flight speed 104 kmh (65 mph)

Nest Canada wide.

Northern Shoveler Duck

Size: 42–50 cm (17"–20"), wingspan to 82 cm (33")
Range: Alaska, Canada, USA to Central America and West Indies; Europe, Russia, Asia

- named for their spatula or shovel-shaped bill
- bill has comb-like 'teeth' to strain food from the water
- take more animal matter than other dabbling ducks
- **courtship** involves repeated bobbing of the head by the male when near a female
- flight speed 85 kmh (53 mph)

Nest in Yukon, and British Columbia to Manitoba.

The word wigeon comes from the French '*vigeon,*' meaning whistling duck.

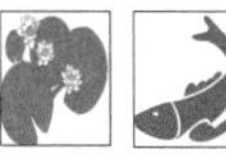

American Wigeon Duck

Size: 45–57 cm (18"–23"), wingspan to 87 cm (35")
Range: Alaska, Canada, USA to Central America and West Indies

- possess a characteristic, wheezy, laughing noise
- known to take food out of the mouths of American coots and diving ducks
- flocks sometimes turn and wheel rapidly in unison
- flight speed 35 kmh (22 mph)

Nest Canada wide.

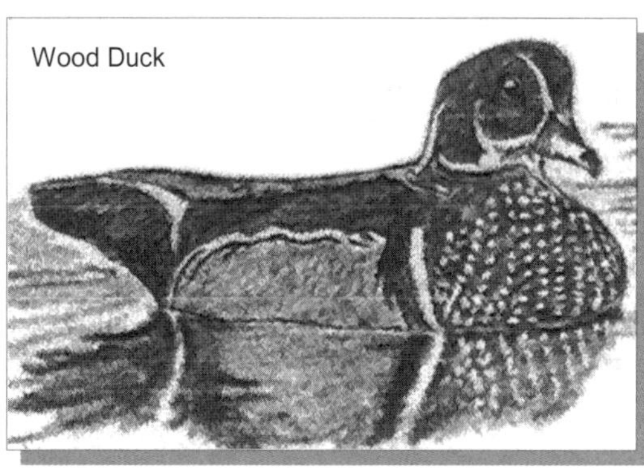
Wood Duck

Wood Duck

Size: 42–50 cm (17"–20"), wingspan to 75 cm (30")
Range: Canada, USA to Cuba

- eat more fruit and nuts than any other duck species
- Latin name means "*promised bride,*" suggesting the male is formally dressed
- walk and run with greater ease than most ducks, and frequently perch in trees
- nest as high as 15 m (50 ft) from the ground in tree cavities
- are often **dump nesters**, laying their eggs in the nests of other wood ducks
- population was almost wiped out when the early settlers cleared all the trees for farmland
- flight speed 88 kmh (55 mph)

Nest across southern Canada.

Cinnamon Teal

Size: 35–42 cm (14"–17"), wingspan to 65 cm (26")
Range: Canada, USA, Central and South America

- named for the reddish-brown colour of the males
- up and down movement of the head usually means they are about to take flight
- males often stay with their mates through the **incubation** period and raising of the young
- the only teal species to breed in both North and South America

Nest in interior British Columbia and southern Alberta.

Blue-winged Teal

Size: 35–40 cm (14"–16"), wingspan to 77 cm (31")
Range: Canada, USA to South America

- don't feed by tipping the tail up, but skim the surface or reach below the water with their head and neck
- have the longest **migration** in the duck family, covering 9,600 km (6,000 mi)
- flight speed 77 kmh (48 mph)

Nest Canada wide.

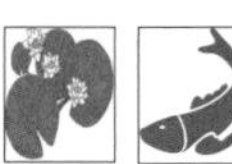

Green-winged Teal

Size: 32–40 cm (13"–16"), wingspan to 62 cm (25")
Range: Alaska, Canada, USA to Central America and Bahamas

- a very hardy species, they are among the last to reach winter habitats, and the first to depart
- flocks execute sharp turns in unison like shorebirds
- flight speed 64 kmh (40 mph)
- lifespan up to 20 years

Nest Canada wide.

Did You Know...

Some birds are eaten by fish! Bird species that nest or feed around water often fall victim to large angler fish, cod, bass, sharks and monkfish, among others.

Northern pike take an estimated 3.5 million waterfowl chicks each year in the delta areas of western Canada.

World Species 9
Canadian Species 1

Stiff-tailed Ducks - subfamily Oxyurini

Characteristics

These small, chunky, diving birds are the most **aquatic** members of the duck family, and nearly helpless on land. Their short, sturdy legs are set so far back on their body that walking is extremely difficult. They have dense, shiny **plumage** and small, rounded wings, which cannot lift them off the water without pattering along the surface with large, powerful feet. The long, narrow, stiffened tail feathers function as a rudder while swimming underwater.

Behaviour

They are more skillful underwater than other diving ducks, and can sink slowly below the surface without a ripple or a sound, coming up the same way.

Diet

These ducks eat a variety of **aquatic** vegetation on or just below the surface, and can be found in marshes, lakes and ponds.

Reproduction

The bizarre **courtship** display of the males consists of cocking their tails over their back, inflating the lower neck and beating on it with their bright blue bill, producing bubbles as they eject the air from their feathers. This is followed by a burp from the open bill.

Five to seventeen cream eggs are **incubated** 23 days. The young fly 42–49 days after hatching. These ducks are unique among the duck family in that the male helps care for the young. Females are voiceless, and males are generally silent.

Family Status

There are nine species in the world, with one found in Canada. Along with the cinnamon teal, they are the only waterfowl to breed in both North and South America. Introduced to Europe by man, their rapid expansion there is threatening native duck species.

Ruddy Duck

Size: 35–40 cm (14"–16"), wingspan to 60 cm (24")
Range: Western Canada, USA to Central America and the Bahamas

- named for the rust-red breeding **plumage** of the male
- do not go through **eclipse moult**, but slowly change from breeding **plumage**
- if disturbed, they would rather dive than fly
- **migrate** only at night
- nest is a basket-like structure built of marsh plants and attached to growing weeds
- lay enormous eggs; a **clutch** of 14 eggs weighs three times more than the female
- often **dump nesters**, laying their eggs in the nests of grebes and other ducks

Nest in eastern British Columbia, Alberta and southern Saskatchewan and Manitoba.

World Species 59
Canadian Species 2

The Eagle Family - Accipitridae

Characteristics

Eagles are members of the hawk family, collectively known as raptors, or birds of prey. They are distinguished by the weapons they use to overcome their prey: short, hooked beaks; strong feet ending in long, curved claws or talons; and very acute eyesight. Roughened pads on the soles of their feet help them grasp prey.

The Canadian species range in size from 82–107 cm (33"–43"), and their **plumage** is varying shades of brown with white markings. Like all raptors, the females are larger than the males. Their bodies are strong, compact and wide-breasted with large, rounded heads. The bold look of their profile is formed by a bone projecting as an eyebrow ridge above the eye. They have long, broad, rounded wings and rounded tails. Breast and limb muscles are very strong.

Behaviour

Unmated bald eagles are generally solitary, but will gather in groups of up to 4,000 during fall salmon runs, feasting on the easily accessible fish. Mated pairs of bald and golden eagles have been seen to hunt cooperatively, with one bird harrying the prey until it is exhausted, and the other moving in for the kill, which is then shared.

Bald and golden eagles are resident in North America year round, although there is seasonal movement down from the Arctic in the autumn months. **Migration** occurs along mountain ridges, and they **migrate** only during the day, as they ride the warm **thermals** which die at sunset.

Diet

Eagles live on the flesh of mammals, birds, reptiles, fish and even insects. They hunt only by day, as their prey is located by sight. Because of their large size, they can gorge themselves and then go without food for weeks. They are known to pirate food from hawks, osprey and other eagles, harassing them until they drop or abandon their meal. Eagles also eat carrion, and are often killed when eating poisoned carcasses set out to trap coyotes.

Reproduction

Eagles are noted for the enormous size of their nests which are constructed of sticks, twigs, weeds and roots, and lined with moss, lichen and fur. They are built in trees or on cliff ledges, and may be used for several years, or by succeeding generations. One bald eagle nest used for 35 years was built up until it weighed 1,814 kg (4,000 lbs) when it collapsed. Eagles mate for life, and both sexes help construct the nest, although the female does most of the work.

One to four white eggs are laid at two to four day intervals and the 31–46 day **incubation** starts with the first egg laid. This leads to a great variety in size of the young, and the older, stronger eaglet often kills its nest mates, ensuring its own survival. Both parents feed the young, who are born helpless and covered with down. Young eagles take their first flight 65–75 days after hatching.

Family Status

Eagles are found around the world in a variety of habitats. One species, the Madagascar serpent eagle, was thought to be extinct in the 1930's, but a very small population has recently been discovered.

 **Bald Eagle**

Size: 85–107 cm (34"–43"), wingspan to 6 m (7.5 ft)
Range: Alaska, Canada, USA; Russia

- the word bald, or balled, meant 'shining white' in Middle English, and not hairless
- males weigh 3–4 kg (8–9 lbs), females 4.5–6 kg (10–14 lbs)
- young take four to five years to achieve the white head and tail of adults
- build the largest nest of any pair of birds in the world: 5–6 m (7–8 ft) deep, up to 9 m (12 ft) across
- nearly eliminated in the continental USA due to the use of crop pesticides in the 1950's and 1960's
- bounties were paid on their killing as late as 1962 in Alaska, as they were thought to be stock killers
- national bird of USA
- flight speed to 70 kmh (44 mph)
- lifespan up to 48 years

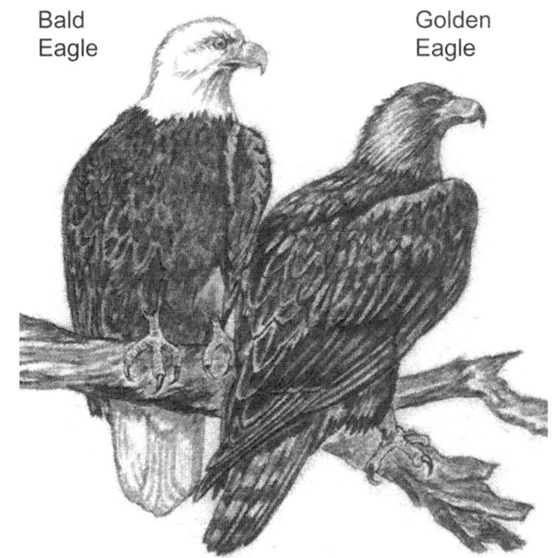

Nest Canada wide except for the Great Plains.

The word eagle comes from the Latin word for the north wind, which darkened the sky.

  **Golden Eagle**

Size: 82–95 cm (33"–38"), wingspan to 6 m (7.5 ft)
Range: Alaska, Canada, USA; Europe, Asia, North Africa

- able to spot a hare on the ground from nearly 3.2 km (2 mi) in the air
- males weigh 3–4.5 kg (8–10 lbs), females 4–6 kg (9–13 lbs)
- named for the colour of the feathers on the neck and head
- thrive where terrain is rugged and people are few
- nest is 0.9–1.2 m (3–4 ft) deep and 2–3 m (8–10 ft) across
- 20,000 were killed in bounty programs in Texas and New Mexico from 1940–1960
- once thought to be killers of domestic stock, but in fact 70% of their diet is rabbit
- most Sioux war bonnets used tail feathers of young golden eagles
- is the heraldic eagle which has been used on shields and crests since ancient times
- were the official emblem of the Roman army in 87 BC, and have been the emblem of Mexico since Aztec times in 1325 AD.
- can attain a dive speed up to 320 kmh (200 mph)
- flight speed to 51 kmh (32 mph)
- lifespan up to 46 years

Nest Yukon, Northwest Territories, northern British Columbia, Alberta, Ontario and Quebec.

World Species 58
Canadian Species 5

The Falcon Family - Falconidae

Characteristics

Falcons are the speed demons of the bird world, and every line of their 23–62 cm (9"–25") body is built for fast flight. Their **plumage** is shades of browns and grays, with white and black markings. The sexes look the same, and the females are larger than the males. Like all raptors, or birds of prey, they have a strongly hooked bill and taloned feet, but falcons have a bullet-like head, a short neck and broad, powerful shoulders. Their bills have two cutting serrations on the upper **mandible**, with two corresponding notches in the lower. These 'teeth' are used to break the neck of their prey if the force of the talons does not immediately kill the animal. Falcons also have nostrils specially modified to allow for freer breathing in fast flight. The long wings are wide close to the body, then taper into points. The wing structure, plus their narrow tail, allows for quick maneuverability in the air. Their legs are thick and strong, to withstand the sudden impact of striking their prey.

Behaviour

Falcons take most of their food in the air, and their dark eyes give them exceptionally acute eyesight. They can often be seen watching from a prominent perch, waiting for movement. Striking their prey with the great force of their talons, death is usually instantaneous. Due to the necessity of having to see their prey, falcons hunt only during daylight hours.

Diet

Although the majority of their diet consists of birds, small mammals or insects are also taken. While hawks tend to land before eating, many falcons eat while flying.

Reproduction

Courtship displays in all species are swift, aerial and may be followed by ritual feeding of the female by the male. None of the falcon species build their own nest, and no nesting material is added to the nestsite. They lay two to eight cream eggs with dark markings on bare rock ledges, in tree cavities or the abandoned nests of hawks, eagles or crows. **Incubation** of 27–33 days begins when the second last egg is laid, and the females are fed by the males while **brooding**. The young are born helpless, covered in down, and fly 25–49 days after hatching.

Family Status

Falconry, or the use of raptors for killing other birds, has been practiced since 2,000 BC. The sport eventually became dominated by tradition, and in the Middle Ages the protocol was: kestrels were flown by peasants, merlins were flown by ladies and peregrines by princes, but only the king or emperor could fly a gyrfalcon. This sport has contributed to the decline of many species, as birds are still illegally taken from the wild to hunt for man.

Falcons inhabit all types of terrain, from the Arctic tundra to tropical forests and scorching deserts. The world's most threatened falcon is the Mauritius kestrel, with just over 100 of these birds alive in 1999. The quelili, or Guadeloupe caracara, has been extinct since 1900, deliberately exterminated by man because it was thought they preyed on domestic goats.

 **Peregrine Falcon**

Size: 37–50 cm (15"–20"), wingspan to 115 cm (46")
Range: Alaska, Canada, northern USA; Europe, Asia, Africa, Australia

- special corneal muscles in the eye compensate for the rapidly decreasing distance in a dive
- special baffles in the nostrils permit them to breathe despite the rush of air in a dive
- considered the fastest bird in the world, they have been clocked at speeds in excess of 400–440 kmh (250–275 mph) in a dive
- achieve maximum speed in a dive by folding their wings back, then increase their speed by beating them in that position
- the population east of the Mississippi was eliminated between 1940's and 1960's due to heavy pesticide use on crops
- do not breed until their third year
- nesting sites in North America have increased fivefold since 1975, and they have adopted tall buildings in cities to nest on
- once one of the most widely distributed birds in the world

Nest generally in Yukon and Northwest Territories, but now found in various cities as well.

Peregrine Falcon

 **Prairie Falcon**

Size: 42–50 cm (17"–20"), wingspan to 105 cm (42")
Range: Western Canada, USA to Mexico

- excel at catching birds in flight, often eating in the air
- official mascot of the US Air Force Academy
- numbers are declining due to rodent poisoning programs and nest robbing by falconers
- flight speed 48 kmh (30 mph)
- lifespan up to 10 years

Nest in southern Alberta and Saskatchewan.

 **Gyrfalcon**

Size: 50–62 cm (20"–25"), wingspan to 135 cm (54")
Range: Alaska, Canada, northern USA; Europe, Asia, Greenland, Iceland

Gyrfalcon

- largest falcon in the world, weighing 0.7–1 kg (2–3 lbs)
- have three color phases—black, white and grey
- a mated pair have two or three alternative nest sites used in different years
- the only diurnal raptor to winter in the Arctic
- 89% of their diet is ptarmigan

Nest on the Arctic tundra.

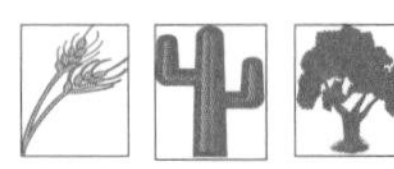 **American Kestrel**

Size: 23–30 cm (9"–12"), wingspan to 61 cm (24")
Range: Canada, USA, Central and South America

- most widespread and common of the North American falcons
- also known as 'sparrow hawks', even though birds make up a small part of their diet; in Europe they are known as 'windhovers'
- often hover in the air to scan the ground for food: insects, small mammals, reptiles; can spot a beetle from 30 metres (100 ft)
- do not need to drink water, as sufficient moisture is obtained from their prey
- one bird can eat 290 mice yearly
- flight speed to 62 kmh (39 mph)
- lifespan up to 17 years

Nest Canada wide.

Falcon comes from the Latin word for sickle, referring to the curved beak and talons.

  **Merlin**

Size: 25–34 cm (10"–13"), wingspan to 66 cm (26")
Range: Alaska, Canada, USA to South America & West Indies; Europe, Asia

- formerly known as 'pigeon hawks'
- catch birds in mid-air with feet and talons
- often use abandoned nests of crows, magpies or other hawks
- males arrive back in spring before the females; mated pairs return to same general area each year
- flight speed to 72 kmh (45 mph)

 Nest Canada wide.

World Species 125
Canadian Species 16

The Finch Family - Fringillidae

Characteristics

The finch family consists of small, 10–25 cm (4"–10"), seed eating birds with stout conical bills, strong skulls, large jaw muscles and powerful **gizzards**, all adaptations for dealing with hard seeds. Beaks are internally modified for holding and shelling seeds. A seed is wedged into a special groove at the side of the mouth and crushed by raising the lower jaw onto it. The husk is then peeled off with the tongue, releasing the kernel, which is then swallowed. **Plumage** is highly variable and often brightly coloured. The sexes do not look alike.

There is a great variation in beak shapes, according to the type of seeds eaten. Goldfinches have long, tweezer-like bills and are the only species able to eat the seeds of teasel, which lie at the bottom of long, spiked tubes. Pine grosbeaks have rounded bills adapted to cones, and crossbills have crossed mandibles to open scales on cones.

Behaviour

Most species are strong fliers, and the **temperate** zone species often **migrate** although some remain in Canada during the winter. These small birds are highly **gregarious,** and are usually found in small flocks in the winter months. During breeding season, they separate and form breeding pairs.

Diet

Although the majority of their food is seeds, some species occasionally eat insects and berries.

Reproduction

Pairs establish small **territories**, usually just a small area around the nest, which is defended by the male with vigorous song. The females build open, cup-like nests of twigs, rootlets and other plant material in trees, bushes or even on the ground. Two to seven bluish green eggs with dark markings are laid, and **incubated** by the female 10–14 days. The male feeds the female while **brooding**, and helps her feed the young, who are born blind and helpless. Chicks fly 8–14 days after hatching. Adults carry large quantities of seeds in their **gizzards**, and **regurgitate** them to the young birds. Many seed-eating birds raise their young on insects for the high protein content, but crossbills, redpolls and pine siskins feed their young only seeds, which is rare in birds.

Family Status

Finches have been kept as pets for centuries, valued for their musical song, bright colours and simple seed diet. The family includes such familiar birds as the canary, and is found worldwide except for Antarctica, Australia and Madagascar. Three species are now extinct. The Bonin Island grosbeak, localized to one island near Japan, and the Puerto Rican bullfinch were exterminated by predators introduced by man. Another equatorial island dweller, the Sao Thome grosbeak, was eliminated when the forests were cut down to plant coffee plantations, and has been classed as extinct since 1900.

Which species consumes the most ants?

(see page 193 for the answer)

Indigo Bunting

Size: 12–15 cm (5"–6"), wingspan to 22 cm (9")
Range: Southern Canada, USA to Central America and West Indies

- the only North American finch to appear blue all over
- fiercely **territorial**, and holds a small **territory** by protracted singing
- young males are known to imitate the song of an older established male, who has already scared away other birds
- flight speed 32 kmh (20 mph)
- lifespan up to 8 years

Nest from southern Manitoba to Maritimes.

Lazuli Bunting

Size: 12–15 cm (5"–6"), wingspan to 22 cm (9")
Range: Western Canada, USA to Mexico

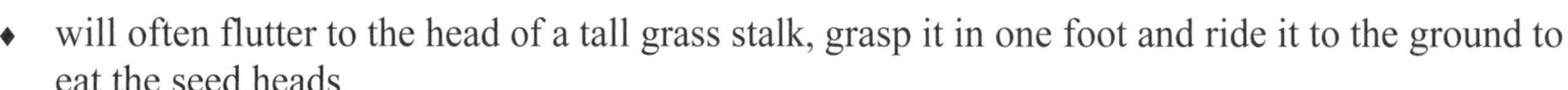

- will often flutter to the head of a tall grass stalk, grasp it in one foot and ride it to the ground to eat the seed heads
- males sometimes have more than one mate
- found up to 3,050 m (10,000 ft) in the Rocky Mountains

Nest in southern British Columbia, Alberta, Saskatchewan.

Northern Cardinal

Size: 19–23 cm (7"–8"), wingspan to 30 cm (12")
Range: Southeastern Canada, USA to Central America

- named for their rich red colour, the same as the robes worn by cardinals of the Catholic church
- unlike most bird species, female cardinals sing as much as the males
- males are highly **territorial** and will fight their own images in windows
- male has at least 28 different songs, and sings throughout the year
- practice **anting** to rid themselves of pests
- often have three or four **clutches** per year; the male cares for one **clutch** while the female **incubates** the eggs of the next one; male feeds female on nest
- mate for life
- state bird of seven states
- lifespan up to 28 years

Nest in southern Ontario, Quebec and the Maritimes.

Red Crossbill

Red Crossbills

- Nest in British Columbia, across Canada in forest zone

White-winged Crossbill

- Nest across Canada in forest zone.

Size: 12–17 cm (5"–7"), wingspan to 27 cm (11")
Range: Alaska, Canada, USA; Europe, Russia, Siberia

- may nest year round if seeds are plentiful
- often feed while hanging upside down
- store seeds in their **crop** to be eaten on really cold winter nights while roosting
- so adept at opening cones that it is estimated they can eat 3,000 seeds in one day
- although they share the same range, red crossbills prefer pine cones, while white-winged prefer cones of spruce, tamarak and cedar
- crawl around in the trees like a small parrot, using the bill and feet to grasp branches
- often eat clay to absorb the resin from pine seeds, and salt from winter roads

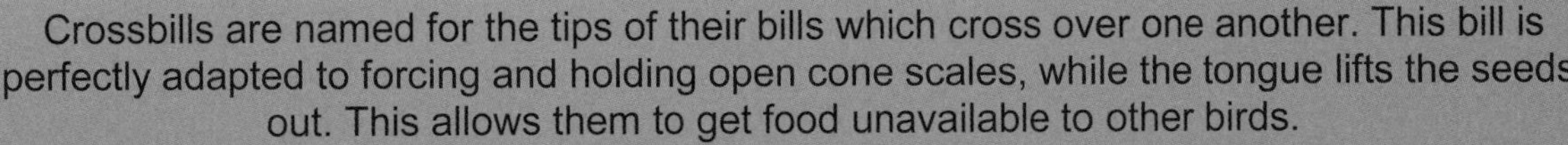

Crossbills are named for the tips of their bills which cross over one another. This bill is perfectly adapted to forcing and holding open cone scales, while the tongue lifts the seeds out. This allows them to get food unavailable to other birds.

◆

Famous for their strange population fluctuations, huge numbers of these birds occasionally move entirely out of their range during the winter. It is thought this happens in years of low food supply, and it may take years before the birds return to the original area.

Types of Beaks

Finches of North America

These tiny birds range in size from 12–17 cm (5"–7"), with a wingspan to 25 cm (10"). They are found in high mountain coniferous forests, rocky alpine tundra and woodlands.

Cassin's Finch - Western Canada, USA to Mexico

- conifer buds are their preferred food when snow is on the ground
- attracted to rock salt blocks, and salt on roadways
- two **clutches** per year

Nest in southwestern British Columbia.

Grey-crowned Rosy Finch - Western Canada, USA

- during nesting season, they develop a **gular pouch** to carry even more seeds
- have an unusual behaviour called mate guarding that centres on the female; wherever she goes, the male goes with her to drive away other males
- lay pear-shaped eggs

Nest in British Columbia, Yukon and Arctic islands.

House Finch - Western Canada and USA, eastern Canada and USA

- 86% of their food is weed seeds; young fed a diet of dandelion seeds
- lifespan up to 10 years

Nest across southern Canada.

Originally a western species, in the 1940's house finches were sold in New York as Hollywood finches. When laws changed, dealers released their birds, who formed a wild population in the east. The two groups are slowly expanding their range towards each other.

Purple Finch - Canada, USA

- in **courtship**, the male dances around the female with his wings beating so fast they become a blur, until he rises into the air, chirping softly throughout
- two **clutches** per year in the west, one in the east
- lifespan up to 12 years

Nest across Canada except for the Great Plains.

American Goldfinch

Size: 10–12 cm (4"–5"), wingspan to 22 cm (9")
Range: Southern Canada, USA

- young are raised entirely on seeds which are partially digested by the adults and **regurgitated**
- nest is so thick-walled it will hold water, and unprotected chicks have drowned in heavy rain
- state bird of Washington, New Jersey, Minnesota and Iowa
- lifespan up to 8 years

Nest across southern Canada.

Grosbeaks

Grosbeaks are larger members of the Finch family from 15–25 cm (6"–10") with wingspans to 37 cm (15"). Their name literally means 'thick-beak,' as their powerful bills crush even the hardest nuts and pine seeds. They are found in wooded areas of both coniferous and deciduous forests.

Black-headed Grosbeak - Western Canada, USA to Mexico

- nest is built by the female in three to four days
- males share **incubation** duties
- consume large numbers of harmful insects and are very valuable to farmers
- lifespan up to 5 years

Nest in southern British Columbia and Alberta.

Evening Grosbeak - Canada, USA

- in spring the outer covering of the bill peels off, exposing a blue-green colour
- name comes from the erroneous belief that they only sing in the evening
- highly **gregarious** and travel in large flocks
- lifespan up to 13 years

Nest in British Columbia and across southern Canada except for the Great Plains.

Pine Grosbeak - Alaska, Canada, northern USA; Europe, Russia

- largest member of the grosbeak family
- has a **gular pouch** for extra seed storage
- nest in mountains up to 3,050 m (10,000 ft)
- lifespan up to 8 years

Nest in Yukon, Northwest Territories and north eastern Canada.

Rose-breasted Grosbeak - Canada, USA to Mexico

- male often sings while on the nest, and sometimes at night
- unlike most bird species, the females also sing
- mates appear affectionate, sometimes touching bills in **courtship**
- male sometimes helps build nest; both sexes **incubate** the eggs
- several males may fight fiercely for one female, hovering over her and singing
- lifespan up to 24 years

Nest in northern British Columbia, Alberta to Maritimes.

  **Common Redpoll -** Alaska, Canada, western USA; Eurasia, Europe

Nest in Yukon, Northwest Territories, Nunavut, Arctic tundra.

  **Hoary Redpoll** - Alaska, Canada, Northwest Territories; Europe, Russia

Nest on Arctic tundra.

Size: 12–14 cm (5"–5.5"), wingspan to 22 cm (9")

- adult males weigh approximately 19 gr (2/3 ounce)
- flocks make a constant twittering noise
- non-**migratory**
- bathe in winter by burrowing into wet snow
- nests are lined with caribou hair and ptarmigan feathers
- lifespan up to 7 years

  **Pine Siskin**

Size: 10–12 cm (4"–5")
Range: Alaska, Canada, USA

- attracted to the minerals in clay, ashes, cement and salt blocks
- the name siskin comes from the Scandinavian word for 'a chirper,' referring to a similar European species
- females are known to dismantle old American goldfinch nests and use the materials to build their own
- highly **gregarious**, often in mixed flocks with redpolls and goldfinches
- lifespan up to 11 years

Nest in Yukon, British Columbia, Alberta, Saskatchewan and across central Canada.

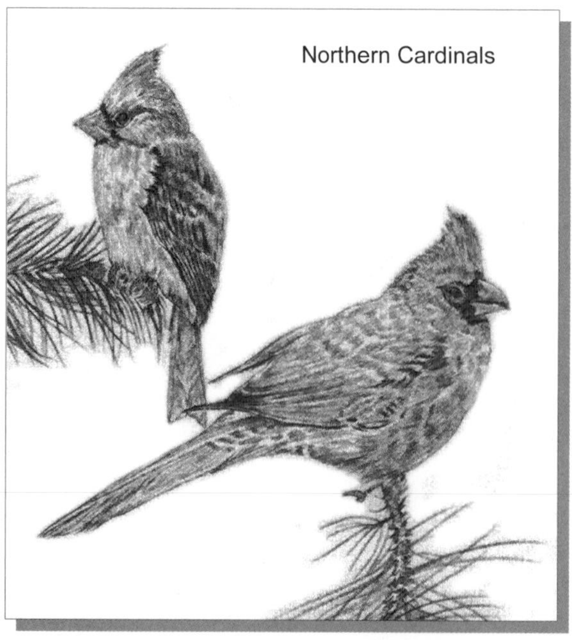

Northern Cardinals

World Species 374
Canadian Species 16

The Flycatcher Family - Tyrannidae

Characteristics

Flycatchers are small to medium sized birds, 12–23 cm (5"–9"), of dull brown, grey or olive. Some species have elongated tail feathers, and most can raise their crown feathers to form a crest. They have large heads and broad, flattened bills strongly hooked at the tip. Prominent bristles at the base of the bill protect the eyes during foraging and aid in snagging insects. Like most perching birds, their feet and legs are short and weak.

Behaviour

Named for their behaviour, these birds prefer to perch on the top of shrubs, where they dart out to snatch a flying insect with an audible click of the bill, then return. Some tropical species also pluck insects from foliage. If an insect is too large to swallow, they hold it under their feet and bite off pieces. Bees or wasps are held in the bill, and knocked against a branch to remove the stinger before being eaten.

This family has a habit of aggressive behaviour towards larger birds. **Territories** and nests are defended vigorously and noisily.

Diet

Although the majority of their diet is insects, some berries and small fish are also eaten.

Reproduction

Nests are made of plant material and spider webbing, and vary from cup-like structures to cavities in trees, domed nests or bulky pendant nests with side entrances. Two to seven cream or pinkish white eggs with dark markings are laid. **Clutch** sizes are larger in the temperate species, where there are fewer insects than in the tropics. Larger **clutches** increase the chance of successfully producing offspring. **Incubation** lasts 12–17 days, and the young leave the nest 12–18 days after hatching. While only the females **incubate** the eggs, both parents feed the young. Males mate with only one female each year.

Family Status

This family is located around the world and covers the Americas. No other **New World** bird family occupies every habitat and breeds from southern Canada to the tip of South America. Most flycatchers live in the tropics, and the Canadian species **migrate** there in the fall.

Flycatchers throughout the world eat thousands of pounds of insects daily, thus benefiting man enormously.

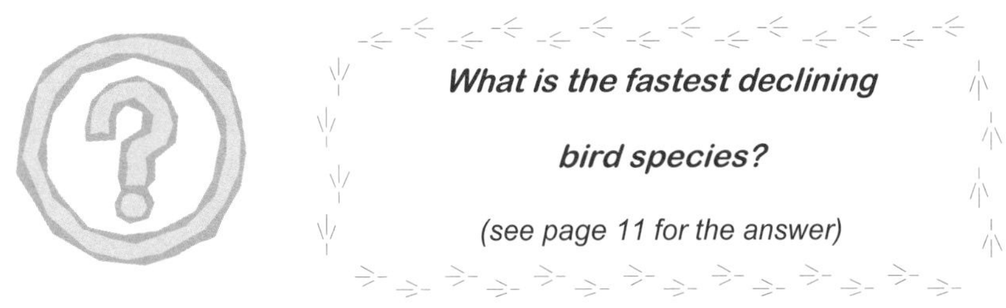

(see page 11 for the answer)

Empidonax Flycatchers

*This group of flycatchers are drab, with pale eye rings and wing bars. All are 12–15 cm (5"–6") in length. From spring to summer, their **plumage** grows duller from wear.*

 **Acadian Flycatcher -** Eastern Canada, USA to Central America and Cuba

- misnamed birds, as they never reach Acadia (Nova Scotia)
- shallow basket nest is suspended by its rim on the outer ends of horizontal branches 1.2–6 m (4–20 ft) up

Nest in southeastern Canada.

 **Alder Flycatcher** - Alaska, Canada, USA to Central and South America

- summer in dense thickets near water
- indistinguishable from the willow flycatcher, except for their song

Nest across Canada.

Hammond's and dusky flycatchers are closely related and difficult to distinguish. The populations were separated when the ice fields advanced and the forests were divided into western and eastern refuges. When the flycatchers returned to the newly forested northern half of the continent, each had developed differing habitat needs, allowing them to coexist without competing for nesting sites and food.

  **Dusky Flycatcher** - Yukon, western Canada, USA to Mexico

- adults weigh about 11 gr (1/3 oz)
- nest in small trees or shrubs

Nest in British Columbia, southwestern Alberta.

 **Grey Flycatcher** - British Columbia, western USA to Mexico

- inhabit sagebrush and juniper lowlands
- longish bill is pinkish-orange on the lower half
- colours blend with the blue-grey of the sagebrush, helping conceal them from predators

Nest in southwestern British Columbia.

  **Hammond's Flycatcher** - Alaska, Yukon, western Canada, USA to Central America

- summer at higher elevations than other flycatchers, up to 3,350 m (11,000 ft)
- nest in tall fir trees near the very top

Nest in British Columbia.

Empidonax flycatchers *continued*

 **Least Flycatcher** - Yukon, Canada, USA to Central America

- smallest flycatcher species
- the male vigorously defends a **territory** of about 0.4 ha (1 acre) with aggressive call
- give a "*che-bec*" call up to 60 times per minute during the breeding season
- males feed females while they **incubate**, and both parents feed young for up to 20 days after they leave the nest
- lifespan up to 5 years

Nest Canada wide.

 **Willow Flycatcher -** Southwestern Canada, western USA to South America

- once considered one species with the alder flycatcher, called Traill's flycatcher
- lifespan up to 4 years

Nest in southern British Columbia, Alberta, Saskatchewan and Manitoba.

 **Yellow-bellied Flycatcher** - Canada, USA to Central America

- eat more ants than any other flycatcher
- nest is located on or near the ground, well hidden in sphagnum moss
- may live for several days on mountain ash berries during stormy weather
- lifespan up to 4 years

Nest in Northwest Territories, northern Alberta to Maritimes.

Tyrant flycatchers are the largest and most diverse family of birds in the **New World**, and are more common in the western part of North America. Their family name *Tyrannidae* comes from their aggressive behaviour towards other birds.

◆

It has been estimated there are 751,000 species of insects on earth, and there are hundreds or possibly thousands that have yet to be identified. Their population totals many millions of creatures, and is so large that no one knows the exact size.

 **Great-crested Flycatcher**

Size: 20–23 cm (8"–9"), wingspan to 35 cm (14")
Range: Southeastern Canada, eastern USA

- if a selected tree cavity is too deep, the pair will fill it with leaves and trash to within 46 cm (18") of opening and then build their nest
- cup nest is made of plant material and cast off snakeskin
- males fight over **territory**, sometimes striking with their claws and tearing out the feathers of their opponent
- lifespan up to 11 years

Nest from southern Manitoba to the Maritimes.

Great-crested Flycatcher

 **Olive-sided Flycatcher**

Size: 17–20 cm (7"–8")
Range: Alaska, Yukon, Canada, USA to South America

- summer from sea level to 3,350 m (11,000 ft) in the Rocky Mountains
- eat only winged insects, no spiders, caterpillars or other larvae

Nest Canada wide except for the Great Plains.

  **Pacific-slope Flycatcher**

Size: 12–15 cm (5"–6")
Range: Alaska, western Canada and USA to Central America

- previously called western flycatcher
- one of the most widespread flycatchers in the west
- nests are built in tree cavities, wood piles or on tree crotches, buildings or bridges

Nest in British Columbia.

Eastern Kingbird

Size: 20–23 cm (8"–9"), wingspan to 37 cm (15")
Range: Western Canada, USA to South America

- fearlessly attack hawks, crows and magpies, diving at them and sometimes landing on their back; have been known to 'attack' low-flying airplanes crossing their **territory**
- eat more than 200 kinds of insects, seeds of 40 different kinds of plants, and berries plucked from the bushes while hovering
- nests may be located in tree cavities, on top of posts or in rain gutters
- flight speed 37 kmh (23 mph)

Nest Canada wide.

> Kingbirds are so named because of their domineering character and habits.
>
> ◆
>
> These birds vigorously defend their summer breeding **territory** in open country, but in winter they travel in large flocks and prefer forest habitat, eating mostly fruits.

Western Kingbird

Size: 20–23 cm (8"–9"), wingspan to 40 cm (16")
Range: Canada, eastern USA to Central America

- attack crows, ravens, hawks and other larger birds who venture into their **territory**
- more social than other kingbirds, and several pairs may nest in the same tree
- use dried snakeskin in the nest
- flight speed 27 kmh (17 mph)
- lifespan up to 7 years

Nest in southern British Columbia, Alberta, Saskatchewan and Manitoba.

Eastern Phoebe

Size: 15–17 cm (6"–7")
Range: Canada, USA to Mexico

- one of the hardiest North American flycatchers
- eat tiny fish, as well as insects
- like to be near water
- nest is made of mud and moss
- often build new nests on top of those used in previous years
- lifespan up to 9 years

Nest from Alberta to Maritimes.

Say's Phoebe

Size: 17–20 cm (7"–8")
Range: Alaska, Yukon, western Canada and USA to Mexico

- named for their call
- **regurgitate** the hard parts of insect bodies in small **pellets**
- often hover in midair

 Nest in Yukon, British Columbia, Alberta, Saskatchewan.

Wood Peewee

Size: 15–17 cm (6"–7")

Eastern:
Range: Southeastern Canada, eastern USA to South America

Nest from southern Manitoba through to Maritimes.

Western:
Range: Alaska, Yukon, western Canada and USA to South America

Nest in Yukon, British Columbia, Alberta and Saskatchewan.

- adults weigh about 10 gr (1/2 ounce)
- bees, wasps and ants make up 40% of the diet, flies are another 44%
- eastern species cover the outside of their nest with lichen to camouflage it with the branch
- lifespan up to 7 years

Did You Know...

Birds use an enormous variety of materials in their nests. Flycatchers are fond of lining theirs with cast-off snakeskin, which is thought to deter predators. If snakeskin is not available, they will use cellophane, insect skins or even onion skins.

The record for strange nesting items goes to a pair of wrens who built a 1.1 kg (2.5 lb) nest using only office supplies - paper clips, straight pins, safety pins, rubber bands, thumbtacks, rawhide shoelaces, a darning needle, paper fasteners, insulated wire, matches and toothpicks were just some of the 1,791 countable items used!

World Species 9
Canadian Species 1

The Gannet Family - Sulidae

Characteristics
Gannets are 87–100 cm (35"–40") seabirds with spindle-shaped bodies, long pointed wings, and short, strong, legs with webbed feet. Most gannets are white, and their **plumage** is waterproof. Their long tails are wedge-shaped: soaring birds look like white crosses. They have colourful, sharp, straight bills with serrated cutting edges to hold slippery prey. Like all birds of the open ocean, gannets have **salt-excreting glands** which allow them to drink sea water and ingest it with their food. Air sacs beneath the skin of the neck and breast cushion the impact of steep dives into the water. Their nostrils close when they dive, and they breathe out of the corner of their mouth.

Behaviour/Diet
These birds waddle on land but are expert fliers. Flocks of gannets scan the ocean from heights of 3–30 m (10–100 ft) looking for schools of fish. When one is located, they plunge straight down with their wings folded, and just before impact completely flatten their wings against their body. These birds dive at more than 18 m (60 ft) per second, then chase their prey under the surface. Gannets can dive from 30 m (100 ft) in the air to 30 m (100 ft) below the surface. They often accompany ocean vessels to feast on the disturbed flying fish. Fish up to 35 cm (14") are swallowed whole, and they can eat more than 0.7 kg (2 lbs) in one session.

Reproduction
Coming ashore only to breed, gannets build their nest of seaweed and grasses on cliff ledges or oceanic islands in colonies of thousands. Highly **territorial**, they vigorously defend the area immediately around their nest. One pale blue egg is **incubated** beneath the feet for 44 days, and young are **brooded** on top of the webs of the feet. Young are hatched naked and blind, but are soon covered with white down. Both sexes **incubate** and care for the young, who are fed **regurgitated** fish. They are fed so well they have very large fat reserves when they **fledge**. This makes it easier for them to dive for fish, but harder to avoid predators. Young are able to fly 84–87 days after hatching.

Family Status
Gannets are found throughout the **temperate** oceans of the world, and have been a familiar sight to sailors for thousands of years. They are so tame they often land on ships and make no effort to escape. As a result, they became a staple diet for sailors, but have survived because their nesting places are usually inaccessible to man.

 **Gannet, Northern**

Size: 87–100 cm (35"–40"), wingspan to 180 cm (72")
Range: Eastern Canada, USA to Florida; British Isles

- adult **plumage** is not reached until 3–4 years, and they do not breed until 4–5 years of age
- stay out at sea for the first three years of life
- always return to their usual nesting area and some of them have been occupied for thousands of years

Nest along offshore Newfoundland and Labrador.

World Species 20
Canadian Species 5

The Goose Family - Anserini

Characteristics
Geese are large, familiar members of the waterfowl group, with webbed feet and waterproof **plumage** of browns, grays and whites. Both sexes look the same, but the males are larger. Geese are intermediate in size between ducks and swans, and Canadian species range from 52–107 cm (21"–43"). Their neck feathers are furrowed vertically and in threat display they vibrate, rather than raise them. Unlike ducks, geese do not go through an **eclipse moult** where they replace all their feathers at once. Geese **moult** their flight and tail feathers after breeding, and are flightless for at least six weeks. Their legs are farther forward on the body than those of either ducks or swans, which gives them better balance on land, and they often graze far from water.

Behaviour
Highly **gregarious**, geese are found in large flocks with one bird acting as sentry, keeping a lookout for danger and warning the others. Because geese mate for life, their social displays are more inconspicuous than those of other species. Mutual **preening** of head and neck feathers, mutual head movements and wing lifting, and clucking to each other help maintain pair bonds. Geese are highly vocal birds, with a variety of loud, trumpeting sounds.

The **temperate** species all **migrate**, although there is a sub-population of Canada geese that do not. Fall **migration** is done in either long lines, or 'V' formations. This formation is thought to be used because it cuts down wind resistance, and the lead bird is often replaced by another flock member. This allows all the birds to share the position of greatest wind resistance.

Diet
These birds are vegetarians, eating huge quantities of grasses, roots, grains and pasture plants on land or in marshes. Because grass has a low nutrient quantity, they must eat huge amounts of it to obtain energy, and then continually eliminate the indigestible portion.

Reproduction
Females build their nest over water or among marsh vegetation. Like ducks, geese cannot pick up items in their bill, and the nest is made by pulling in nearby items, thereby forming a protective circle. The nest is lined with down plucked from the female's breast, which is pulled over the eggs when she leaves to feed. One white egg is laid daily until the **clutch** has three to six eggs, and the 21–28 day **incubation** does not start until the **clutch** is complete. This ensures all the young are the same age when hatching. They remain in the nest overnight, and the following morning the mother leads them to water. Young goslings can swim at one day old, but cannot fly until 38–86 days after hatching.

Parents do not feed the **precocial** young, but they do guard them, and often form nursery groups where one pair looks after the goslings of several birds while the adults feed.

Family Status
Geese are found throughout the world, and have been domesticated for thousands of years. In 390 AD, the Romans kept flocks outside the city gates to warn of approaching intruders.

Brant Goose

Size: 55–62 cm (22"–26"), wingspan to 1.2 m (48")
Range: Northern and coastal Canada, north coasts of USA; Greenland, Russia, Eurasia

- named for the Latin word for 'burnt' because of their charcoal grey colour
- do not fly in 'V' formation, but in long, wavy lines
- possess **salt-excreting glands** which allow them to drink sea water and eat saltwater plants
- also eat crustaceans, mollusks and marine insects
- nest further north than any other goose

Nest on Arctic tundra.

In the Middle Ages, it was thought that geese grew on trees.

Canada Goose

Size: 62–107 cm (25"–43"), wingspan to 1.6 m (65")
Range: Alaska, Canada, USA to Mexico

- the most well known and widespread of all North American waterfowl
- fly in 'V' formation to cut down wind resistance; there is a flock hierarchy with families dominating
- one of the earliest spring **migrants**, traveling day or night and returning to the same nesting area each year
- some populations non-**migratory** if there is open water year round
- among very few birds with strong family bonds; family stays together for a year
- have been introduced to various parts of the world and numbers are increasing everywhere
- one of the few birds to benefit from modern agricultural methods and expanding golf courses, where they dine on the green grass
- flight speed 72 kmh (45 mph)
- lifespan up to 20 years

Nest Canada wide.

Canada Goose

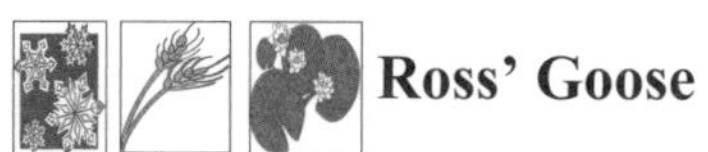

Ross' Goose

Size: 52–65 cm (21"–26"), wingspan to 1.3 m (54")
Range: Alaska, western Canada and USA to Texas

- the sides of their upper bill are covered with warty protuberances; the reason for these is unknown
- a relatively rare species
- nest in loose colonies
- named for Chief Factor of the Hudson's Bay Company in 1861

Nest on Arctic tundra.

Snow Goose

Size: 62–78 cm (25"–31"), wingspan to 1.5 m (60")
Range: Northwest Territories, Canada, USA to Mexico

- one colour phase is called a 'blue goose'
- fly very high in 'V' formation or long curved lines
- population numbers in the millions, and is increasing annually
- nest is always located within 8 km (5 mi) of salt water
- **migrate** 2,736 km (1,700 mi) in 70 hours
- flight speed 80 kmh (50 mph)

Nest on Arctic tundra.

Greater White-fronted Goose

Size: 65–85 cm (26"–34") wingspan to 155 cm (62")
Range: Alaska, western Canada, USA to Mexico

- the only North American goose with yellow feet
- travel in 'V' formation, often very high
- nest is merely a scrape on a hummock in the tundra

Nest on Arctic tundra.

The idea of Mother Goose came from an early queen of France, who was kind to everyone and a favourite with the people. She was called "Bertha Goosefoot" because of her large floppy feet. After her death, peasants told stories about her and transformed her into the mythical Mother Goose.

World Species 20
Canadian Species 6

The Grebe Family - Podicipedidae

Characteristics

Grebes are 30–73 cm (12"–29") duck-like water birds related to no other species, and considered to be among the oldest living families of birds. Their dense, waterproof **plumage** is short, close, and typically dark grey, black or brown with white undersides. During breeding season, males develop brightly coloured plumes and markings. They are one of the most perfectly adapted species for life in the water, with slender, pointed bills that have saw-like edges to hold slippery food; lobed toes with partial webbing; and strong legs at the rear of the body for propulsion. They are, however, very clumsy on land, and move about with difficulty.

Behaviour

Grebes feed, sleep and court on water. They dive to 6 m (20 ft) below the surface, can stay submerged up to 30 seconds, and swim rapidly below the water. If frightened, they may dive under and resurface with only the bill and eyes out of the water, sitting quietly until danger has passed. Possessing a very small tail, they must have a running start across the water to become airborne. They are weak but rapid fliers. Grebes are not noisy birds, but can utter a series of soft wails, chuckles, croaks, trills, squeaks and whinnies.

Diet

These birds have a habit, unique in the bird world, of feeding their young and themselves their own feathers. This is thought to protect the stomach lining from sharp fish bones. Grebes eat a variety of small fish, aquatic insects and crustaceans.

Reproduction

Grebes participate in an elaborate **courtship** ritual where both birds repeat each others movements of head and neck, then rise straight up with head and neck extended and run across the surface of the water with wings held behind them. Both adults help to build a nest of piled up reeds and cattails that is sometimes floating, anchored to vegetation.

Two to ten whitish blue or green eggs are **incubated** 20–25 days. **Incubation**, shared by both parents, starts before the **clutch** is complete, and the young hatch at two day intervals. Before leaving the nest, the parents cover the eggs with vegetation. This not only hides them, but provides warmth as the plants of the nest decay. The **precocial** young are downy, and striped black, white and brown. When in the water, the parents carry the chicks on their backs and if danger threatens, they tuck them under their wings and dive. The young can dive and swim feebly at birth, and are fed feathers and small fish by the parents. Age when the young first fly is unknown.

Family Status

The soft, thick breast feathers of grebes were once used to make women's capes, muffs and hats, and many populations were decimated by the demand for the **plume trade** in the 1800's. Grebes live throughout the world, but most species are found in the western hemisphere. Those in **temperate** climates **migrate**, flying at night and swimming close to the shore during the day.

Eared Grebe

Size: 30–32 cm (12"–13")
Range: Western Canada, USA to South America; Eurasia, Africa

- prefer to escape danger by diving rather than flying
- population was decimated in the19th century to decorate hats for the **plume trade**

Nest in southern British Columbia, Alberta, Saskatchewan and Manitoba.

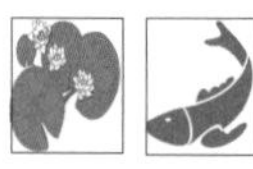

Horned Grebe

Size: 30–37 cm (12"–15"), wingspan to 60 cm (24")
Range: Alaska, Canada, USA to Central America; Eurasia

- named for their tufts of ear feathers
- feed in water 1.5–7.5 m (5–25 ft) deep, and can stay under the surface up to three minutes
- diet is almost exclusively fish

Nest in Yukon, Northwest Territories and British Columbia through to Manitoba.

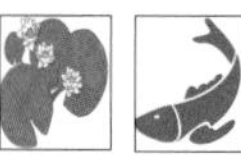

Pied-billed Grebe

Size: 30–37 cm (12"–15"), wingspan to 60 cm (24")
Range: Canada, USA to Central and South America

- the most common grebe in North America
- when apprehensive, they sink slowly, expelling air from the body and feathers to lower their specific gravity, then swim with only the head above water
- two **clutches** per year

Nest Canada wide.

Red-necked Grebes

Red-necked Grebe

Size: 42–55 cm (17"–22"), wingspan to 80 cm (32")
Range: Alaska, Canada, north and coastal USA to Central America

- females are sometimes **dump nesters**, laying their eggs in the nests of other birds, leaving them to do the **incubating** and rearing of the young

Nest in Yukon, Northwest Territories and British Columbia through to southern Ontario.

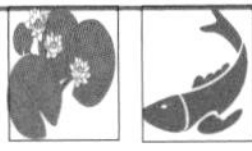

Western Grebe

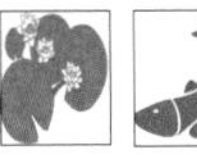

Clarke's Grebe

Size: 55–73 cm (22"–29"), wingspan 100 cm (40")
Range: Western Canada, USA to Mexico

- largest North American grebe
- have light and dark colour phases, and prefer mating of dark to dark birds and light to light
- **migration** is primarily east-west
- Clarke's grebe is sometimes considered a sub-species of the western grebe
- females often lay eggs in the nests of other birds
- colony nester

Both species nest in southern Alberta, Saskatchewan and Manitoba.

Courtship dance of Western Grebes

World Species 18
Canadian Species 9

The Grouse Family - Tetraonidae

Characteristics
Grouse are a family of 30–75 cm (12"–30") plump-bodied, fowl-like birds that have adapted to many harsh environments. **Plumage** is cryptically marked shades of brown, white and grey to aid in concealment. The males are larger than the females, and the sexes do not look alike. They all have compact bodies with short, strong, curved bills and short, rounded wings. Their strong legs are feathered wholly or in part, and some species have elongated hind claws, or spurs.

Most members of the family live in **temperate** or cold climates, and exist on low nutrient, vegetarian foods. In order to break down their high fiber diet, they have specialized digestive systems.

Behaviour
These **terrestrial** birds fly swiftly, but only for short distances, and most grouse species are non-**migratory**, ranging locally looking for food. On cold winter nights, the birds burrow into snow drifts for more warmth.

Many males of this family are noted for their spectacular social gatherings and **courtship** displays. This behaviour ranges from song flights on individual territories to communal **drumming**, dancing and calling. The dance arena where they perform their **courtship** rituals is called a 'lek'.

Diet
Grouse are grazers and browsers, eating shoots, buds, leaves, berries and even pine needles found on or close to the ground.

Reproduction
Members of this family are ground nesters, laying their eggs in a scrape in the ground among vegetation. Large **clutches** of four to seventeen greenish or pinkish buff eggs with dark markings are laid, and **incubated** 20–34 days by the female. The **precocial** chicks develop rapidly and begin feeding on insects and other foods immediately after hatching. Some take their first fluttering flights as early as seven days.

Family Status
Grouse are found in the tundra, prairies, alpine meadows, brushland and coniferous and mixed forests of the northern hemisphere. They have always been considered game birds important to the economy, and the harvest is controlled by limits and licensing systems.

One sub-species of the greater prairie chicken known as the 'heath hen' has been extinct since 1932, the victim of massive over-hunting for their meat. Greater prairie chickens have been **extirpated** from Canada.

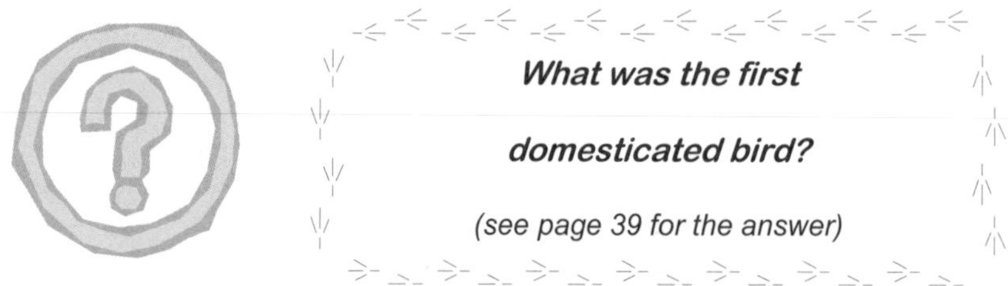

 **Blue Grouse**

Size: 45–52 cm (18"–21")
Range: Alaska, western Canada and USA

- also called dusky or sooty grouse
- do not **migrate**, but winter in coniferous forests and summer in deciduous forests in the same range
- the common grouse species of the western mountains

Nest in Yukon, British Columbia, southwestern Alberta.

  **Ruffed Grouse**

Size: 37–47 cm (15"–19"), wingspan to 62 cm (25")
Range: Alaska, Canada, USA

- named after the ruff of dark feathers on their neck
- **courting** males make a **drumming** sound with their wings which can be heard for a 0.4 km (1/4 mi)
- most popular of all upland game birds
- state bird of Pennsylvania
- flight speed up to 60 kmh (40 mph)
- lifespan up to 7 years

Cherokee Indians considered the meat of the ruffed grouse taboo for pregnant women because they laid large numbers of eggs, but few birds survived.

Nest Canada wide.

 **Sage Grouse**

Size: 52–75 cm (21"–30")
Range: Southwestern Canada, western USA

- largest North American grouse
- birds roost together at night in a circle, with all of them facing outwards
- permanent resident of sagebrush plains and salt desert scrub
- depend on the disappearing sagebrush plant for leaves, shoots and shelter
- not a popular game bird because their diet of sagebrush taints the meat
- lifespan up to 7 years

Nest in southern Alberta and Saskatchewan.

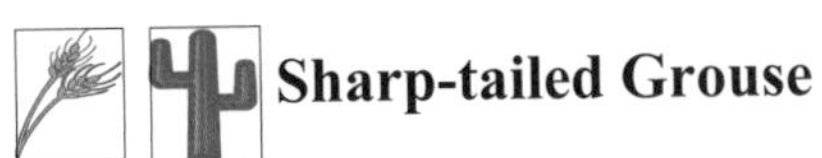

Sharp-tailed Grouse

Size: 52–75 cm (21"–30")
Range: Alaska, Canada, northern USA

- prefer to walk rather than fly
- in the spring, males gather on dancing grounds, inflate the air sacs in their throats to utter hollow booming notes, and raise and fan the tail while quivering their wings
- disappeared from Oregon and New Mexico in the past decade
- flight speed 50 kmh (30 mph)
- lifespan up to 7 years

Nest in Northwest Territories and Alberta through Ontario.

Sharp-tailed Grouse

Spruce Grouse

Size: 37–42 cm (15"–17")
Range: Alaska, Canada, northern USA

- also called 'fool hens' because of their tameness
- usually a tree dweller, eating the buds of conifers
- male **courtship** display consists of tail partly spread, red combs erect, making whirring and snapping sounds with his wings
- not a popular game bird because their diet of spruce needles taints the meat

Nest Canada wide except for the Great Plains.

Did You Know...

Most birds take a bath every day to dislodge parasites and dead skin—in water, dust, rain or even in the sun. Bathing in water facilitates the oiling, ***preening*** *and cleaning of the feathers. Small birds such as hummingbirds fly through a shower or even across the top of dew covered plants before* ***preening.***

If no water is available, desert birds take dust baths, wriggling around in loose dirt and throwing it up on their bodies with their wings. Sun bathing is done when the birds encounter an extremely hot surface, where they sit down and spread their wings. They remain in this position for only a few minutes, before flying to a cooler area to preen.

Ptarmigan

These birds are found further north than any other land bird. For protection against cold temperatures, they have a dense mat of feathers on their feet which grow thicker in the winter months. As a unique adaptation to preserving their camouflage, ptarmigan ***moult*** *their feathers three times during the year - barred grey or brown in autumn; white in winter; and yellower barred* ***plumage*** *with bolder patterns in spring. They are the only birds in the world to have three different coloured* ***plumages****.*

White-tailed Ptarmigan

Size: 30–32 cm (12"–13")
Range: Alaska, western Canada and USA

- smallest member of the grouse family
- in winter, birds are completely white except for their black eyes and bill
- the only ptarmigan with an all white tail
- live only on the highest mountains up to 4,300 m (14,000 ft)
- females sit on their eggs so tightly people can nearly step on them before they move
- lifespan up to 15 years

Nest in Yukon, British Columbia and southwestern Alberta.

Rock Ptarmigan

Size: 32–37 cm (13"–15")
Range: Alaska, northern Canada; Greenland, Arctic Ocean to Eurasia

- also called Arctic or 'polar grouse'
- in winter, birds are completely white except for their black eyes, bill and tail
- the most Arctic dwelling ptarmigan, preferring higher, barren hills

Nest in Yukon, Northwest Territories, Nunavut and Arctic islands.

Ptarmigan comes from the Gaelic '*tarmachan*,' which means mountaineer.

Willow Ptarmigan

Size: 37–42 cm (15"–17")
Range: Alaska, northern Canada; Europe, Asia

- male **courtship** involves short flights into the air, making barking sounds as he flutters down
- fierce battles between males often result in feathers plucked and blood flowing
- both parents attend the young until they are 60 days old
- male remains with female during the **incubation** period, viciously defending the nest against predators

Nest in British Columbia, Yukon to Nunavut, and northern Manitoba to Labrador.

World Species 82
Canadian Species 23

The Gull & Tern Families - Laridae

Characteristics
Laridae are 23–77 cm (9"–31"), grey, black or white seabirds. Juvenile gulls are brownish grey. The sexes are similar, but males are slightly larger. They are not strong fliers, but their long narrow wings are adapted for easy gliding flight and soaring in the updrafts. As with most seabirds, they drink fresh or salt water, with their **salt-excreting glands** removing the excess salt. These birds swim well using their webbed feet.

Although they are in the same family, there are some basic differences between gulls and terns. In flight, gulls point their bill forward while terns point their bill and head down. Gulls alight on water, while terns dive into it for fish. Terns are smaller than gulls, with more slender bodies and deeply forked tails, which is why they are sometimes called 'sea-swallows.'

Behaviour
With numerous scavenging sites now provided by man, some gull species are greatly expanding their ranges and numbers. Many are known for carrying shellfish aloft and dropping them on hard surfaces to break them open. They will also tread their feet on the sand to bring small animals to the surface. **Diurnal** and **gregarious** birds, all members of this family roost in large groups at night. They have shrill voices, with complex vocabularies.

Diet
Gulls originally fed on fish, shellfish, insects, small mammals, birds, their eggs and young, and carrion. Human garbage has now been added to the diet of many, but not all, species. Terns feed on fish, squid and shrimp obtained by plunge diving, but will also eat insects.

Reproduction
In general, the larger species breed on shorelines and the smaller ones in marshes and swamps. Nest sites are variable, ranging from urban rooftops to marshes, cliffs, offshore islands, lagoons, coastal sand bars or even trees. The nest is a scrape lined with plant matter or a mass of twigs, sticks, seaweed and grasses. One to four greenish or pinkish buff eggs are laid, and **incubated** 18–32 days by either the female or both parents, depending on the species. Both parents feed the young by **regurgitation**. In some of the larger gull species there is a red spot near the bill tip. When small chicks peck at this spot, it stimulates the parents to **regurgitate**. Once the chicks leave the nest 21–56 days after hatching, they form loose flocks with other young birds. Most species are communal nesters if food is plentiful, and terns breed in huge colonies numbering hundreds of birds. When disturbed, young gulls and terns may swim out to sea to escape predators. This is a dangerous habit, since they are not always accompanied by an adult and they might easily get lost.

Family Status
Gulls and terns live on coasts, freshwater lakes, rivers and marshes around the world. These birds show little fear of man if not molested. In some areas, gull eggs were once regarded as a delicacy and both the eggs and the adult birds were eaten, a practice made illegal in 1900. Many species of tern were hunted for the **plume trade** to decorate women's hats.

Gulls of Inland Waters

In spite of their nickname of 'seagull', some gull species frequent inland lakes, marshes and rivers, as well as coastal areas. They range in size from 30–77 cm (12"–31"), and have wingspans to 65 cm (29").

Bonaparte's Gull - Alaska, Canada, USA to Central America

- smallest gull in the western hemisphere
- in winter, the black head becomes white with a round black spot behind each eye
- one of the few gull species to nest in trees
- drop onto insects or fish from a hovering position

Nest across northern Canada from British Columbia to Ontario.

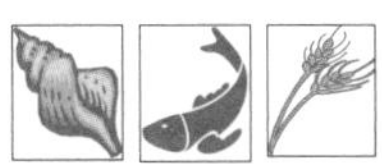
California Gull - Western Canada, USA

- one of the most useful birds to agriculture, with the majority of their diet being insects
- saved the crops of early settlers in Utah from a grasshopper plague; a monument to them was constructed in Salt Lake City and they are now the state bird of Utah
- lifespan up to 12 years

Nest in Alberta and Saskatchewan.

Franklin's Gull - Central Canada and USA to South America

- one of the few black-headed gulls
- also called 'prairie dove' as they are the common gull of summer prairies
- often seen following farm equipment during cultivation
- eat mostly insects in the summer
- nest in large colonies in prairie marshes
- named after Sir John Franklin, Arctic explorer
- unusual in the gull family in that they winter south of the Equator in South America

Nest in Alberta, Saskatchewan and Manitoba.

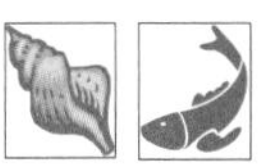
Great Black-backed Gull - Eastern Canada, USA, West Indies; Europe, Iceland, Russia

- one of largest North American gulls with a wingspan of 1.5–1.6 m (60"–66")
- also called 'saddleback gull'
- prey on other seabirds, gulping down both eggs and young birds, and stealing their fish
- domineering over other gulls on the nesting grounds
- lifespan up to 19 years

Nest along coastal Labrador and Newfoundland.

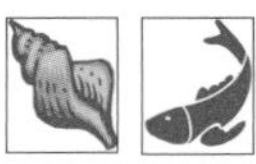 **Herring Gull** - Alaska, western Canada & USA to Central America; Europe

- have pale pink legs
- best known and most widespread gull of North America and Europe
- flocks often ascend vertically in a large circle, flying together in graceful circling flight
- spit up **pellets** of undigested food items: bones, claws etc.
- flight speed to 60 kmh (40 mph)
- lifespan up to 45 years

Nest Canada wide except for Great Plains and Rocky Mountains.

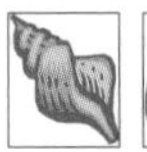   **Mew Gull** - Alaska, western Canada to Central America; Europe

- named after one of their calls
- a Eurasian species common along the Pacific coast of North America
- descend to ocean surface to catch sand eels or dip bill into water while hovering
- lifespan up to 24 years

Nest in Yukon, Northwest Territories and northwestern British Columbia.

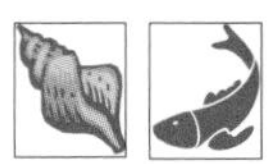 **Ring-billed Gull** - Canada, USA to Florida and Mexico

- the most abundant gull in North America
- young do not reach adult **plumage** until the third year
- when inland, they live on rodents, insects, worms and grubs
- a common sight at garbage dumps, parks and fast food outlets
- flight speed 55 kmh (35 mph)
- lifespan up to 20 years

Nest in Alberta, Saskatchewan and southern Manitoba to the Maritimes.

> Flocks of gulls at airports around the world present a major hazard to aircraft and have been responsible for extensive damage to jet engines.

Mew Gull

Herring Gull

California Gull

Gulls of the Tundra and Open Ocean

These birds are seldom seen inland, and spend all their time at sea or along the coasts. Many nest on the Arctic tundra, and ***migrate*** *offshore. Sizes range from 25–67 cm (10"–27"), with wingspans to 72 cm (33").*

Glaucous Gull - Alaska, northern Canada, Atlantic coast to Central America; Greenland

- one of the largest gull species
- essentially a bird of prey living on young birds, eggs, lemmings, fish, mollusks, crustaceans
- lifespan up to 21 years

Nest on Arctic tundra.

Glaucous-winged Gull - Alaska, western Canada and USA to Central America

- most abundant and widespread gull of the Pacific coast
- drop barnacles, mollusks and sea urchins onto rocks from high in the air
- **omnivorous**, eating carrion, fish, garbage, shellfish
- flight speed to 45 kmh (28 mph)
- lifespan up to 22 years

Nest on Arctic tundra.

Iceland Gull - Nunavut, eastern Canada & USA to Virginia; Greenland, Iceland, Europe

- **omnivorous**, eating carrion, fish, crustaceans
- an uncommon gull of the North Atlantic

Nest on Arctic tundra and Baffin Island.

Ivory Gull - Arctic islands; Greenland, Eurasia

- rarely seen outside of the Arctic
- the only gull species that is pure white
- one of the hardiest gulls in the world, living constantly near snow and ice
- called 'ice partridge' in Newfoundland
- scavengers, eating carrion, lemmings, insects, crustaceans, mollusks, young birds

Nest on Arctic tundra.

Little Gull - Eastern Canada, north eastern USA; Europe, Asia

- smallest gull species in the world at just 25 cm (10") long
- a Eurasian species now nesting in North America

Nest from Great Lakes to Hudson Bay.

Gulls of the Tundra and Open Ocean *continued*

Ross' Gull - Arctic ocean, Alaska; Greenland, Russia

- a rarely seen gull because of their remote range
- the only gull with a wedge-shaped tail
- small groups often nest on ice or hover along channels of open water in the Arctic

Nest on Arctic tundra.

Sabine's Gull - Alaska, Northwest Territories, coastal Canada and USA; Greenland

- breed in the Arctic and migrate at sea to South Africa and Peru
- the only Canadian gull with a well forked tail

Nest on Arctic tundra.

Thayer's Gull - Arctic ocean, Coastal Canada and USA to California and Florida

- classed by some experts as a sub-species of the herring gull
- lifespan up to 45 years

Nest on Arctic tundra.

Western Gull - Southwestern Canada, coastal USA to Mexico

- not often seen inland beyond the reach of tides
- force much larger pelicans and cormorants to give up their catches of fish

Nest on southwestern coast of British Columbia.

Did You Know...

A bird's vocal repertoire may include up to 20 different calls and songs, each serving a function in communicating with others of its kind. All birds have call notes, but only those classed as songbirds have recognizable songs, which are often elaborate patterns of notes grouped into phrases. Call notes, on the other hand, are brief notes of one or two syllables.

Songs are used to attract mates and defend ***territory****. Call notes are used as a warning, a distress call, a 'feed-me' call by the young, to gather the flock together, and let other birds know where they are.*

 **Black-legged Kittiwake**

Size: 40–45 cm (16"–18"), wingspan to 90 cm (36")
Range: Atlantic coast of Canada, USA to West Indies; Greenland, Europe, Russia

- drink only salt water, and are the most oceanic member of the family
- named for their call
- come ashore only to nest in colonies of up to 200,000 birds
- cement together mud, grasses and seaweed by treading to make a nest; this hollow prevents the eggs from rolling off the cliffs
- called 'tickle-ace' in Newfoundland
- lifespan up to 15 years

Nest on Arctic tundra.

  **Arctic Tern**

Size: 35–42 cm (14"–17"), wingspan to 87 cm (33")
Range: Arctic Ocean, Alaska, northern Canada down Atlantic coast to Antarctica; Europe, Iceland, Scandinavia, Russia

- have the longest **migration** of any bird in the world—36,000 km (22,000 mi) from their Arctic nesting ground to the Antarctic
- flying from one end of the world to the other, they don't see the sun set for eight months of the year, and see more daylight in their lifetime than any other animal
- lifespan up to 34 years

Nest on Arctic tundra.

  **Black Tern**

Size: 23–35 cm (9"–10")
Range: Canada, USA to South America; Russia, Europe to Africa

- populations are in decline due to loss of marsh habitat
- dive bomb intruders around the nest, sometimes spraying them with red excrement
- flight speed 48 kmh (30 mph)
- lifespan up to 17 years

Nest Canada wide.

Caspian Tern

 **Caspian Tern**

Size: 47–57 cm (19"–23"), wingspan to 1.3 m (55")
Range: Canada, coastal USA to West Indies; Russia, Africa, India, Australia

- largest tern in the world
- scientific name means 'water-swallow'
- least sociable of all terns, travelling singly or in small groups
- nest in small colonies or sometimes in single pairs
- lifespan up to 26 years

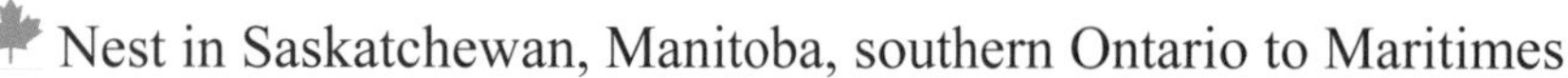

Nest in Saskatchewan, Manitoba, southern Ontario to Maritimes.

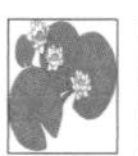   **Common Tern**

Size: 32–40 cm (13"–16"), wingspan to 77 cm (31")
Range: Canada, coastal USA to Central America; Europe, Asia to North Africa

- fishermen watch these terns to see where to put their nets, as the small fish eaten by the birds are always followed by larger ones
- most commonly seen tern of the Atlantic coast
- during **courtship**, the male flies back and forth over the colony, holding a fish in his bill

Nest from Alberta to Maritimes.

  **Forster's Tern**

Size: 35–40 cm (14"–16"), wingspan to 75 cm (30")
Range: Canada, coastal USA to Central America; Europe, Asia to North Africa

- insects are taken in flight and from the surface of the water
- when diving for fish, they fold their wings and submerge completely
- nest in colonies near saltwater, and in single pairs near freshwater
- flight speed 16 kmh (10 mph)

Nest in Alberta, Saskatchewan and Manitoba.

 **Roseate Tern**

Size: 35–42 cm (14"–17"), wingspan to 75 cm (30")
Range: Coastal Canada and USA to South America; Europe, Middle East, Africa, India, Asia, Australia

- named for their pinkish coloured breast
- lifespan up to 9 years

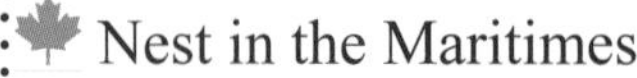

Nest in the Maritimes.

World Species 149
Canadian Species 10

The Hawk Family - Accipitridae

Characteristics

These birds are often referred to as birds of prey, but this is not an exclusive description, as many birds eat some insect or animal matter. A more correct term for the hawk family is raptor, which means a predatory bird that has evolved a specialized beak and talons to catch their food. The hawk family is divided into three groups according to their shape and behaviour—accipiters, buteos and harriers.

Plumage is mottled, usually blended browns or greys on the back and whitish on the front, often streaked or barred. Females are usually larger than the males. All raptors have strongly hooked bills, open nostrils in the soft, leatherlike skin of the upper bill; short necks; rounded heads; and feet ending in sharply curved talons. Roughened pads on the soles of the feet help them grasp prey.

Their piercing eyes are yellow, orange or brown, and their fierce appearance is accentuated by a bony shield over the eyes. The eyesight of raptors is probably the keenest of any living animal. Their eyes are so large they move little in their sockets, and raptors must direct their vision by turning their heads. They have both binocular and monocular vision, essential for an animal that hunts by sight.

Behaviour

Hawks are **diurnal** hunters, active only during daylight hours when they can see their prey. Raptors in the **temperate** zones **migrate** to warmer areas in the winter. **Migration** takes place only during the day, and always over land. The most economical method of flight is to ride the **thermals**, which die down at sunset, and these columns of air are not found over water.

Diet

Raptors are valuable allies to the farmer, as their diet consists of crop-eating mice, rats, voles and other small mammals; insects; and birds.

Reproduction

All members of the hawk family build their own nest of sticks and twigs, located in trees, cliff ledges or on the ground (harriers). The larger species often use the same nest for years. Both sexes help build the nest, but the females do most of the work. **Incubation** is done either by the female alone or both sexes, depending on the species. Two to nine greenish or bluish white eggs are laid at two to four day intervals, and the 21–38 day **incubation** starts with the first egg laid. This results in a great variation in size of the young, and the older chicks often kill the smaller, weaker ones. The young hatch blind and helpless, covered in down. They take their first flight 23–48 days after hatching.

Family Status

Hawks are found on all continents except Antarctica and some oceanic islands, and in all habitats. Throughout their entire range, they are threatened by man's use of pesticides, which cause thinning of the eggshells so the eggs are crushed when **incubated**. While many of these chemicals have been banned in North America, they are still widely used in the birds' wintering grounds in Central and South America.

***Accipiters** are agile, forest dwelling hawks that have short, rounded wings for short bursts of speed, and long tails for excellent maneuverability. Capable of sharp twists and turns in flight, these hawks feed primarily on small birds, taken by darting low and swiftly in and out of woods.*

Northern Goshawk

Size: 47–67 cm (19"–27"), wingspan to 1.1 m (47")
Range: Alaska, Canada, USA to Mexico; Europe, Asia

- biggest and most rare accipiter
- their name originated in Europe as 'goose-hawk'
- extremely audacious when hungy, they often disregard the presence of man
- female is the dominant partner; she **incubates** and **broods** the young, and defends the territory
- nest is built by both sexes and may be 1.5 m (5 ft) across and 1 m (3 ft) deep
- **incubating** female turns the eggs with her beak every 30 minutes
- flight speed 61 kmh (38 mph)
- lifespan up to 19 years

Nest across Canada except for the Great Plains.

Cooper's Hawk

Size: 35–52 cm (14"–21"), wingspan to 90 cm (36")
Range: Canada, USA to Costa Rica

- also known as 'chicken hawks' for their bold attacks on farm poultry
- after catching their prey in their talons, they sometimes fly to water to drown it
- flight speed 45 kmh (28 mph)
- lifespan up to 7 years

Nest from southern British Columbia through to Quebec.

Sharp-shinned Hawk

Size: 25–35 cm (10"–14"), wingspan to 67 cm (27")
Range: Alaska, Canada, USA to Central America and West Indies

- is the smallest accipiter, but tackles prey much larger than itself
- females may be half again as large as males
- young birds have yellow eyes which gradually change to the red of the adults at about three years of age
- also called 'little blue darter'
- a new nest is built each year and may be up to 60 cm (24") across
- flight speed 45 kmh (28 mph)
- lifespan up to 12 years

Nest Canada wide.

***Buteos** are soaring hawks with wide tails and long, broad wings. They circle much higher than accipiters, watching the ground for prey then swooping down and pouncing. These birds eat small mammals such as rats, mice, rabbits and ground squirrels. Some ground dwelling birds, insects and carrion are also eaten.*

Broad-winged Hawk

Size: 32–47 cm (13"–19"), wingspan to 97 cm (39")
Range: Canada, eastern USA to South America

- the smallest buteo, about the size of a crow
- tamest of all hawks and are quiet and gentle
- toads are their favorite food in the spring
- nest takes three to five weeks to build and may be up to 60 cm (24") across
- **incubation** is shared by both sexes, but only the female has a **brood patch**
- flight speed 64 kmh (40 mph)
- lifespan up to 7 years

Nest in central Alberta and Saskatchewan, and southern Manitoba through to Maritimes.

Ferruginous Hawk

Size: 55–62 cm (22"–25"), wingspan to 1.4 m (56")
Range: Central Canada and USA to Mexico

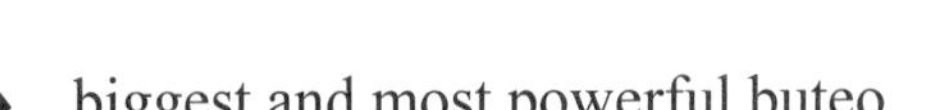

- biggest and most powerful buteo
- often sit at the edge of a mammal burrow, waiting for them to come out
- named for their rusty red plumage
- also called 'squirrel hawk' because of their fondness for ground squirrels
- often include chunks of dried cow or horse manure in their nest, which may be used year after year and can be 4.5 m (15 ft) high
- flight speed 56 kmh (35 mph)
- lifespan up to 20 years

Nest in southern Alberta and Saskatchewan.

Red-shouldered Hawk

Size: 42–60 cm (17"–24"), wingspan to 1.2 m (50")
Range: Southeastern Canada, USA to Mexico

- also called 'red-bellied hawk'
- have a strong attachment to their nesting **territory**; in one woodland either the same pair or succeeding generations used the same area for 45 years
- add material to the same nest annually
- flight speed 54 kmh (34 mph)
- lifespan up to 20 years

Nest in southern Ontario and Quebec.

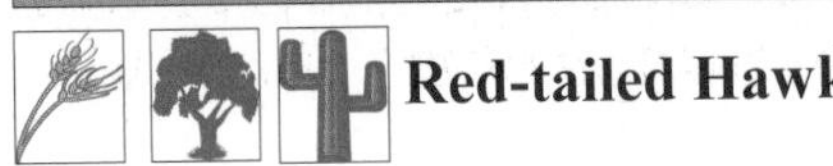

Red-tailed Hawk

Size: 47–62 cm (19"–25"), wingspan to 1.4 m (58")
Range: Alaska, Canada, USA to Central America and West Indies

- the most abundant and widespread hawk in North America
- can see mice on the ground from 30 m (100 ft) in the air
- **courtship** is done in the air, where the female turns over and presents her claws to the male in mock combat
- pairs mate for life and keep the same **territories** each year
- population is declining steadily because of persecution and habitat loss
- flight speed 64 kmh (40 mph)
- lifespan up to 29 years

Nest Canada wide.

Rough-legged Hawk

Size: 47–60 cm (19"–24"), wingspan to 1.4 m (56")
Range: Alaska, NWT, western Canada and USA

- the only buteo that routinely hovers like an American kestrel or osprey
- may spiral high in the air until they are only a speck in the sky
- tame and unsuspicious of man
- the number of eggs laid depends on the availability of lemmings
- roost in small groups in the winter
- nest further north than any other buteo

Nest on Arctic tundra, Northwest Territories and northeastern Canada.

In Iceland, it was believed that if a person carried the tongue of a hawk beneath his own, he would understand the birds' language.

Swainson's Hawk

Size: 42–55 cm (17"–22"), wingspan to 1.3 m (54")
Range: Alaska, western Canada and USA to South America

- a gentle hawk, living in harmony with other birds as they prey on rodents and insects
- wait at the entrance to ground squirrel burrows and catch them when they appear
- same nest is often repaired and used each year
- young leave the nest about 30 days after hatching and chase insects on the ground
- **migrate** 27,360 km (17,000 mi) round trip to South America, often travelling in huge flocks
- flight speed 24 kmh (15 mph)
- lifespan up to 9 years

Nest in British Columbia, Alberta and Saskatchewan.

Harriers *are slim raptors with long, narrow wings and long tails. They fly close to the ground, gliding slowly while looking for rodents. Because they fly so low to the ground their sight is limited, and they also hunt by sound, which other hawks are unable to do.*

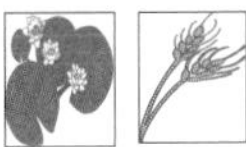

Northern Harrier

Size: 40–50 cm (16"–20"), wingspan to 1.2 m (48")
Range: Alaska, Canada, USA to South America; Europe, Asia

- a pronounced facial disk funnels sound to their ears, allowing them to hunt by ear
- males are grey, while females are cryptically marked with shades of brown for ground nesting camouflage
- the only member of its genus in North America
- also called 'marsh hawks', for their habit of flying a few feet above marshes, prairies and meadows
- hover in front of prairie fires to pick up escaping mice
- breed according to the population cycle of voles; low numbers mean few if any eggs are laid, while large numbers of voles mean large numbers of eggs
- numbers are decreasing because of the draining of marsh lands, their prime hunting habitat
- flight speed 61 kmh (38 mph)
- lifespan up to 16 years

Nest Canada wide.

Harriers are so named because of the way they 'harry' or harrass their prey.

Swainson's Hawk

Red-tailed Hawk

World Species 63
Canadian Species 6

The Heron Family - Ardeidae

Characteristics

The Ardeidae family is comprised of herons and bitterns. Herons are long-legged, long-necked wading birds, while bitterns are smaller with shorter necks and legs. **Plumage** is shades of blues, greys, blacks and browns with white markings. In herons, both sexes have black crests which can be raised at will, and bitterns have a mane of long feathers on the neck and throat for the same purpose. All have broad, rounded wings, and are usually associated with water. Their bill is long and spear-like, and the tail is short.

Members of this family possess two or three pairs of **powder down** patches. When rubbed with the bill, these feathers crumble into a powder which is then used to clean the feathers. Once it has been distributed, the powder is combed out with their third toe, which is flattened and serrated. This toe is called a **feather comb**.

Behaviour

Herons and bitterns fly with straight backs, their necks tucked well back on their shoulders in an 'S' shape with feet trailing loosely behind. Flight is a steady, slow flapping. Although they do not have webbed feet, they do alight on the water.

These birds perch in trees, stand quietly in the shallows or wade along the shores of ponds, marshes and other waterways searching for food. Large food items are not speared, but swallowed whole, with the indigestible parts **regurgitated** as **pellets**. They stand straight legged, and walk in a slow, stately manner, sometimes stirring the bottom with their feet to flush prey from the mud.

Diet

Herons and bitterns eat frogs, mice, crustaceans, eels, insects and small fish.

Reproduction

Male herons advertise for a mate by performing displays from the nest site, located high in a tree. Once a female responds, a platform nest of sticks is built by both sexes, and they share **incubation** and feeding duties as well. Bitterns build a nest of reeds and sedges just above the water level on matted roots in marshes. One to seven bluish green eggs are laid, and **incubated** 17–29 days. The helpless downy young grab the parents' bill to receive **regurgitated** food. Chicks leave the nest 10–42 days after hatching. All members of this family nest in colonies called 'heronries'.

Family Status

The heron family is found worldwide except for the polar areas and some oceanic islands. Herons were nearly wiped out by hunting for the **plume trade** in the 19th century, when it was the fashion to decorate women's hats with feathers. Bitterns were once a delicacy in England, with only the richer classes being able to afford them. Today however, these birds are under threat from the constant draining of the marshlands, and loss of other habitat.

One species, the Bonin night-heron, has been extinct since 1879 due to predators introduced to its island home.

American Bittern

Size: 60–85 cm (24"–34"), wingspan to 1.2 m (50")
Range: Canada, USA to Central America and West Indies

- calls of the males are among the loudest in the bird family, and the boom uttered during breeding season can be heard more than 5 km (3 mi) away
- the hollow booming noise is produced by gulping in air, then forcing it out from the distended esophagus; an air sac in the chest acts as a resonator
- their eyes are placed so that they can see forward when in 'freeze' position, and down when feeding

Nest Canada wide.

> Bitterns are famous for their 'freezing' posture.
>
> Their protective colouration of soft browns and dark markings is enhanced by their habit of standing perfectly rigid with their bill pointed upwards. Their striped undersurface blends so well with the reeds they become virtually invisible, and will even sway back and forth if there is a breeze.

Least Bittern

Size: 27–35 cm (11"–14"), wingspan to 45 cm (18")
Range: Southeastern Canada, USA to South America

- smallest member of the heron family
- escape from intruders by running through reeds above the water, grasping several stems in each foot
- the male chooses the nest site and builds it, while the female brings him materials
- when their chicks hatch, the adults carry the eggshells away
- young assume freezing pose at three to four days old
- **migrate** at night

Nest in southern Ontario and Quebec.

Great Egret

Size: 92–102 cm (37"–41"), wingspan to 1.3 m (55")
Range: Southern Canada, USA

- also called 'angel bird', 'plume bird'
- in spring, both sexes develop a cape of long flowing plumes up to 1.3 m (54"), growing from the back
- nest is 6–12 m (20–40 ft) up in trees, always near water
- feed during the day and roost in flocks at night
- nearly wiped out for the **plume trade**
- flight speed 51 kmh (32 mph)
- lifespan up to 22 years

Nest across southern Canada.

Snowy Egret

Size: 55–65 cm (22"–26"), wingspan to 1.1 m (45")
Range: Southern Canada, USA

- have black legs and bright yellow feet, which turn orange in the breeding season
- one of the daintiest marsh birds
- use one foot to stir the bottom of ponds to frighten prey into view
- breeding **plumage** includes long, soft, waving plumes on the head and back
- slaughtered by the thousands for the **plume trade**
- flight speed 48 kmh (30 mph)
- lifespan up to 16 years

Nest across southern Canada from Alberta to the Maritimes.

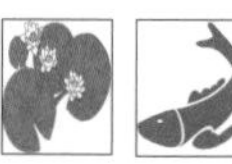

Black-crowned Night-Heron

Size: 57–70 cm (23"–28"), wingspan to 1.1 m (45")
Range: Southern Canada, USA to South America; Europe, Asia, Africa, India, Malaysia

- primarily nocturnal, with relatively large eyes
- male chooses the nest site and brings the material, while the female builds the nest
- flight speed 56 kmh (35 mph)
- lifespan up to 21 years

Nest from southern Alberta through to the Maritimes.

Members of the heron family hunt for food by standing motionless in the water, waiting for small fish to swim close. They are caught in the bill, and swallowed whole. Larger fish are speared with the bill, turned around so the head is facing down the throat, and then swallowed.

One African species, the black heron, has developed the habit of shading the water with his wings, opening them up and pulling them over his head. This fools the fish into thinking there is a sheltered area to swim into, and when they get close, he grabs them.

 **Great Blue Heron**

Size: 1.0–1.3 m (42"–52"), wingspan to 1.5 m (62")
Range: Alaska, Canada, USA to South America and West Indies

- largest and most common heron in Canada
- live in both salt and fresh water habitats
- nests may be used annually and can reach 1.2 m (4 ft) across
- nest from ground level to 30 m (100 ft) up in trees
- defensive action of the young is to **regurgitate** food down on an intruder
- flight speed 56 kmh (35 mph)
- lifespan up to 21 years

Nest across southern Canada.

Great Blue Heron

  **Green Heron**

Size: 45–55 cm (18"–22"), wingspan to 65 cm (26")
Range: Southeastern Canada, USA to South America

- live in both salt and fresh water habitats
- scrape the bottom of the pond with one foot, then peer down to examine the area for moving prey
- flight speed 54 kmh (34 mph)

Nest in southern Ontario and Quebec.

World Species 319
Canadian Species 5

The Hummingbird Family - Trochlidae

Characteristics

Hummingbirds are tiny, nectar drinking birds named after the droning sound of their wings in flight, which beat up to 90 times per second in the smaller species. They range in size from the smallest bird in the world at 5 cm (2 1/4"), to 21 cm (8 1/2"). Most species are iridescent blue or green overall, with markings of red, purple or white, and the males are more brilliantly coloured.

Everything about these little birds is unusual. Their slender, pointed bills are adapted to probing flowers for nectar, and their tongues are tubular and brush-tipped to collect it. They have the unique ability to hover and feed at the hearts of flowers, where they have no competition from other birds. Pointed wings sweep back at their sides, and allow them to fly backwards, shift sideways and fly straight up and down. They rotate their shoulder joint to turn their wings completely over on both the back and forestrokes. This permits the forepart of the wings to cut the air, checking the tendency to move. Because of the enormous effort expended to hover continually, hummingbirds have unusually large flight muscles which are 22%–34% of their body weight. Their legs and feet are used only for occasional perching, and are small and weak.

Behaviour

Hummingbirds feed on the wing and even bathe while airborne, either in the rain or by brushing against wet foliage. Their head is large in relation to their body, and they do not tuck their bill into the back feathers when sleeping, as other birds do. They fluff their body feathers and tilt the head back so the bill points upwards at an angle. On cold nights, they possess the ability to become dormant until dawn, when they can again feed at flowers. Many species follow the seasonal blooming of flowers up and down the continent, and some **migrate** very long distances. They feed heavily before **migrating**, adding more than 50% of their body weight in fat layers under the skin. Direct flight speed has been measured at 50–65 kmh (30–40 mph).

Diet

As well as collecting nectar, hummingbirds also snatch insects from mid-air and spiders from plants. They have the highest metabolic rate of any living vertebrate, and must feed almost continually, consuming 50% of their body weight in sugar daily. They have a tiny **crop** where they can store food for overnight sustenance. Males establish feeding **territories** from which they chase other males, bees and hawk moths.

Reproduction

Aggressive and quarrelsome among themselves, hummingbirds are extremely **territorial** when nesting. Females build the nest, **incubate** the eggs and raise the young on their own, driving away other hummers, including the male of the pair. Nests are a round cup of plant fibers, down, and moss bound together with spider webbing and attached to a tree branch. The openings are elastic, closing when the female leaves. Two tiny white eggs are **incubated** for 15–16 days, and the young are fed on **regurgitated** food. Chicks are able to fly 20–22 days after hatching.

Family Status

Hummingbirds are found only in the **New World**, from Alaska to Tierra del Fuego, and from the lowlands to 4,900 m (16,000 ft) in Ecuador. The family originated in South America and is now found over much of North America as well.

Anna's Hummingbird

Size: 9–10 cm (3.5"–4"), wingspan 12 cm (5")
Range: Western Canada and USA to Mexico

- the only hummingbird to regularly winter in the USA
- unlike most hummingbirds, these are able to sing a thin, squeaky warble
- depend more on insects and spiders for food than other hummingbirds
- **courtship** display involves the male rising upwards until he is just a speck in the sky, and then shooting vertically downward at tremendous speed
- weigh about 5.8 gr (1/5 ounce)

Nest in southwestern British Columbia.

The Cuban bee hummingbird is the smallest bird in the world, measuring just 5.6 cm (2.25"). These tiny creatures are often mistaken for large insects in flight.

♦

The smallest eggs in the world belong to the Vervain hummingbird from the Caribbean. Approximately the size of a small bean, they are 10 mm (0.39").

Black-chinned Hummingbird

Size: 9–10 cm (3.5"–4")
Range: Southwestern Canada, western USA to Mexico

- two or three **clutches** per year
- weigh approximately 3 gr (1/11 ounce)

Nest in southern British Columbia.

Black-chinned Hummingbird

Calliope Hummingbird

Size: 7–9 cm (2.75"–3.5"), wingspan to 11 cm (4.5")
Range: Western Canada and USA to Mexico

- smallest bird in North America
- nest up to the timberline at 4,600 m (15,000 ft)
- nest is always placed under a larger branch for protection
- female often builds her nest atop those used in previous years, until several are stacked up
- weigh approximately 2.5 gr (1/10 ounce)

Nest in southern British Columbia.

 Ruby-throated Hummingbird

Size: 7–10 cm (3"–4"), wingspan to 12 cm (5")
Range: Alaska, Canada, USA to Central America, West Indies

- wings beat at 70 times per second, accelerating to 200 times per second during **courtship**
- attack and chase larger birds from their territory
- **migrate** across the Gulf of Mexico, covering 800 km (500 mi) non-stop in 18 hours
- go as far north as Alaska, and are the only hummingbirds nesting east of the Mississippi
- two or three **clutches** per year
- weigh approximately 3 gr (1/11 oz)
- lifespan up to 5 years

Nest across southern Canada from Alberta to Quebec.

 Rufous Hummingbird

Size: 8–10 cm (3.5"–4"), wingspan to 11 cm (4.5")
Range: Alaska, Yukon, western Canada and USA to Mexico

- so attracted to red that they investigate red towels, red fruit boxes, red cans and bandanas
- summer farther north than any other hummingbird
- female sometimes builds a new nest on top of an old one
- both sexes are aggressive in defending **territory,** driving away larger birds and small mammals
- weigh approximately 3 gr (1/11 oz)

Nest in British Columbia, southwestern Alberta.

The Ibis Family - Threskiornithidae

Characteristics

Ibis are 47–105 cm (19"–42") long-legged, wading birds with long necks and bills. **Plumage** is highly variable throughout the family, but all species have a bare facial area encircling the eyes. Their highly sensitive bill finds food more by touch than by sight. Their feet are partially webbed, and the long, broad wings make them strong fliers. In sustained flight the head and neck are stretched forward with the long legs trailing behind. Slow flapping wing beats alternate with short glides.

The family is divided into the ibis with thin, **downcurved** bills and the spoonbills, with broad, flattened bills. They are closely related to the stork family.

Behaviour

Highly **gregarious**, members of this family live in large groups and travel widely in search of feeding grounds in freshwater lagoons, lakes, bays and marshes. All species can swim well. The majority of the species have no voice; those that do vocalize have a weak call.

Diet

Fish, insects, mollusks, crustaceans, and small mammals are eaten.

Reproduction

These birds feed, nest, and roost in swamps, marshes, trees and on the ground. Colony nesters, both sexes take turns guarding the nest site. Three to four greenish blue eggs are laid in a deep nest of twigs, plants and debris, and **incubated** 21–22 days. Both parents feed the young **regurgitated** food. Ibis nest in mixed colonies with herons, bitterns and egrets.

Family Status

Ibis are found worldwide in tropical and warm **temperate** regions. They have been valued since prehistoric times for their role in controlling animal pests in crops. Ancient Egyptians revered the sacred ibis as the god Thoth, whose duty was to record the lives of all people. Many hundreds of these birds were mummified and buried in the temples with the Pharaohs. They are no longer found in Egypt, and are confined to more southerly locations in Africa.

 **White-faced Ibis**

Size: 47–105 cm (19"–42")
Range: Alberta, USA to Central America and Hawaii

- blue facial skin becomes white in breeding season
- isolated breeder in southern Canada with the breeding population increasing annually
- ibis are primarily tropical birds and this is the only western and northern straggler
- population in the USA is declining due to pesticides
- flight speed 53 kmh (33 mph)
- lifespan up to 14 years

 Nest in southern Alberta, Saskatchewan and Manitoba.

World Species 6
Canadian Species 3

The Jaeger Family - Stercorariidae

Characteristics
Jaegers are 61 cm (24") oceanic, piratical birds of the north and south oceans. **Plumage** is generally dark brown or black. Sexes look alike, but the females are larger. They resemble their close relatives the gulls, but have a hawk-like fleshy pad across the base of the upper bill, and elongated central tail feathers that extend 5–20 cm (2"–8") beyond the others. The short, stout bill is strongly hooked at the tip, and short, strong legs end in webbed feet with sharply curved claws. The wings are long and slender, and usually held angled at the joints in flight.

Behaviour
These are the most numerous birds of prey in the Arctic, and play the same **carnivorous** role hawks, falcons and vultures do on land. Strong **rapacious** pirates of the high seas, they live largely by chasing smaller seabirds and forcing them to disgorge their meals. 'Jaeger' means hunter in German, referring to their habit of taking food from other birds.

Diet
On their Arctic nesting grounds they eat lemmings, rodents, carrion, young birds, berries, fish, mollusks and garbage left by man. Throughout the rest of the year fish make up most of their diet.

Reproduction
Jaegers perform spectacular aerial displays and calls when they first arrive on the breeding grounds. Pairs then select regular look-out posts on a mound or rock near the nest site, which is a mere scrape in the ground. One to three olive brown eggs with dark markings are laid, and **incubated** 23–28 days by both parents. **Incubating** birds leave the nest before an intruder reaches it, mobbing him or trying to distract him with a display of flapping and tumbling. Chicks are covered in grey down, and leave the nest 21–42 days after hatching. Jaegers breed in scattered pairs of loose colonies along the coast and on bare ground inland.

Family Status
Seldom seen from shore, jaegers are strong, fast fliers that wander over the seas to South America. In winter, they spend all their time at sea, often settling on the water, drifting objects or ships. Jaegers and their close relatives, the skuas, are found on land only in the Arctic.

Which bird sees more daylight in their lifetime than any other animal?

(see page 85 for the answer)

 **Long-tailed Jaeger**

Size: 50–75 cm (20"–33"), wingspan to 75 cm (30")
Range: Alaska, northern Canada; Greenland, Europe, Russia

- the smallest jaeger species
- **circumpolar** breeding range along the coasts of the entire Arctic Ocean
- rarely seen because they **migrate** in mid-ocean
- so dependent on lemmings for food that in summers of lemming scarcity may move to summer elsewhere
- adults feign injury to lead intruders from nest

Nest on Arctic tundra.

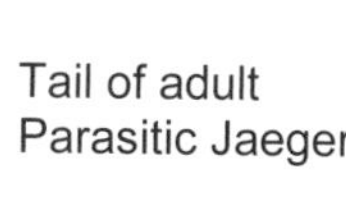
Tail of adult
Parasitic Jaeger

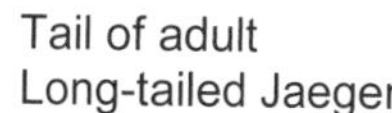
Tail of adult
Long-tailed Jaeger

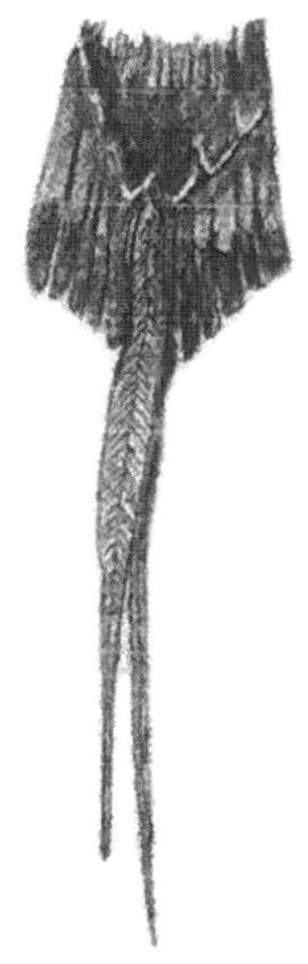

  **Parasitic Jaeger**

Size: 37–52 cm (15"–21"), wingspan to 90 cm (36")
Range: Alaska, northern Canada; Greenland

- also called an 'Arctic hawk'
- **migrate** 18,500 km (10,000 mi) at sea to winter in the oceans off South America and Africa
- join Arctic terns on their long **migration**, to pirate food from them
- do not breed until three to five years of age
- lifespan up to 30 years

Nest on Arctic tundra.

  **Pomarine Jaeger**

Size: 50–57 cm (20"–23"), wingspan to 1.2 m (48")
Range: Alaska, northern Canada; Greenland, Europe, Russia

- largest and most powerful jaeger species
- name comes from the Latin word for having the nostrils roofed over by a horny plate
- when hunting, they fly 4–7 m (15–25 ft) above the tundra, alighting when a lemming is seen and grabbing it in their bill
- breed along coasts and islands of the entire Arctic Ocean

Nest on Arctic tundra.

Pomarine Jaeger

World Species 86
Canadian Species 1

The Kingfisher Family - Alcedinidae

Characteristics

Kingfishers are chunky, compact birds with short necks and large heads accentuated by erectile crests. Their waterproof **plumage** is generally bright blue or green with contrasting patches of white, red or brown. Sexes look alike. They have stumpy tails; short, rounded wings; and long, sharp, pointed bills. Short legs end in small, weak feet with three toes pointing forward and one pointing backward.

Behaviour/Diet

All members of this family tend to be noisy and raucous. Flight is rapid and direct but usually not far, as they habitually perch on a branch or tree stump near water. Kingfishers are solitary except for the mating season.

Their diet is mainly fish, which are seized by diving headfirst underwater. The bird perches until prey is sighted, then aims, tenses and dives headfirst with the body straight as an arrow and the beak open. Fish are grabbed with the beak, not stabbed. A protective membrane covers the eye surface as they enter the water. When they grab a fish, they pivot and flap back to the surface, propelling themselves out of the water. The whole action takes about a 1/3 of a second. They then return to their perch, bang the fish against the branch until it is dead, flip it around until the head is facing down the throat, and swallow it whole. Amphibians, crustaceans and insects are also taken.

Reproduction

Kingfishers nest at the end of a self-dug horizontal burrow in the riverbank. These burrows, dug with the bill and feet, are 0.9–2.1 m (3–7 ft) long with a round nesting chamber at the far end. Kingfishers mate for life and both sexes guard their **territory**, chasing off interlopers of the same species. Eggs are laid on bare soil, and shared **incubation** starts when the clutch is complete. Chicks attempt to fish on the day they leave the nest, but parents continue to feed them until they are proficient at feeding themselves. There is a high chick mortality rate through drowning.

Family Status

These birds are close relatives of the kookaburra, bee eaters, rollers and hornbills. Although they have a worldwide distribution, most kingfisher species are found in the tropics.

Belted Kingfisher

Size: 27–35 cm (11"–14")
Range: Alaska, Canada, USA to Central America and West Indies

- self-dug burrow takes from three days to three weeks to construct
- sometimes dive below the surface of the water to escape predators
- disgorge **pellets** of fish bones and scales
- chicks become surrounded with fish bones and scales, as the same nest is used for many years
- flight speed 58 kmh (36 mph)

Nest Canada wide.

World Species 398
Canadian Species 3

The Kinglet & Gnatcatcher Family - Sylviidae

Characteristics

Sylviidae are small, chubby, active, insect eating birds with long, thin, pointed bills. Generally from 7–15 cm (3"–6") long, kinglets are greenish brown with bright crowns visible when they are excited. Gnatcatchers are pale greyish blue with long mobile tails which are often cocked upwards and flipped about. These are among the smallest North American birds, and for their size, have a surprisingly loud, melodic song.

Behaviour

These tiny birds move actively through the leaves and needles, and are particularly adapted to feeding in conifers. Because they weigh so little, they are able to feed at the very top of the branches. In winter they travel in mixed flocks with chickadees, nuthatches and woodpeckers in the northern woods, as they do not **migrate**. During the colder seasons they search out hibernating insects and their larvae.

Diet

Kinglets pick insects, larvae and spiders from the bark of trees, while gnatcatchers also catch flying insect prey. Some fruit, seeds and tree sap are also eaten.

Reproduction

Song plays an important part in the breeding cycle in defining **territory** and attracting a female. Once paired, the birds claim a small **territory**, and elaborate, globular nests are built of plant materials, mosses and spider webbing, located in trees from 0.6–6 m (2–200 ft) up. Kinglets build domed nests, while gnatcatchers' nests are open. For a small bird, kinglets lay huge clutches of 10–11 bluish cream eggs. Both sexes **incubate** 12–13 days, and both feed the young. The chicks leave the nest 10–12 days after hatching.

Family Status

This large family of insect eaters is found throughout the world except for the polar areas. They are also known as **Old World** warblers, and in spite of their small size these little birds have featured as food in some Mediterranean countries, where they are sold as 'pickled birds'. In England, kinglets are called 'goldcrests.'

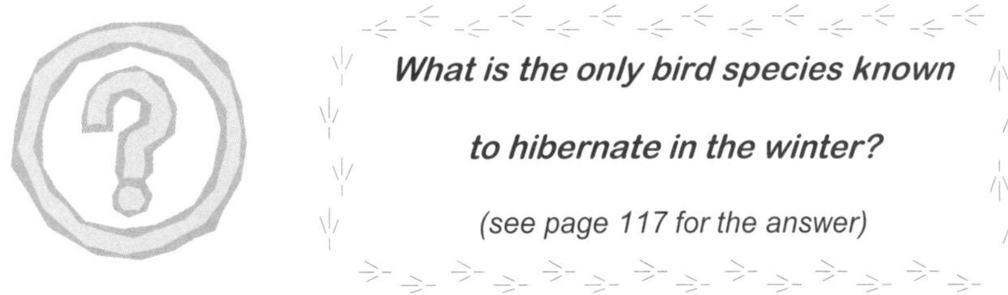

(see page 117 for the answer)

 **Blue-grey Gnatcatcher**

Size: 10–12 cm (4"–5"), wingspan to 15 cm (6")
Range: Southeastern Canada, USA to Central America and West Indies; Europe, Asia

- nest is anchored to a branch with spider webbing
- named for their feeding habit of catching gnats out of the air
- fidgety, slender and frail birds that are intensively active

Nest in southern Ontario.

 **Golden-crowned Kinglet**

Size: 8–10 cm (3"–4"), wingspan to 17 cm (7")
Range: Alaska, Canada, USA to Central America; Europe, Asia

- fearless of people, they often come into cabins and can even be stroked
- nest is 8–10 cm (3"–4") across and 5–8 cm (2"–3") deep
- nest is so small eggs are deposited in layers
- eggs are 12 mm (1/2") long

Nest across northern Canada.

The word kinglet refers to the bright feathers on their head and the small size of these birds. They were thought to be like little kings with golden or ruby crowns.

These bright crown feathers can be raised as crests, and are raised and lowered repeatedly.

 **Ruby-crowned Kinglet**

Size: 8–10 cm (3"–4"), wingspan to 17 cm (7")
Range: Alaska, Canada, USA to Central America;
Europe, Asia

- red feathers on the crown can be flashed or hidden at will
- winter farther south and nest farther north than golden-crowned
- have a characteristic habit of nervously flicking their wings
- song is an excited musical chattering

Ruby-crowned Kinglets

Nest Canada wide except for the Great Plains.

World Species 75
Canadian Species 2

The Lark Family - Alaudidae

Characteristics

Larks are an **Old World** family of small, 17–20 cm (7"–8") perching birds renowned for their liquid, flute-like song. **Plumage** is usually shades of brown streaked with black to help them hide in vegetation. The wings are long and pointed, and both sexes look alike. Unlike most perching birds, their hind claw is long and straight.

Behaviour

Larks are highly **gregarious**, and large flocks can be seen in open, grassy country and cultivated fields. Inconspicuous birds, they forage on the ground and walk or run, rather than hop. When threatened, they often crouch in vegetation or stand motionless to aid in their camouflage, instead of flying. Larks are famous for their elaborate and beautiful **courtship** songs, uttered while flying over their nesting **territory**. Their song is remarkable for its melodious quality and the vehemence with which it is delivered.

Diet

The diet is varied, with most eating seeds, insects, berries, spiders, mollusks and crustaceans. The family has a variety of beak shapes adapted to a wide range of foods.

Reproduction

Living in vast open spaces, larks are ground nesters. Two to four greyish white eggs spotted with brown are laid in a loose cup of dead grass, hidden in the vegetation. The female builds the nest and **incubates** the eggs for 11–12 days. The young leave the nest 9–12 days after hatching, but do not fly until 21 days of age. The male defends the nest site and supplies the **incubating** female with food.

Family Status

Larks are found throughout much of the world with the greatest concentration of species in Africa.

The horned lark has a unique **circumpolar** distribution. In Europe and Asia they are restricted by other lark species to high mountains, stony plateaus and Arctic tundra. In North America, however, being the only widespread lark species, they have colonized open habitats throughout the continent. They are also the only lark species to have reached South America.

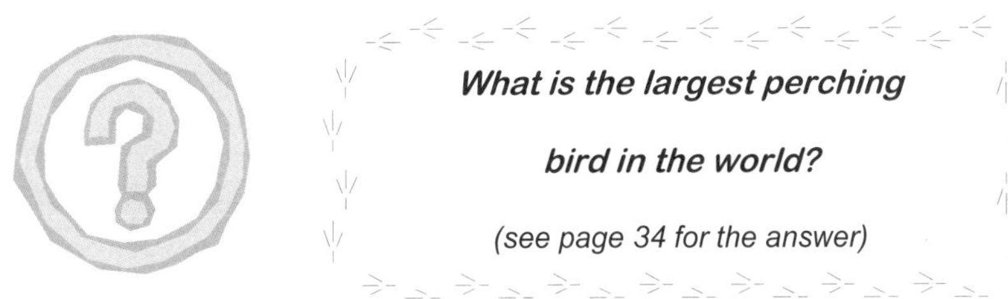

 **Horned Lark**

Size: 17–20 cm (7"–8"), wingspan to 35 cm (14")
Range: Alaska, central Canada and USA to Mexico; Europe, Asia

- black 'horns' on the head are actually feather tufts
- babies have vividly coloured mouth linings with black dots pointing down their throats, to aid parents in feeding
- non **migratory**
- flight song is begun on a climb to more than 24 m (800 ft) where the male circles, and then closes his song with a headlong drop to the earth with closed wings
- two or three **clutches** per year
- flight speed 86 kmh (54 mph)

Nest across Canada.

Horned Lark

 **Skylark**

Size: 17–20 cm (7"–8"), wingspan to 35 cm (14")
Range: South western Canada; Eurasia, Africa

- native to Eurasia and North Africa
- males have loud, clear warbling which may be sustained up to five minutes while hovering in the air above their **territory**; then fold their wings and drop like a stone
- 100 birds were introduced to Vancouver Island in the early 1900's; this small population is declining steadily
- North American population is found only in southwestern British Columbia and northwestern USA
- lifespan up to 8 years

Nest in southwestern British Columbia.

In 1999, wheat soaked with an agricultural insecticide killed as many as 27,000 birds—primarily horned larks, red-winged blackbirds, brown-headed cowbirds and common grackles—in a southern Illinois field.

World Species 8
Canadian Species 1

The Long-tailed Tit Family - Aegithalidae

Characteristics
This is a family of very active, tiny 8–10 cm (3"–4") birds that weigh as little as 5 gr. (1/5 oz). **Plumage** is basically black or brown and white, and all species have graduated tails with the central feathers the longest. The tail makes up more than half the overall length of the bird. Both sexes look alike. Their short, stubby bills enable them to search out the smallest prey.

Behaviour
These **gregarious** birds are extremely busy, constantly moving through the trees and bushes looking for food. Because of their small size, they are able to feed at the very tips of the branches. The flock keeps in touch with each other by uttering high pitched, penetrating calls, and they have no song. During cold weather, the birds roost together in tightly packed groups.

Diet
All members of this family are highly insectivorous, eating a variety of insects, spiders and other small **invertebrates**. Some seeds and grains may also be taken.

Reproduction
These little birds are famous for their construction of elaborate hanging nests. Made of plant matter bound together with spider silk and covered with lichen, they are gourd or bag-shaped, with a hole in one side near the top. A horizontal passage leads to a bowl shaped area where the eggs are laid. Nest sizes vary from 17–25 cm (7"–10") long, and 25–30 cm (10"–12") wide. It can take the pair up to seven weeks to complete construction. Each nest is lined with an enormous number of feathers—more than 2,000 have been recorded. Five to seven white eggs are laid, and **incubated** by both sexes in turn for 12 days. **Incubating** birds often have a bent tail from sitting in the tiny nest. Young leave the nest 14–15 days after hatching, but remain with their parents even after they have **fledged**. Two or even three **clutches** are raised each year.

Unlike most species, flocks do not disperse in the breeding season. Unusually for the bird family, long-tailed tit nests are attended by up to six adults. These helpers may be previous young of the pair, or other adults who have lost their eggs to predators.

Family Status
This family is found throughout Europe and Asia, with only one species in North America.

Bushtit

Range: Southwestern Canada, western USA to Central America

- one of the smallest North American birds at 8–10 cm (3"–4")
- all males and newly hatched young have dark eyes; adult females have cream coloured eyes
- travel in loose flocks of 20–50 birds
- found up to 2,438 m (8,000 ft) in the Rocky Mountains, as well as coastal and desert areas

Nest in southwestern British Columbia.

World Species 4
Canadian Species 4

The Loon Family - Gaviidae

Characteristics

Loons are large, 57–90 cm (23"–36") diving birds with sleek, elongated bodies. **Plumage** of greys, blacks and white is thick, hard and compact, but the feathers of the head and neck are soft and velvety. The sexes look alike, with the females slightly smaller. When sitting on the water, these birds are wider than they are high, which gives them increased stability. They are tailless with long, thick necks and dagger-like pointed bills and small pointed wings. Loons can sink slowly below the surface of the water by expelling air from their body and feathers.

Specialized to an **aquatic** life, their webbed feet are placed so far back on the body they are unable to walk on land. Unlike most birds, loons have many bones that are solid, rather than filled with air, as this added weight helps them dive. They have been found at 60 m (200 ft) below the surface. The only birds that dive deeper are the penguins. Except for one species, loons need a long running start from the water surface to become airborne. Once airborne, they can reach speeds of 90 kmh (60 mph) in level flight.

Behaviour

These birds are seen singly or in pairs, and all are **migratory.** They travel from the northern freshwater lakes to inshore tidal waters to spend the winter. The eerie, wailing cries the loon makes while flying over his **territory** originated the term 'crazy as a loon.' Their voice is distinctive, consisting of guttural notes as well as the loud cries.

Aggressive displays are used to discourage intruders of the same species. These include rapidly swimming towards the intruder with the rear of the body submerged, neck extended stiffly and bill lifted into the air.

Diet

Mainly fish eaters, prey is seized in the bill, not speared. They also eat crustaceans, mollusks, frogs and **aquatic** insects.

Reproduction

Loons breed on freshwater lakes, and nests are built close to shore or on low-lying islets where a flattened scrape in the ground is lined with grass. One to three greenish brown eggs marked with brown are laid. Both parents **incubate** 27–30 days and care for the young, who are unable to fly until they are about two months old. The young leave the nest one to two days after hatching, and take to the water right away. Small chicks often climb up on their parents' backs, a survival adaptation to prevent the downy chicks from becoming soaked. Chicks are not fed **regurgitated** food, but whole fish starting at one day of age. When the young have **fledged**, the parents go through a wing **moult** period, and are flightless until they grow new feathers. Loons do not breed until their third year.

Family Status

A **holarctic** family, loons are found across the northern portion of North America and Eurasia. In Europe they are called divers. In Greenland, loon skins were once used to make ornamental blankets or wall carpets. Today, the loon population is in sharp decline, due to lack of isolated breeding lakes, acid rain and lead poisoning from ingesting fishing weights.

Common Loon

Size: 62–90 cm (28"–36"), wingspan to 1.4 m (58")
Range: Alaska, Canada, USA; Iceland, Greenland

- **territory** sizes range from entire lakes of 40 ha (100 acres) to bays of 6–8 ha (15–20 ac)
- must run across the surface of the water for 18 m (60 ft) or more to become airborne
- dive to 60 m (200 ft) and remain below for nearly a minute
- mate for life, and use the same nest site annually
- nest as close to water as possible
- national bird of Canada
- flight speed 99 kmh (62 mph)
- lifespan up to 7 years

Nest Canada wide.

Common Loons

Pacific Loon

Size: 57–72 cm (23"–29"), wingspan to 1.2 m (50")
Range: Alaska, northern Canada to coasts of Mexico; Eurasia

- more social than other loons, and **migrate** in small flocks
- winter along the Pacific coast of Canada
- once considered the same species as the **Old World** Arctic loon
- flight speed 78 kmh (49 mph)
- lifespan up to 18 years

Nest in Yukon, Northwest Territories and Nunavut.

The word loon comes from the Scandinavian word *'lom'*, meaning a lame or clumsy person, in reference to their awkwardness on land.

Red-throated Loon

Size: 60–67 cm (24"–27"), wingspan to 1.1 m (45")
Range: Alaska, Canada to coasts of Mexico and Florida; Iceland, Europe, Russia

- most widely distributed and smallest loon
- the only loon able to take off from land or leap straight up from the water
- dives are shallower and shorter than those of other loons
- breed farther north than any other loon species
- flight speed 60 kmh (38 mph)
- lifespan up to 23 years

Red-throated Loon

Nest in Yukon, Northwest Territories, Nunavut and on Arctic islands.

Yellow-billed Loon

Size: 75–90 cm (30"–36"), wingspan to 1.3 m (55")
Range: Alaska, western Canada; Scandinavia, Russia

- largest member of the loon family
- mainly a Eurasian species
- rarest of the five loon species in Canada
- once considered a weather profit by the Eskimos

Nest in Northwest Territories, Nunavut and on Arctic islands.

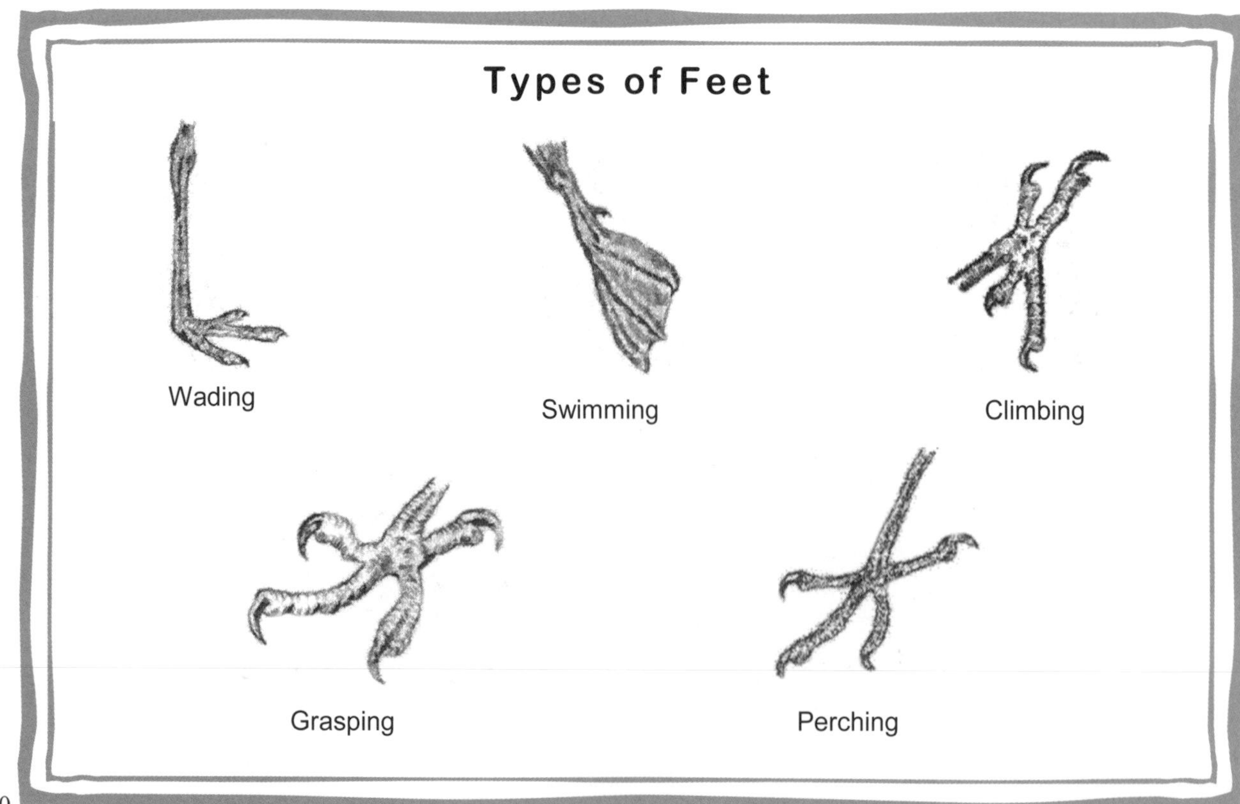

World Species 6
Canadian Species 3

The Merganser Family - Mergini

Characteristics
Mergansers are 40–67 cm (16"–27") diving birds with streamlined bodies adapted to the underwater pursuit of fish. Most species have a crest, and the sexes differ markedly in **plumage.** Like the aquatic loons and grebes, mergansers can sink slowly into the water by expelling air from their feathers. Their feet are placed well back on their body to act as a propeller, and as a result they are awkward on land. Skillful divers, they capture their prey underwater in their long, slender, tooth-edged bill, adapted for holding slippery prey. After the breeding season, males of most species go through an **eclipse moult.**

Behaviour
Mergansers are the fastest fliers in the duck family, and reach speeds up to 160 kmh (100 mph). In flight, the bill, neck and body are rigidly held horizontal, unlike the other members of the duck family who relax their necks. They are often found in pairs or small family groups.

Diet
These birds eat a variety of **aquatic** food: fish, frogs, crustaceans, mollusks, insects and plants.

Reproduction
Mergansers nest in tree cavities or ground depressions. All nests are lined with down from the female's breast and feathers. One egg is laid per day until the **clutch** contains 6–18 yellowish or greenish eggs. **Incubation** does not start until the **clutch** is complete, which ensures that all chicks will be the same age and size when they hatch. The female **incubates** the eggs alone for 29–37 days, and stays on the nest the first day after hatching so the young imprint on her. At four days of age, chicks born in tree cavities leave the nest by leaping to the ground, and follow the female to water. Young mergansers fly 60–70 days after hatching.

Family Status
One species, the Auckland Island merganser, has been extinct since 1910 due to overhunting and the introduction of pigs, rats and mice to the island. Unlike many other duck species, mergansers are not hunted as game birds, as their fishy diet gives their meat an unpleasant taste.

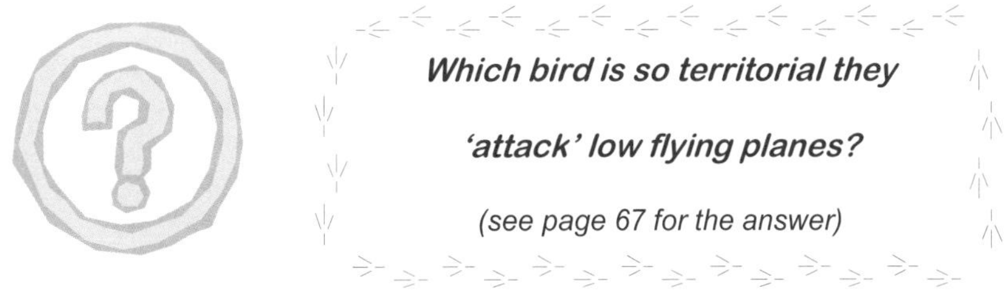

Common Merganser

The word merganser is Latin for 'diving goose.'

Size: 52–67 cm (21"–27"), wingspan to 97 cm (39")
Range: Alaska, Canada, USA to Mexico; Iceland, Eurasia

- largest merganser species, and largest of all inland ducks
- nest in tree cavities
- often work as a group, driving a school of fish into the shallows where they are easier to catch
- must run along the surface, beating their wings, to become airborne
- known as 'goosanders' in Europe

Nest Canada wide except for the Great Plains.

Hooded Merganser

Size: 40–47 cm (16"–19"), wingspan to 65 cm (26")
Range: Alaska, Canada, USA to Mexico

- male has black-bordered, fan-shaped white crest which he raises and lowers repeatedly
- the smallest merganser in North America
- rise straight from the water in full flight
- flight is totally silent and in a direct, straight line
- dive quickly, using wings and feet to maneouver underwater
- tree cavity nester

Nest across Canada.

Hooded Merganser

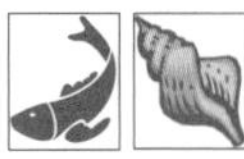

Red-breasted Merganser

Size: 40–45 cm (16"–18"), wingspan to 87 cm (35")
Range: Alaska, Canada, coastal USA; Greenland, Iceland, Europe, Russia

- hunt with their head submerged as they look for food, or swim with head and neck stretched out and bill skimming the surface of the water
- must run along the surface of the water to become airborne
- most **gregarious** merganser species, traveling in flocks of hundreds
- flock may swim in line to drive fish into shallow water, where they are more easily caught
- ground nesters, the female is sometimes a **dump nester**, laying her eggs in the nests of other birds

Nest across Canada except for British Columbia and the Great Plains.

World Species 30
Canadian Species 4

The Mockingbird and Thrasher Family - Mimidae

Characteristics
Mockingbirds are medium-sized, 20–30 cm (8"–12") perching birds famed for their superb song and mimicry. Slender, long-tailed birds, their **plumage** is various shades of greys and browns with white markings. Both sexes look alike. They have short, rounded wings, and strong bills which are slightly or strongly **downcurved.**

Behaviour
All birds in this family are fine singers. Both sexes sing throughout the year, and even at night during the breeding season. Solitary and highly **territorial,** their defensive behaviour is not confined to the breeding season. These active, aggressive birds live in open shrubby habitats.

Some members of this family are famed for their mimicry, imitating the songs of other birds, frogs, crickets, pianos, metal squeaks, barking dogs and many other sounds. Females are attracted to the males with the greatest vocal abilities.

Diet
Ground dwelling birds for the most part, members of this family eat insects, seeds, berries, fruit, spiders and worms. Thrashers use their long bills to dig in the ground or toss leaves aside to locate food.

Reproduction
Bulky, open cup nests are built of grass, twigs and rootlets in a bush or dense tree from 3–15 m (1–50 ft) above the ground. Three to six bluish green eggs spotted with brown are laid, and **incubated** for 10–15 days. Both parents prepare the nest and feed the young, showing great courage in its defense. They generally have two or even three **clutches** per season. The young leave the nest 9–15 days after hatching.

Family Status
This family is found only in the **New World.** Mockingbirds were once captured as young birds and sold as caged pets because of their beautiful song. Although this practice is now illegal in North America, it is still practiced in parts of South America. The symbol of the southern United States, the mockingbird is famous for its rapturous singing at night among the magnolias and oak trees.

Which bird family feeds feathers to their young?

(see page 74 for the answer)

Grey Catbird

Size: 20–23 cm (8"–9"), wingspan to 30 cm (12")
Range: Southern Canada, USA to Central America

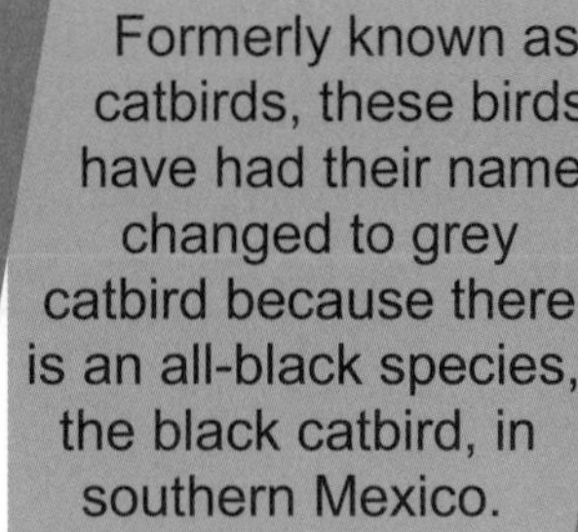

- named after their cat-like, mewing call
- no other bird is plain slate grey with red under the tail
- remarkably fearless of man and tamable
- **migrate** at night
- accomplished mimic of other bird songs
- flight speed 25 kmh (16 mph)
- lifespan up to 10 years

Nest across southern Canada.

Northern Mockingbird

Size: 23–27 cm (9" -11"), wingspan to 37 cm (15")
Range: Southern Canada, USA, Mexico, Central America; introduced to Hawaii

- scientific name means 'bird of many tongues'
- have been recorded imitating the songs of 32 species within 10 minutes
- a strong defender of their **territory**, they often dive at dogs, cats and people who get too close
- female **incubates** the eggs on her own
- state bird of five southern USA states
- flight speed 35 kmh (22 mph)
- lifespan up to 15 years

Nest across southern Canada.

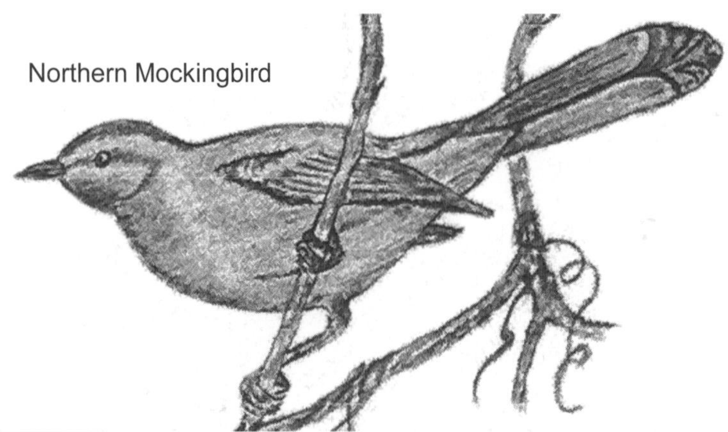

Brown Thrasher

Size: 25–30 cm (10"–12"), wingspan to 35 cm (14")
Range: Southern Canada, eastern USA

- extremely shy birds, living in thickets and shrubbery
- mimic the calls of other birds in a continual, ongoing chatter
- both parents **incubate** the eggs
- state bird of Georgia
- flight speed 35 kmh (22 mph)
- lifespan up to 12 years

Nest from southern Alberta to Quebec.

Sage Thrasher

Size: 20–23 cm (8"–9")
Range: Southwestern Canada, western USA

- used to be called mountain mockingbirds although they live from sagebrush plains to 1,800 m (6,000 ft) in the Rocky Mountains
- shy and difficult to approach
- run around on the ground like a robin
- male performs aerial **courtship** display
- nest only in the disappearing sage prairies
- flight speed 46 kmh (29 mph)

Nest in southern British Columbia, Alberta and Saskatchewan.

Did You Know...

Birds of many different families mimic the sounds they hear around them. Blue jays give a perfect rendition of the call of the red-shouldered hawk. Crows have been heard to imitate the whine of a dog, the cry of a child, the squawk of a hen and the crowing of a young rooster. Captive crows imitate simple spoken words and human laughter. The little Carolina wren has been reported to sing the songs of twelve different bird species.

European starlings have perfected double mimicry, giving the cry of the northern flicker and then drumming on wood. In captivity, they can even be taught to whistle and articulate words. One clever starling in England performed such a perfect imitation of a ringing telephone, that the householder came in from the garden to answer it!

World Species 70
Canadian Species 5

The Nightjar Family - Caprimulgidae

Characteristics

Nightjars are 17–32 cm (7"–13") birds with large flat heads, short necks, large eyes and a mouth sometimes fringed with bristles. Their **plumage** is generally brown, grey or blackish with dark markings, and because it is loose, soft and fluffy, it gives them silent flight. The bill is relatively small and weak, but very wide so that they have a huge **gape**. They have long, pointed wings and small, weak feet on short legs. The middle toe is elongated, and used as a **feather comb.**

Behaviour

These birds are active at night, dusk and dawn. Flight is a darting one with quick, erratic wing beats as they chase their prey. They have special adaptations for catching flying insects—long bristles along the upper edge of the beak direct prey into the mouth, and when an insect hits the palate, the jaw muscles cause the mouth to snap closed like a mouse trap.

During the day, they sleep concealed in the trees, perching lengthwise along the branches, not crosswise as other species do. From this position, the male utters his curious loud burring song. Their cryptically coloured **plumage** helps them blend in with the bark of the trees.

Diet

Their diet consists of flying insects and occasionally small birds, caught on the wing. They also swallow small stones to help their **gizzard** process the hard shells of their insect prey.

Reproduction

Two greenish white eggs marked with brown are laid directly on the ground in a partially shaded area. No nesting materials are used. In most species, parents share **incubation** duties for 19–20 days, and both feed the young. If their open nest site becomes too hot, the parents will move the eggs to another location. The chicks are clad in dark, spotted brown which makes them extremely difficult to see when they crouch in the vegetation. Young fly 20–21 days after hatching.

Family Status

This family is also referred to as 'goatsuckers', which comes from an ancient erroneous belief that they sucked the milk from goats at night. Nightjars have a world-wide range, with their greatest diversity in tropical regions where insect populations are largest. Because of the difficulties in locating these **nocturnal** birds, it is likely that some species still remain undiscovered in the tropics.

One species, the Jamaican Pauraque nightjar has been extinct since 1859 due to the rats introduced to its island home, which preyed on eggs and young birds.

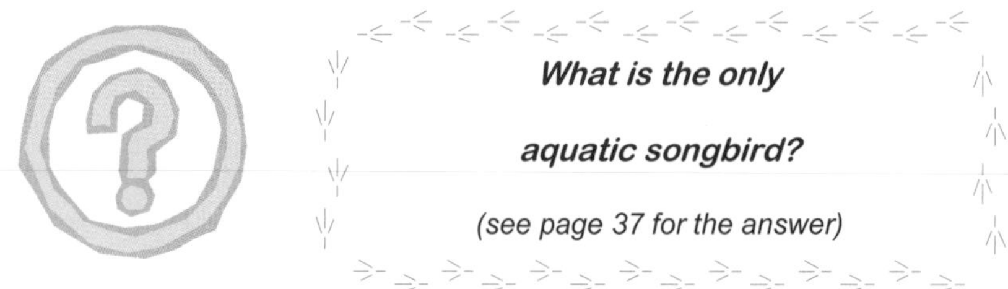

(see page 37 for the answer)

Chuck-will's Widow

Size: 27–32 cm (11"–13"), wingspan to 62 cm (25")
Range: Southeastern Canada, eastern USA to South America

- largest member of the nightjar family
- named for their call
- have a 5 cm (2") wide mouth when open
- their eyes shine at night from reflected light, much like those of cats
- have silent, moth-like flight
- male sings at dusk and on nights of half moon or brighter
- also catch and eat small, whole birds

Nest in southern Ontario.

The song of these birds is a loud, rapid churring which rises and falls, sustained for as long as five minutes. Its effect is particularly jarring as it occurs at night, hence the family name. Aside from the **nocturnal** churring song, many species communicate by clapping their wings together.

Common Nighthawk

Size: 20–25 cm (8"–10"), wingspan to 60 cm (24")
Range: Canada, western USA to South America

- drink water in flight by skimming the surface with their bill open
- **migrate** in flocks up to 1,000 birds
- can eat 500 mosquitoes in a day
- male feeds the **incubating** female and helps her feed the young
- flight speed 35 kmh (22 mph)

Nest Canada wide.

Common Poorwill

Size: 17–20 cm (7"-8")
Range: Southwestern Canada, western USA and Mexico

- the only birds known to **hibernate** over the winter; their heart and respiration rates drop, and their body temperature falls from 41°C to 6°C (105°F to 6°F) for up to five months
- named for their call
- at night, their eyes shine pink in reflected light
- live in arid stony hills, grasslands and mountains up to 3,050 m (10,000 ft)

Nest in southern British Columbia, Alberta and Saskatchewan.

 **Common Whip-poor-will**

Size: 23–25 cm (9"–10"), wingspan to 47 cm (19")
Range: Southeastern Canada, USA to Central America

- named for their call heard at dawn and dusk
- repetitious calls were once considered to predict the future for marriages and deaths
- eyes shine red with reflected light at night
- female alone **incubates** the eggs
- young are hatched most often when the moon is full and parents are best able to hunt

Nest from southern Saskatchewan to the Maritimes.

Common Whip-poor-will

Did You Know...

Birds have a greater resistance to cold than mammals. Heat loss is reduced by their coat of feathers which insulates them with confined air; their legs and feet do not have exposed fleshy parts; and their body temperatures are higher than those of mammals.

*Only one species of bird is known to enter true **hibernation** in the winter, the common poorwill. In many species of birds, if the body temperature falls to 21°C (70°F), they will die. Non-**migratory** birds have several adaptations to survive a Canadian winter, such as fluffing their feathers to trap more insulated air. Some insect eating birds that **migrate** may be caught in sudden spells of freezing cold in spring or fall, and will die of exposure.*

*In 1974, people in northern Europe picked up an estimated 250,000 cold, tired and hungry barn swallows. The Swiss Federal Airways, Swissair, and other airlines carried the birds southward, where they revived and continued their **migration** to the south.*

World Species 25
Canadian Species 3

The Nuthatch Family - Sittidae

Characteristics

Nuthatches are stubby little tree-climbing birds, 8–15 cm (3"–6"), with short tails, strong bills and short legs. **Plumage** is generally blue-grey with patterns in black, white and chestnut. Their feet have long toes with strong claws adapted for climbing up and down vertical surfaces.

Behaviour

These birds are best known for their habit of wedging nuts or seeds in the bark of trees, then hammering or 'hacking' at them with their bill until they open. The word nuthatch is a corruption of the early English 'nuthack'.

Being entirely **arboreal,** nuthatches are extremely agile in the trees, moving upwards, sideways, or downwards along the trunk. They can even walk upside down along the underside of branches. Nuthatches are the only tree-foraging birds that feed moving headfirst down the trunk, thus finding food overlooked by other birds.

Their song is a simple repetition of a single note. These birds are solitary during the summer months, but may often be found in mixed flocks with chickadees, kinglets and other small birds in winter, as they are not **migratory.**

Diet

The diet consists of nuts, seeds and insects. Nuthatches are one of the few bird species that use tools, and two species have been seen using small twigs to draw grubs out of a hole.

Reproduction

Courtship displays involve the male drawing the attention of the female to the brightest parts of his **plumage** by ruffling and spreading his feathers. Four to eight creamy white eggs marked with brown are laid in a tree cavity from 1.5–30 m (5–100 ft). The nest is lined with dry leaves or bark shreds. **Incubation** of 12–16 days is shared by both sexes, and the young fly 14–22 days after hatching. The male helps the female feed the young.

Family Status

Nuthatches are found in both the **Old** and **New World,** although there are none in South America or Africa.

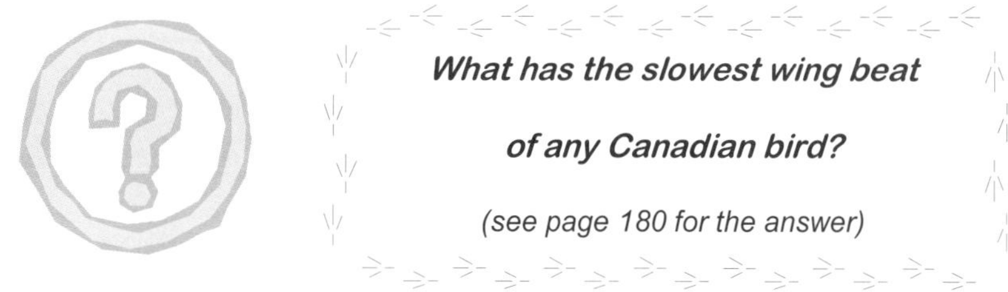

Pygmy Nuthatch

Size: 8–10 cm (3"–4")
Range: Southwestern Canada, western USA and Mexico

- the smallest North American nuthatch
- live in ponderosa pines up to 3,050 m (10,000 ft)
- travel in small family flocks
- at night, they roost together in tree cavities; there is one report of 100 birds in one hole
- lifespan up to 7 years

Nest in southern British Columbia.

Red-breasted Nuthatch

Size: 10–12 cm (4"–5"), wingspan to 20 cm (8")
Range: Alaska, Canada, USA

- also called 'Canada nuthatch'
- pry open cone scales with the bill and extract the seeds within
- smears pine pitch around the entrance hole of the nest to keep predators from entering
- lifespan up to 7 years

Nest Canada wide.

Red-breasted Nuthatch

White-breasted Nuthatch

Size: 12–15 cm (5"–6"), wingspan to 27 cm (11")
Range: Southern Canada, USA, Mexico

- very agile; can catch falling nuts in midair, run down a swaying rope or hang upside down, swinging from a tiny branch
- sing throughout the year
- sometimes pluck hair from live squirrels to line their nest
- resident pairs remain together year round in a **territory** of 10–20 ha (25–50 acre)
- lifespan up to 9 years

Nest in forest zones across Canada.

World Species 1
Canadian Species 1

The Osprey Family - Pandionidae

Characteristics

Osprey are large, 52–60 cm (21"–24") birds of prey with long, tapering wings. **Plumage** is brown above with white undersides, and is compact, which helps blunt the impact and reduce wetting when plunging into water. Their feathers have a peculiar oily odour that even permeates the eggs. The sexes look alike, although the females are larger.

They have been placed in a separate family because they are the only raptor that hovers above the water and plunges feet first for fish. Their strong feet end in claws all the same length, and sharp talons. Their toes are covered with tiny spikes to aid in gripping slippery prey, and they have a reversible outer toe, which enables them to grab prey with two toes in front and two in back.

Behaviour

Osprey hunt by cruising over the water at heights up to 60 m (200 ft). Wings are folded back and the talons are brought forward to strike just as they hit the water surface. Sometimes they completely submerge. After a successful catch, they rise from the surface, shake the water from their feathers and arrange the fish so that the head is pointing forward, thus reducing wind resistance. The fish is then carried to a favourite perch to be eaten.

Diet

Although the majority of their diet is fish, they also eat amphibians, reptiles, birds and sea snakes.

Reproduction

Platform nests of sticks on trees, cliffs or platforms are used year after year, with new material added each spring until they reach nearly 1.8 m (6 ft) across and weigh 225 kg (500 lbs). Two to four pinkish white eggs marked with brown are **incubated** by the female 32–34 days. The male feeds the female while she sits, and helps her feed the young. **Incubation** starts with the first egg laid, so the chicks hatch at different times, and the older, stronger one may kill his sibling if food is scarce. The young fly 52–53 days after hatching. Osprey do not breed until they are three years old, and mate for life.

Family Status

This is one of the most widely distributed birds in the world, living in the Americas, Europe, Asia, Africa, China and Australia. As with many birds of prey, their population suffered a drastic decline in the 1950's and 60's due to pesticides obtained from their food.

 **Osprey**

Size: 52–60 cm (21"–24"), wingspan to 1.8 m (72")
Range: Alaska, Canada, western and coastal USA

- can carry fish up to 1.2 m (4 ft) in length
- flight speed 43 kmh (27 mph)
- lifespan up to 32 years

Nest Canada wide except for the Great Plains.

World Species 151
Canadian Species 16

The Owl Families - Tytonidae and Strigidae

Characteristics

Owls are small to large birds of prey ranging in size from 12–72 cm (5"–29"). **Plumage** is soft and dense, in shades of grey, white or brown with darker markings. Sexes look alike but females are larger, except for the burrowing owl. The bill is strong, short and hooked at the tip; the head is large; and the neck is short. Unlike other birds, owls have serrations on the front edge of their wings which enable them to fly silently. The short legs are covered with feathers, end in sharp talons, and have a reversible outer toe.

The barn owl is placed in the separate family *Tytonidae* because they have a heart-shaped facial disk, no ear tufts and some skeletal differences. True owls have round facial disks, and many species have ear tufts. The tufts are merely upraised feathers which aid their camouflage. The ears are located on the side of the head, concealed by the edges of the facial disk, which functions acoustically by collecting sound waves and funneling them to the ears.

All owls have excellent sight with large, forward facing eyes that give them binocular vision. Because the eyes are tubular, they move only slightly in their sockets so owls must rotate and bob their heads for vision and accurate judgment of distance. Their night vision far exceeds that of other birds, and they can see up to 100 times better than humans at night. They have a third eyelid or **nictitating membrane** that protects their highly sensitive eyes in bright daylight.

Behaviour

Most owl species are **nocturnal**, but some do hunt by day. They hunt by flying slowly and silently a few metres above the ground, listening for prey. Strongly **territorial**, owls have both roosting and nesting sites within their home area. Although most species are solitary, the small burrowing owl does live in colonies.

Diet

Owls consume large numbers of rodents destructive to agriculture, as well as insects, birds, spiders, reptiles and fish. The indigestible bones, fur, insect casings and feathers are coughed up in small **pellets**.

Reproduction

Courtship among owls includes display flights, posturing, bobbing and wing clapping. A wide variety of nesting sites are used by this family, from tree cavities to ground nests, cliff nests or even burrows in the ground. From 1–10 white eggs are laid, depending on the species. The females of most species **incubate** the eggs for 26–42 days, and are fed by the male while sitting. In the smaller species, the young fly at 27–34 days after hatching, while the larger species take 42–70 days. **Incubation** starts when the first egg is laid and successive eggs follow at one or two day intervals. When the last egg hatches, the first is several days old, down covered and much larger. In times of food shortage smaller chicks die, helping ensure the survival of the strongest.

Family Status

Owls are found around the world from the Arctic to cool temperate regions in the southern hemisphere. They occupy almost every habitat. Six world species are now extinct and there are five species on Canada's endangered list due to loss of habitat.

Barn Owl

Size: 35–50 cm (14"–20"), wingspan to 1.1 m (47")
Range: Southern Canada, USA to South America; Eurasia, Africa, Australia

- the most widely distributed owl in the world
- mice make up 75% of their diet
- pairs mate for life
- do not build a nest, but lay eggs directly on floor of cave, cavity or building rafter
- young birds utter a hissing note like the sound of escaping steam when being fed
- lifespan up to 17 years

Nest in southern Ontario, and coastal British Columbia south of Vancouver.

Barred Owl

Size: 42–60 cm (17"–24"), wingspan to 1.2 m (50")
Range: Canada, USA to Central America

- also called 'hoot owl' or 'black-eyed owl'
- active day or night
- can hear the squeak of a mouse from 46 m (150 ft) away
- frequently drink water and bathe in open water even in winter
- said to wade into water to catch fish
- use the same nest site annually; both sexes **incubate** eggs
- lifespan up to 23 years

Nest in British Columbia, northern Alberta, Saskatchewan and southern Manitoba through to the Maritimes.

Boreal Owl

Boreal Owl

Size: 20–30 cm (8"–12")
Range: Alaska, Canada, northern USA; Eurasia

- also called 'Richardson's owl'
- strongly **nocturnal**, roosting in thick cover during the day
- virtually fearless of man; Eskimos thought their ease of capture was because they couldn't see in daylight
- dependent on old woodpecker holes for nesting
- lifespan up to 15 years

Nest in British Columbia and across northern Canada.

Burrowing Owl

Size: 23–27 cm (9"–11"), wingspan to 60 cm (24")
Range: South central Canada, western USA to South America

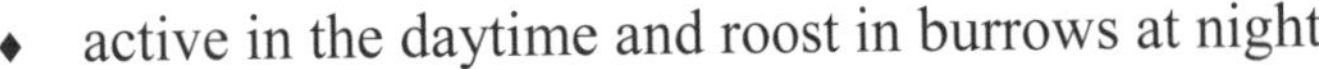

- active in the daytime and roost in burrows at night
- endangered due to habitat loss and pesticide use on their insect prey
- nest in abandoned burrows of prairie dogs or ground squirrels
- have the largest **clutches** of any North American owl, occasionally up to 12 chicks
- do not share a burrow with rattlesnakes as once thought; the defensive sound made by young chicks sounds like the rattle of a snake
- flight speed 19 kmh (12 mph)
- lifespan up to 11 years

Nest in southern Alberta and Saskatchewan.

Flammulated Owl

Size: 15–17 cm (6"–7")
Range: Southwestern Canada, western USA to Central America

- have two distinct colour phases: red and grey
- the only small North American owl with dark eyes
- eat primarily insects captured with their feet

Nest in British Columbia.

Great Grey Owl

Great Grey owl

Size: 60–82 cm (24"–33"), wingspan to 1.5 m (60")
Range: Alaska, Canada, northern USA

- Canada's largest owl
- active during the day
- smaller eyes than most owls are an adaptation to **diurnal** hunting
- do not build nests but will enlarge an old one
- do not **migrate,** but will irrupt into hunting areas with high rodent population cycles

Nest in Yukon, Northwest Territories and British Columbia to Ontario.

People have always been fascinated with owls because they are at home in the world of darkness which is so alien to us. They have been considered harbingers of death, disease and bad luck for centuries, but the Japanese believed they had the power to ward off evil. They became symbolic of intelligence because it was thought they had the power to predict the future. Their nocturnal habits and ominous hooting sounds became associated with the occult and the otherworldly in ancient times.

Great Horned Owl

Size: 45–62 cm (18"–25"), wingspan to 1.5 m (60")
Range: Alaska, Canada, USA, Central and South America

- called the 'winged tiger' for their hunting ability
- have attacked men wearing fur hats, mistaking them for prey
- non-**migratory**; usually the first species of bird to breed each winter, so the young owls are old enough to hunt the young of other species
- active day or night
- use a regular feeding post near the nest, where they bring prey to be torn up and eaten
- do not breed until two years of age
- provincial bird of Alberta
- flight speed 64 kmh (40 mph)
- lifespan up to 29 years

Nest Canada wide.

To control rats in oil palm plantations in Malaysia, nest boxes have been placed in the trees to encourage owls. One pair of nesting owls can consume about 1,400 rats per year.

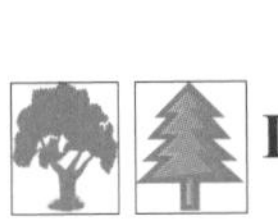

Long-eared Owl

Size: 32–40 cm (13"–16"), wingspan to 1 m (42")
Range: Northern Canada, USA; Europe, Asia

- long black 'ears' are actually feathers which are flattened against the head in flight
- the most secretive owl species, strictly **nocturnal**
- pretend to be wounded to lure intruders away from the nest
- when disturbed on their roost, they raise their ear tufts and compress the feathers, making themselves look like the upright stub of a tree limb
- lifespan up to 27 years

Nest across southern Canada.

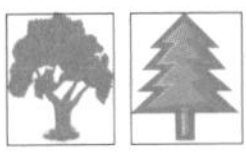

Northern Hawk Owl

Size: 35–42 cm (14"–17"), wingspan to 82 cm (33")
Range: Alaska, Canada

- hawk-like posture and flight give them their name
- more active during the day than other forest owls
- have been seen following farmers loading hay bales onto wagons and pouncing on uncovered mice
- basically non-**migratory** but will retreat from northern-most part of range in winter

Nest across northern and central Canada.

 **Northern Pygmy Owl**

Size: 17–20 cm (7"–8"), wingspan to 37 cm (15")
Range: Alaska, western Canada, USA, Mexico

- have two black spots rimmed with white on the back of the head that look like eyes
- do not possess soft wing feathers to muffle the sound of flight, because they rely on speed and agility instead of surprise
- have a ferocity and strength out of proportion for their size, which is about that of a bluebird
- mainly **nocturnal**, but will hunt during the day

Nest in southern British Columbia and Alberta.

 **Northern Saw-whet Owl**

Size: 17–20 cm (7"–8"), wingspan to 50 cm (20")
Range: Alaska, Canada, USA

- name comes from their two note call
- remarkably tame owls; nearly fearless of man
- their usual food is insects
- lifespan up to 17 years

Nest across southern and central Canada.

Northern Saw-whet owl

 **Eastern Screech Owl**

Size: 17–25 cm (7"–10"), wingspan to 60 cm (24")
Range: Eastern Canada and central and eastern USA

Nest from southern Saskatchewan to Quebec.

 **Western Screech Owl**

Size: 17–25 cm (7"–10"), wingspan to 60 cm (24")
Range: Western Canada and USA

Nest in British Columbia.

- have two distinct colour phases: red and grey
- their call is not really a screech but a soft, mournful whinny that aroused fear and suspicion among early settlers
- lifespan up to 13 years

 **Short-eared Owl**

Size: 32–42 cm (13"–17"), wingspan to 1.1 m (44")
Range: Alaska, Canada, USA to South America; Europe, Asia, Africa

- have a high pitched, rasping call like the bark of a small dog
- fly low over the ground and hover briefly before swooping down
- roost on the ground, occasionally in large groups
- active day or night
- adults will perform 'crippled bird' act to lure intruders from nest
- live in the grasslands of every continent except Australia
- flight speed 42 kmh (26 mph)

Nest across Canada in grassland areas.

  **Snowy Owl**

Size: 50–67 cm (20"–27"), wingspan to 1.6 m (66")
Range: Alaska, Canada, USA to Bermuda; Russia, Europe

- Canada's heaviest owl, weighing up to 9 kg (4 lbs)
- completely encased in feathers from their toes and foot pads to the tip of their beak
- require very large **territories**, up to 10 sq km (4 sq mi) due to the scarcity of prey on the tundra
- hoots can be heard more than 3 km (2 mi) away
- has the most northerly distribution of any owl
- the lemming population determines the number of eggs; if the rodents are abundant up to 13 can be laid
- flight speed 80 kmh (50 mph)
- lifespan up to 14 years

Nest on Arctic tundra.

 **Spotted Owl**

Size: 40–47 cm (16"–19"), wingspan to 1.1 cm (45")
Range: Southwestern Canada, western USA, Mexico

- strictly **nocturnal**, and seldom seen because of their retiring habits during the day
- one of their calls is similar to that of a baying hound
- pairs mate for life
- mates occupy a home range of 1,000 ha (2,500 acres)

Nest in southwestern British Columbia.

World Species 6
Canadian Species 1

The Oystercatcher Family - Haematopodidae

Characteristics

Oystercatchers are large, thick-set shorebirds 37–52 cm (15"–21"). **Plumage** is either completely black or black and white. Sexes are alike, but females are larger. Their bill is bright red in breeding season, but duller the rest of the year, and more than twice as long as their head. Their wings are long and pointed, and they have short tails. Feet and long legs are pinkish-orange or red, and stout with three toes.

Behaviour

Noisy and restless birds, oystercatchers are usually seen in pairs, but occasionally congregate in large flocks. Oystercatchers are one of the few birds that eat bivalve shellfish not available to other species. They pull the mussels off the bed, turn them over, hammer a hole in the shell and cut the muscle that holds the two halves together. They then pry the shell apart and chisel out the meat with their bill.

Diet

As well as mussels, they eat other shellfish, marine worms and sea urchins, and are restricted to coastal areas.

Reproduction

Courtship displays consist of a dance in which one or more birds run around uttering high pitched piping calls. This dance is also performed as a social function by a number of birds. Nesting **territories** are established in the spring. A scrape is made on the shore of the ocean and lined with small pebbles, seaweed and shells. Two to four clay-coloured eggs marked with black are laid, and both parents **incubate** 25–28 days. The **precocial** young are clothed in protective down, and run almost immediately but do not fly until 30–45 days after hatching. The parents use distraction displays of feigned injury and **brooding** at false nests to lure intruders away.

Family Status

Oystercatchers nest in huge colonies of thousands of birds, and the population is not considered in any danger.

Black Oystercatcher

Size: 40–45 cm (16"–18")
Range: Alaska, Pacific coast of Canada and USA

- non-**migratory**, flocks in winter seldom wander more than 48 km (30 mi) from their nesting places
- move sedately with slow, jerky movements
- chicks can run well at three days old and catch insects at five days

Nest on coastal British Columbia.

World Species 6
Canadian Species 1

The Pelican Family - Pelicanidae

Characteristics
Pelicans are **aquatic** birds with crested heads, and short, stout legs with large webbed feet. They are among the largest living birds, reaching 1.2–1.8 m (4–6 ft) in length, with wingspans up to 3 m (9 ft) and weights of 7 kg (17 lbs). **Plumage** is white, grey or brown, and the face has patches of bare skin which become more colourful in the breeding season. Although the sexes look alike, males are larger. They are famed for their enormous beak, which has an elastic pouch suspended from the lower half, used to store food and as a cooling device.

Behaviour
Social and **gregarious** birds, pelicans are highly adapted for swimming and flying. They float high in the water due to additional air sacs located just under the skin, and are strong swimmers. Because of their size, they must run over the surface of the water to become airborne.

Pelicans are capable of long, sustained flight, soaring in synchronized formation over great distances. It is aerodynamically advantageous to flap in time with the bird ahead, thus all pelicans flap or glide simultaneously.

Diet
These birds live on fish, salamanders and crustaceans. Their pouch scoops up water and prey, then the water is squeezed out and the prey swallowed whole. The pouch holds two or three times the capacity of the stomach, or about 13 litres (3 gal) of water. Community fishing is practiced, with several birds driving fish into shallower water. Adult birds eat 5%–10% of their body weight in food each day, or about 2 kg (4 lbs).

Reproduction
Colony nesters, pelicans breed on islands, with larger species nesting on the ground and smaller ones building stick nests in trees. One to six pale blue eggs are **incubated** by both sexes for 35–37 days, and the young are hatched naked and black. Chicks are fed by both parents on **regurgitated** fish which the young take from deep inside the pouch. Young birds leave the nest at 21–28 days, but do not fly until 60–70 days after hatching.

Family Status
Pelicans are found throughout the **temperate** and tropical regions of the world. The white pelican was on Canada's endangered species list in the 1970's but the population has since rebounded.

 **White Pelican**

Size: 1.2–1.7 m (50"–70"), wingspan to 2.7 m (9 ft)
Range: Western Canada, USA to Central America

- largest wingspan of any Canadian bird
- can swallow fish up to 30 cm (12") long and must eat 2 kg (four lbs) a day
- during breeding season, a yellow, hornlike growth develops on the upper bill of the males
- lifespan up to 34 years

Nest from British Columbia to Manitoba.

World Species 3
Canadian Species 3

The Phalarope Family - Phalaropodidae

Characteristics

Phalarope are small, dainty 15–23 cm (6"–9") wading birds with long, thin necks, small heads and long legs ending in slightly webbed toes. They have long, pointed wings, and relatively long bills. Their **plumage** is more dense than other shorebirds, and provides water-proofing and buoyancy. They have a layer of down which provides a raft of trapped air on which they float high and cork-like on the water. Unlike all other bird species, females are more brightly coloured than males. All phalaropes have different **plumages** in summer and winter.

Behaviour

These small birds are the only ones to feed by spinning their bodies around like tops in the water, making many revolutions per minute. This stirs up food from lower levels, and rapid movements of the feet are made for the same reason. They bob their heads back and forth as they swim, dabbing the water with their bill. They also rest and sleep while afloat.

At home both on land and in the water, phalaropes are the only truly oceanic shorebirds, spending much of the year on the ocean. They have **salt-excreting glands** which allow them to drink salt water. Phalaropes are **gregarious,** and usually found in small to large flocks.

Diet

These birds live on **aquatic** insect larvae, mostly mosquitoes, as well as crustaceans and insects.

Reproduction

In the phalarope family, the roles of the sexes are reversed, with the female selecting the male and driving off other females to defend the **territory**. The female lays four olive grey eggs marked with brown, but does not have a **brood patch**. The male builds the nest, which is a mere scrape in the ground, **incubates** the eggs for 10–23 days, and rears the young. The **precocial** chicks take to the water soon after hatching, and first fly around 18–21 days. The female may mate with more than one male, and leaves the breeding area before the eggs hatch. Phalaropes nest in large colonies with other shorebirds.

Family Status

Two species of phalarope are found in the Arctic waters of the world, and the coastal waters of North America. After breeding season, they spread southward over the oceans. Only one species, Wilson's phalarope, frequents inshore lakes and marshes of western Canada and the USA.

Which bird in Canada has

the largest wingspan?

(see page 129 for the answer)

 **Red-necked Phalarope**

Size: 15–20 cm (6"–8"), wingspan to 35 cm (14")
Range: Alaska, northern Canada, coastal Atlantic and Pacific worldwide

- the smallest, most abundant and widely distributed phalarope
- also called 'northern phalarope'
- assemble in hundreds of thousands on the Bay of Fundy during **migration**
- winter at sea off the coasts of South America and Africa

Nest in Yukon, Northwest Territories, Nunavut and northeastern Canada.

The common name phalarope stems from their scientific one, which means 'coot-footed,' in reference to the lobes on the toes.

  **Red Phalarope**

Size: 20–23 cm (8"–9"), wingspan to 40 cm (16")
Range: Alaska, northern Canada, coastal Atlantic and Pacific worldwide

- the most maritime member of the phalarope family
- utter a low, musical '*clink-clink*' which sounds like the tapping together of two small steel bars
- winter at sea off the coasts of South America and Africa

Nest on Arctic tundra.

Wilson's Phalarope

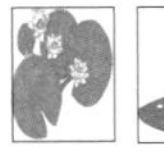  **Wilson's Phalarope**

Size: 20–23 cm (8"–9"), wingspan to 40 cm (16")
Range: Canada, northern and coastal USA to South America

- spin on water up to 60 revolutions per minute, bringing insects to the surface
- most inland dwelling phalarope species
- the only member of the family limited to the western hemisphere
- get most of their food by probing the mud flats and shallow water
- feed as often on land as on water; eat mostly mosquito larvae
- often follow ducks as they stir up food in the marshes
- male develops a **brood patch** during nest building
- winter on the South American pampas, a 6,400 km (4,000 mi) **migration**

Nest in British Columbia, Alberta, Saskatchewan and southern Manitoba and Ontario.

World Species 174
Canadian Species 5

The Pheasant Family - Phasianidae

Characteristics

This family is comprised of pheasants, quail and partridge which vary in size from 12 cm to 2.3 m (5"–92"). **Plumage** is soft and thick, with the males of many species showing iridescent colouring and elaborate patterns. Females are always in shades of buff or brown. Some species have combs, wattles and areas of bare skin on the head and throat. Pheasants have long, ornate tails, while quail and partridge have short, weak tails. Males of all species are much larger than the females. All are heavily built birds with short, rounded wings fitting close to the body and small heads. The short, stout legs have four clawed toes.

Behaviour

A **terrestrial** family, these birds spend their time searching for food on the ground, scratching to expose food hidden under leaves and grasses. Many species roost in small trees at night, although members of the quail family roost on the ground. While they are swift fliers if necessary, flight cannot be sustained for long periods, and they do not **migrate**.

Pheasants are usually found singly or in pairs, while quail and partridge form small flocks outside of the breeding season.

Diet

A variety of seeds, fruit, nuts, peas, grains, leaves, buds, roots, insects, snails, worms and spiders are eaten. As they require **grit** for grinding their food, they can often be found on the roadside eating small pebbles.

Reproduction

A nest of dead leaves and twigs is built on the ground by the female, under cover of vegetation. Large **clutches** of 10–20 greenish white eggs marked with brown are laid. **Incubation** lasts 21–25 days, and in most species is done only by the female. The young hatch within a few hours of each other, as their peeping calls allow them to communicate and synchronize the hatching process. The **precocial** young are covered in thick down, and soon leave the nest to start scratching food. Most can fly short distances at 10–14 days, and are fully grown around seven months.

Male pheasants, who have vivid colouration, compete with nearby males for dominance. The successful bird breeds with all the females in his **territory**. He takes no part in the raising of the young, as he defends his **territory** while the females incubate.

The more subtly coloured quail and partridge males form pair bonds during the breeding season. While the female does all the incubating, both parents look after the young and defend their **territory**.

Family Status

This family contains such familiar birds as jungle fowl, domestic chickens and peacocks. They differ from the similar grouse family by having no feathers on the legs, and no inflatable air sacs. *Phasianidae* are considered important game birds, and occupy nearly all habitats, being absent only from the polar regions.

Northern Bobwhite Quail

Size: 23–25 cm (9"–10"), wingspan to 40 cm (16")
Range: Southeastern Canada, USA, Central America

- name comes from their two note call
- **gregarious** birds most of the year, traveling in coveys of up to 30 birds
- roost at night on the ground, with all birds sitting tightly together and facing outwards
- both sexes utter many conversational notes and utter an assembly call to bring the group together
- can eat 5,000 aphids or 30,000 weed seeds in one day
- on Canada's endangered species list, they are common and widespread in the USA
- flight speed 61 kmh (38 mph)
- lifespan up to 9 years

 Nest in southern Ontario.

Quail have been kept in captivity for thousands of years. They were kept by the Romans as food, and in ancient Greece they were kept as pets where it was the custom for a man to give his lover a pet quail.

In China and Malaysia quail fights were nearly as popular as cockfights and are still allowed there today. Because of their tenacity and fighting nature, they became symbolic of courage and tenacity.

California Quail

Size: 23–27 cm (9"–11")
Range: Southwestern Canada, western USA

- do not fly unless forced to
- highly **gregarious**, feeding in large flocks with one bird acting as sentinel
- utter an assembly call to bring the group together
- roost in trees at night
- females are sometimes **dump nesters**
- flight speed 82 kmh (51 mph)
- running speed 19 kmh (12 mph)
- lifespan up to 9 years

Nest in southern British Columbia.

California Quail

Chukar

Size: 32 –37 cm (13"–15")
Range: Southwestern Canada, USA

- introduced from Asia in the early 1900's to 42 US states and six Canadian provinces as a game bird
- found from sea level to 3,650 m (12,000 ft) and can stand winter temperatures of -35°C (-30ºF)
- prefer to escape danger by running instead of flying
- make local **migrations** from the mountains to the valleys in winter
- **gregarious** birds, members of the flock utter an assembly call to bring them together
- running speed 29 kmh (18 mph)

Nest in southern British Columbia.

Grey Partridge

Size: 30–32 cm (12"–13"), wingspan to 55 cm (22")
Range: Canada, USA; Europe, Asia

- introduced from Europe in the 18th century as a game bird
- introduced to Alberta in 1908 from Hungary, hence the local name of 'Hungarian partridge'
- flocks seldom range more than 0.4 km (1/4 mi)
- multiple females may lay eggs in the same nest
- roost in a circle on the ground, or may plunge into snowdrifts for warmth
- get their moisture requirements from the dew on the vegetation
- flight speed 56 kmh (35 mph)
- running speed 14 kmh (9 mph)

Nest from southern British Columbia through to Maritimes.

Pheasants are named after the river Phasis, where they first originated.

Ring-necked Pheasant

Size: 52–90 cm (21"–36"), wingspan to 80 cm (32")
Range: Southern Canada, USA; Asia, Orient, Russia

- Chinese immigrants introduced them to Oregon in 1800's as a game bird
- in areas where they have been heavily hunted, they prefer to run through the vegetation instead of flying
- range no more than 1.6–3.2 km (1–2 m)
- sometimes seek shelter from rain or predators in animal burrows
- males have harems of up to four females, and establish and hold their own **territory**
- females often lay their eggs in the nests of other females
- state bird of South Dakota
- flight speed 61 kmh (38 mph)
- lifespan up to 8 years

Nest from southern British Columbia through to Maritimes.

World Species 54
Canadian Species 2

The Pipit Family - Motacillidae

Characteristics
Pipits are slender, small to medium-sized, 11–18 cm (5"–8") songbirds living on the ground in grassy areas. They are protectively coloured in **plumage** of brown and white with black markings, and the sexes look alike. They have thin, pointed bills and long legs, toes and tails.

Behaviour
These small birds are strong fliers, and those at the extreme northern and southern limits of their range **migrate** long distances. They actively hunt their food on the ground, and walk and run rather than hop. Most species pump their tails up and down as they walk.

In their winter range, large flocks gather in open fields. When disturbed they rise in unison, wheel, turn, and resume their feeding. The American Pipit feeds on the countless insects on the edges of tundra puddles, and in alpine meadows it visits snow banks. Rising warm air currents transport many insects to high altitudes. Most of these die and are frozen in snow banks, providing food for the pipits.

Diet
Pipits eat a wide variety of insects, spiders, grains and weed seeds.

Reproduction
Like other songbirds of the grassland, their **courtship** behaviour includes song flights with rapid ascents to great height, then a slow, fluttering down to earth like a wind-blown leaf. Ground nesters, a cup of dry grass is concealed in the vegetation, and three to seven greyish white eggs protectively marked with brown are laid. **Incubation** lasts 10–14 days and is done by the female. The young have thick down on their upper parts, and remain in the nest 14–15 days.

Family Status
This family, which also includes the wagtails, has a worldwide distribution except for Antarctica.

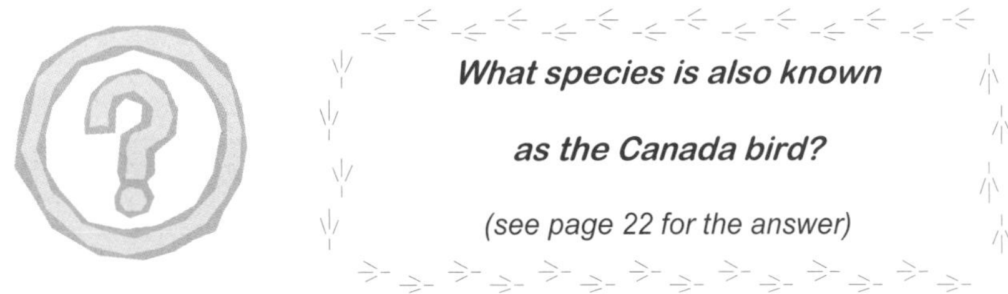

American Pipit

Size: 15–17 cm (6"–7"), wingspan to 25 cm (19")
Range: Alaska, Canada, USA to Central America

- nod their head and pump their tail while walking
- previously thought to be the same species as the **Old World** water pipit
- lifespan up to 8 years

Nest in British Columbia, Yukon, Northwest Territories, Nunavut and northeastern Canada.

Sprague's Pipit

Size: 15–17 cm (6"–7")
Range: Central Canada and USA to Mexico

- famed for their spectacular **courtship** flight, where the male spirals up to 152 m (500 ft) and circles with tail spread, uttering clear, musical notes, then closes his wings and plunges earthward
- more often heard than seen, as they remain hidden in grasses
- so inconspicuous and elusive that 16 years passed between the first and second scientific sightings
- do not run in the open when disturbed, but prefer to hide in dense grass
- range and numbers are declining as they cannot adjust to grasslands converted to crops
- flight speed 45 kmh (28 mph)

Nest in southern Alberta, Saskatchewan and Manitoba.

The scientific name for these birds means 'to chirp', and the common name of pipit is taken from their calls.

World Species 63
Canadian Species 7

The Plover Family - Charadriidae

Characteristics
Plovers are medium sized, 15–32 cm (6"–13") plump-breasted birds of the shore, with long, tapered wings, long legs, thick necks and straight bills which are shorter than the head. **Plumages** are brown, grey or sandy above with white below, and their markings make them difficult to see against the ground. Most have black and white wing markings in flight, and the short tails are rounded and boldly marked. The sexes look similar. Plovers are distinguished from other shorebirds by their heads, which are more round and dove-like.

Behaviour
Gregarious birds outside the breeding season, plovers feed by running along beaches and shorelines, picking up food from the surface. These wary birds are quick to give alarm and when flushed they take swift and direct flight. Strong fliers and swift runners, they also swim well.

Diet
Plovers eat insects, crustaceans and other **invertebrates** picked up in the mud and sand at the waters edge. They feed by running in short bursts and darting at prey.

Reproduction
Courtship involves mutual displays, and both parents take turns scraping out a nesting site on the ground, always near water. During breeding season, pairs maintain a small **territory** from which they drive other plovers. All species use distraction displays such as feigning injury to lead intruders from the nest site. Two to five greyish buff eggs marked with brown are laid, and parents share **incubation** duties for 23–29 days. The eggs have a broken, cryptic color pattern that make them very difficult to see against the sandy or pebbly background of the nest. Both parents care for the chicks, but do not feed them. The **precocial** young leave the nest as soon as they are dry, feeding themselves almost immediately. They can fly 22–34 days after hatching.

Family Status
Plovers are found in most parts of the world except Antarctica, and generally travel in flocks of thousands of birds. However, one Canadian species, the piping plover, is critically endangered due to loss of nesting habitat.

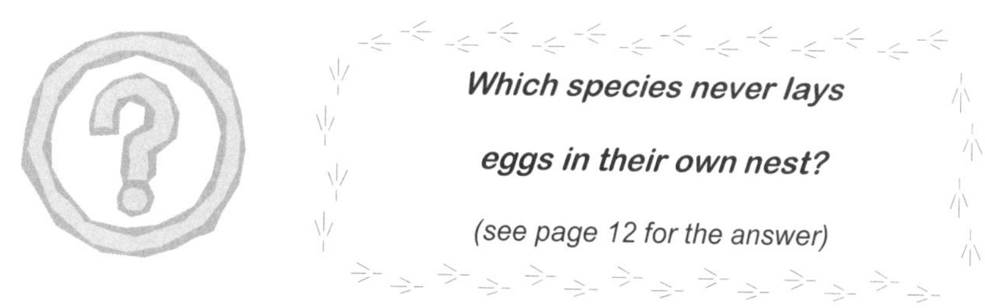

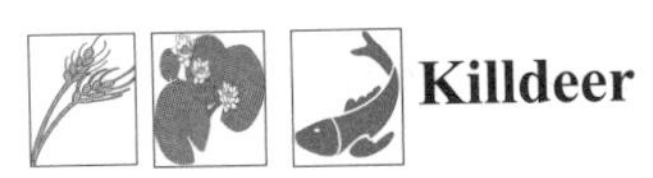

Killdeer

Size: 23–27 cm (9"–11"), wingspan to 52 cm (21")
Range: Alaska, Canada, USA to South America

- the most widely distributed and well known North American shorebird
- have a bright reddish orange patch on their rump
- name comes from their loud cry
- 98% of their food is insects
- often live many miles from water
- flight speed 56 kmh (35 mph)
- running speed 8 kmh (5 mph)
- lifespan up to 6 years

Nest Canada wide.

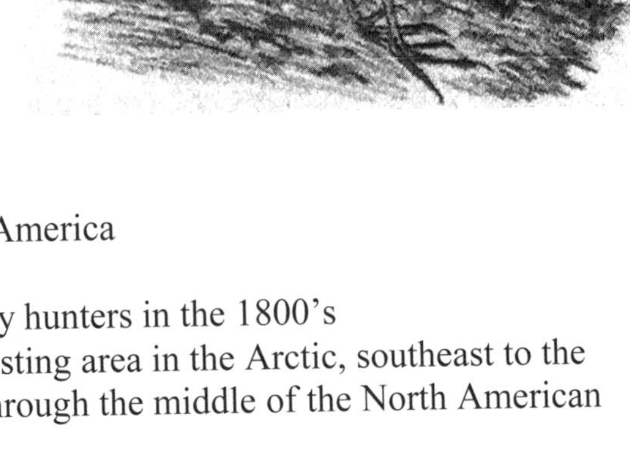

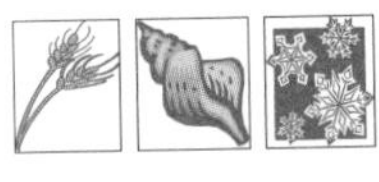

American Golden Plover

Size: 23–27 cm (9"–11"), wingspan to 55 cm (22")
Range: Alaska, northern Canada, coastal USA to South America

- once an abundant bird, they were nearly wiped out by hunters in the 1800's
- **migrate** nearly 32,000 km (20,000 mi) from their nesting area in the Arctic, southeast to the Atlantic coast to South America in the fall, and up through the middle of the North American continent to the Arctic in the spring
- flight speed 112 kmh (70 mph)

Nest in the Yukon, Northwest Territories, Nunavut and Arctic islands.

The word plover is pronounced like 'cover' not 'clover.'

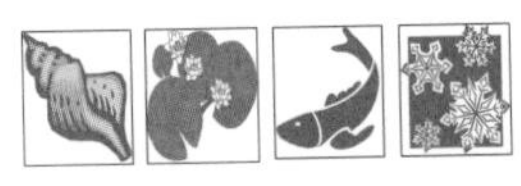

Black-bellied Plover

Size: 27–32 cm (11"–13"), wingspan to 62 cm (25")
Range: Alaska, northern Canada, coastal USA to South America; Europe, Russia, China, India, Africa, Australia, New Zealand

- largest plover species in North America
- extremely shy birds, they are the first of a mixed flock to take flight if startled
- when disturbed, they fly out over the water, circle and land behind the intruder
- flight speed 72 kmh (45 mph)

Nest on the Arctic tundra.

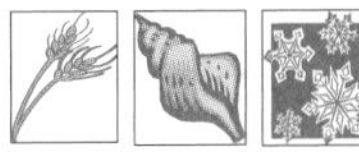

Common Ringed Plover

Size: 15–17 cm (6"–7"), wingspan to 37 cm (15")
Range: Northeastern Canada; Europe, Russia, Greenland, Iceland, Asia, Africa, India

- have one **clutch** per year at the northern limit of their range, and two or three at the southern limit
- the Canadian population **migrates** eastward through Greenland to western Europe

Nest on the Arctic tundra.

Mountain Plover

Size: 20–23 cm (8"–9"), wingspan to 47 cm (19")
Range: Central Canada, central USA

- a misnamed bird, as they live on high plains and semi-desert, not in the mountains
- one of the few shorebirds that live mainly away from water
- eat mostly insects
- after laying the first set of eggs which are **incubated** by the male, the female lays a second set and **incubates** them herself

Nest in southern Alberta and Saskatchewan.

Piping Plover

Size: 15–17 cm (6"–7"), wingspan to 37 cm (15")
Range: Southern Canada, Great Lakes to coastal USA

- so protectively coloured that when they crouch on sand they seem to disappear
- female abandons the family before the young **fledge**, leaving all parental care to the male
- named after their piping call
- lifespan up to 14 years

Nest in southern Alberta, Saskatchewan, Manitoba and the Maritimes.

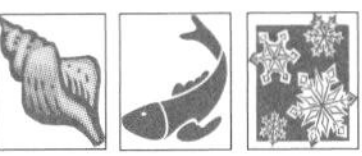

Semi-palmated Plover

Size: 15–20 cm (6"–8"), wingspan to 37 cm (15")
Range: Alaska, northern Canada, coastal USA to South America

- name refers to the partial webbing between the toes
- when feeding, they run, stop and tremble their foot in the mud to make prey move
- flight speed 56 kmh (35 mph)

Nest in Yukon, Northwest Territories, Nunavut, northeastern Canada and the Maritimes.

The Rail Family - Rallidae

Characteristics

Rails are ground dwelling marsh or water birds, 12–50 cm (5"–20"), with short, rounded wings, short tails, large feet, and long toes which help them walk over floating grasses. **Plumage** is generally greys and browns with dark markings, making them hard to see against the marsh background, but moorhens have shades of purple, dark green and turquoise. The sexes look alike although the males are larger. Their flexible wings have a claw-like appendage at the bend that helps them climb about in marsh plants. Bill shapes vary widely, from short and thick to long and **decurved.** In marsh dwelling species, the body is compressed from side to side, originating the term 'skinny as a rail.' This makes it easier for them to run through thick grasses.

Behaviour

Rails are solitary, secretive and more often heard than seen, as their loud, harsh calls give away their presence. These birds do not sing, but make a series of cackles, whinnies, grunts and clucks. They prefer to escape by running through the grasses instead of flying. Due to the difficulty in observing these birds in their marsh habitats, little is known of their behaviour.

Coots are more **aquatic** than rails. They swim and dive well, even to 7.5 m (25 ft) below the surface, and can stay submerged for up to 16 seconds. They are highly **gregarious**.

All members of the family are highly **territorial** and belligerent, often leaping up into the air and lashing out with their feet at invaders.

Diet

Rails consume large quantities of insects, worms, snails, crustaceans, fish and amphibians as well as some plants and seeds.

Reproduction

Nests are made on the ground, in reeds or on floating mats of vegetation. They are often attached to standing stems. Four to twenty-two greenish buff eggs marked with reddish brown are laid, and both sexes **incubate** 18–24 days. The down-covered young leave the nest a few hours after hatching and are fed by both parents. Chicks are able to fly after 42–60 days.

Family Status

Along with the rails, this family also includes coots, crakes, moorhens and gallinules. The rail family is the world's most widespread group of **terrestrial** birds, and is found on every continent except Antarctica. They live in a variety of habitats, with the exception of deserts and polar areas.

Although rails are weak fliers, temperate species **migrate** long distances, traveling at night. Many species found on remote oceanic islands are flightless, making them extremely vulnerable to introduced predators. Fourteen rail species and one gallinule are classed as extinct for this reason.

What is the fastest flyer in the world?

(see page 55 for the answer)

 **American Coot**

Size: 32–40 cm (13"–16"), wingspan to 70 cm (28")
Range: Canada, USA to South America

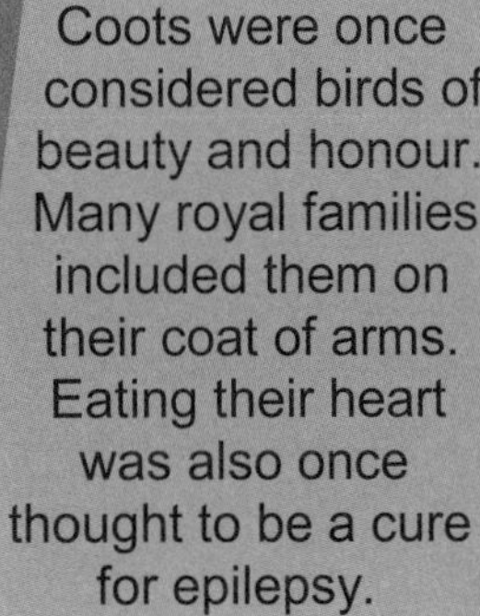

- also called 'mudhen', 'marsh hen', 'water chicken' or 'pull-doo'
- often follow other species closely to eat **aquatic** plants and insects they stir up
- nod their head in time with their leg movements as they swim
- prefer to hide or dive when disturbed
- parents carry eggshells away from the nest when the young have hatched
- downy chicks have bright orange head, neck and shoulders, and a bright red bill
- lifespan up to 9 years

Nest across Canada.

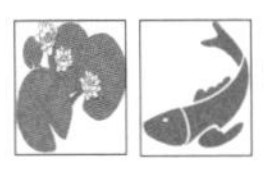 **Common Moorhen**

Size: 30–37 cm (12"–15"), wingspan to 57 cm (23")
Range: Southeastern Canada, eastern USA to South America; Europe, Russia, Japan, Africa, India, Philippines

- previously known as 'common gallinule'
- rarely fly, but when forced to, they flutter along the surface, half flying and half running before dropping back into the water
- when threatened, they submerge into water so just their head is showing and retain their position by hanging on to underwater vegetation with their feet
- parents eat the eggshells after the chicks have hatched
- lifespan up to 6 years

Nest in southern Ontario and Quebec.

The word rail comes from the Old English word *'raale,'* which meant a scraping sound reminiscent of their loud calls.

 **King Rail**

Size: 37–47 cm (15"–19"), wingspan to 62 cm (25")
Range: Southeastern Canada, eastern USA to Central America

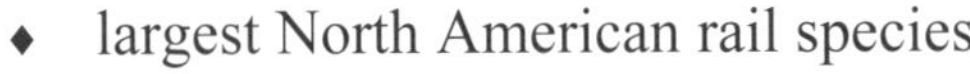

- largest North American rail species
- their distribution coincides closely with that of the muskrat, which creates openings in the marsh, and feeding and drinking places for the bird

 Nest in southern Ontario.

Sora Rail

Size: 20–25 cm (8"–10"), wingspan to 35 cm (14")
Range: Canada, USA to South America

- the commonest and most abundant North American rail
- the name 'sora' originated with the American Indians
- have the longest **migration** route of any rail; 4,800 km (3,000 mi) each way
- diet is 73% weed seeds
- found in both fresh and saltwater marshes

Nest Canada wide.

Virginia Rail

Size: 20–25 cm (8"–10"), wingspan to 35 cm (14")
Range: Canada, USA to South America

- have a distinctive oinking vocalization
- during **migration**, they fly low at night in a direct course over a river or low level land
- found in both fresh and saltwater marshes

Nest across southern Canada.

Yellow Rail

Size: 15–17 cm (6"–7"), wingspan to 32 cm (13")
Range: Canada east of the Rockies, USA

- extremely shy, sparrow sized rail
- also called 'yellow crake'
- vocalization can be imitated by tapping two stones together - '*tick tick*' or '*tick tick tick*'

Nest from Alberta to Quebec.

King Rail

Virginia Rail

World Species 87
Canadian Species 31

The Sandpiper Family - Scolopacidae

Characteristics

Sandpiper is the group name given to small shorebirds, or ground dwelling wading birds from 12–60 cm (5"–24"). **Plumage** has a 'dead grass' pattern of browns, buffs, greys and whites with darker markings. The sexes look alike, and the females are larger. They have slender, tapered bodies; relatively longs legs; short tails; and long, pointed wings. Bill shapes are highly variable and adapted to specialized feeding. The tips of the bill are soft, pliable and very sensitive to the touch; when plunged into the mud they open whenever prey is touched.

Behaviour

All members of this family are high **gregarious**. In flight, the flocks show a remarkable correlation of movement with all birds turning and wheeling in unison. During breeding season, the flocks break into nesting pairs. These birds walk or run rapidly, but can also swim and dive. Most live along the shores of oceans, lakes, marshes and rivers, but the American woodcock has adapted to exist in deciduous forests, hunting in the damp litter of the forest floor.

Diet

Sandpipers live on a diet of insects and their larvae, mollusks, crustaceans, marine worms, spiders, seeds and berries. Food is obtained by probing into mud and sand with the bill, or by picking it up off the surface.

Reproduction

The principal characteristic of this family is their high latitude breeding range, north of 50ºN. Most members of this family engage in elaborate **courtship** flights and displays, accompanied by melodious calls. Displays often include wing tilting and dramatic flights over the tundra. The mating systems are complex and variable throughout this large family.

With the exception of the solitary sandpiper, all species are ground nesters, and the nest is usually a shallow scrape concealed in the surrounding vegetation. A maximum of four eggs are laid, and they are teardrop shaped so they fit close together in the nest. In most species, **incubation** duties are shared by both parents. The fluffy young are **precocial**, and most find their own food from the hour they hatch, although their attentive parents are close by.

Family Status

This huge family consists of sandpipers, tattlers, willet, yellowlegs, curlews, whimbrel, godwits, dowitchers, snipe, surfbird, American woodcock, knots, dunlin, sanderling and turnstones.

Members of the sandpiper family are found throughout the world, and those in the northern hemisphere are **migratory,** with some making journeys of up to (16,000 km) 10,000 mi from the Arctic tundra to the tip of South America.

Many species were formerly hunted as game birds, some to near extinction. They were shot in the hundreds of thousands as they passed over the North American continent, but now only two species can be legally hunted. The status of this family varies, from species existing in the hundreds of thousands to the eskimo curlew, with an estimated population of under 20 birds.

Curlews are shorebirds with long downcurved bills from 5–20 cm (2"–8").

 **Eskimo Curlew**

Size: 30–35 cm (12"–14"), wingspan to 75 cm (30")
Range: Unknown - thought to be Arctic tundra to South America

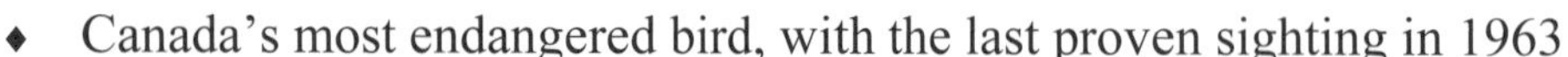

- Canada's most endangered bird, with the last proven sighting in 1963
- possibly extinct - no nest sites have been confirmed for 110 years
- their **migration** route was the most elaborate and hazardous of any bird - from the Canadian tundra, east to the Atlantic, south to South America, north through the Great Plains
- the entire population traveled together, perhaps in the millions, and was slaughtered in huge numbers as they **migrated**

Nesting area unknown.

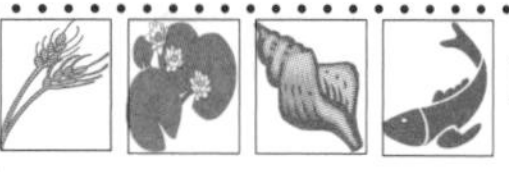 **Long-billed Curlew**

Size: 52–65 cm (21"–26"), wingspan to 1 m (40")
Range: Southwestern Canada, western USA to Central America

- long, **downcurved** bill is up to 23 cm (8 3/4") long
- North America's largest shorebird
- found in fresh and salt water marshes
- do not breed until their third year
- perform spectacular aerial displays while establishing their **territory** in the spring
- adults sit on the nest with their necks stretched out on the ground
- flight speed 56 kmh (35 mph)
- running speed 16 kmh (10 mph)
- lifespan up to 10 years

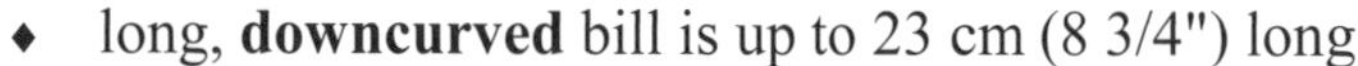

Nest in southern British Columbia, Alberta and Saskatchewan.

 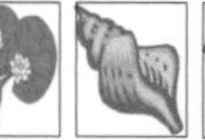   **Whimbrel**

Size: 37–45 cm (15"–18"), wingspan to 77 cm (31")
Range: Alaska, northern and coastal Canada, coastal USA to South America; Iceland, Europe, Russia, Africa, India, Australia, New Zealand

- often fly in 'V' shaped formations
- name comes from an imitation of their call
- flight speed 54 kmh (34 mph)
- lifespan up to 11 years

Nest on the Arctic tundra.

Dowitchers are 25–30 cm (10"–12") shorebirds with wingspans up to 50 cm (20"). They have 5–7 cm (2"–3") long, straight bills.

Long-billed Dowitcher

Range: Alaska, Canada, USA to Central America; Russia

Long-billed Dowitcher

Nest on the Arctic tundra.

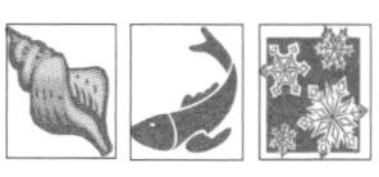

Short-billed Dowitcher

Range: Alaska, Canada, USA to Central America

Nest in the Yukon, and northern Alberta to Quebec.

- often immerse their heads entirely in the water when feeding
- jab their bills into the mud repeatedly to liquefy it and make it easier to bring out prey
- found in fresh and saltwater marshes
- flight speed 69 kmh (43 mph)

Godwits are 35–50 cm (14"–20") shorebirds with wingspans to 75 cm (30"). They have bicolored bills from 7–12 cm (3"–5") long, which turn upwards at the tip. Both were nearly hunted to extinction as game birds.

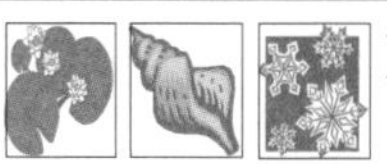

Hudsonian Godwit

Range: Alaska, northern Canada, coastal USA to South America

- **migrate** 12,600 km (9,300 mi) non-stop
- flight speed 72 kmh (45 mph)

Nest on the Arctic tundra.

The name godwit is thought to come from the Anglo-Saxon words for good-eating.

Marbled Godwit

Range: Alaska, western Canada, USA to South America

- spring aerial displays consist of males chasing one another in figure-eight flights, calling loudly all the while

Nest in southern Alberta, Saskatchewan and Manitoba.

The largest grouping in the Scolopacidae is that of the Sandpipers, which are smaller birds with short, straight bills.

  **Dunlin**

Size: 15–20 cm (6"–8"), wingspan to 37 cm (15")
Range: Alaska, northern Canada, coastal USA; Europe, Greenland, Russia, Asia, Africa

- name means a small, dun coloured (brown) bird
- in **migration**, they often travel in such large flocks they look like a swarm of insects from a distance
- flight speed 176 km (110 mph)
- lifespan up to 14 years

Nest on the Arctic tundra.

  **Red Knot**

Size: 23–25 cm (9"–10"), wingspan to 50 cm (20")
Range: Northern Canada, coastal USA to South America; Iceland, Greenland, Europe, Russia

- once one of the most abundant shorebirds in North America, but the population was decimated by over-hunting in the 1800's
- legend says these birds were named after King Canute, or Knut, because both came from Denmark and they were his favorite food
- **migrate** 30,000 km (19,000 mi) from the Arctic to South America
- flight speed 61 kmh (38 mph)
- lifespan up to 13 years

Nest on Arctic tundra.

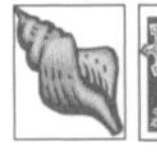  **Sanderling**

Size: 17–20 cm (7"–8"), wingspan to 37 cm (15")
Range: Northern Canada, coastal USA; all continents except Antarctica

- follow receding waves on the shoreline picking up stranded food particles; as the waves return, they run just ahead of them
- circumnavigates the Americas in **migration**, flying east across the top of North America, down the Atlantic coast to South America and north up the Pacific coast to the Arctic
- flight speed 65 kmh (41 mph)

Nest on the Arctic tundra.

Sandpipers *continued*

Baird's Sandpiper

Size: 17–20 cm (7"–8"), wingspan to 40 cm (16")
Range: Alaska, northern Canada, central USA to South America; Greenland

- do not probe the mud with their bill like other sandpipers, but pick food off the surface
- migrate 15,000 km (9,600 mi) yearly

Nest on the Arctic tundra.

Buff-breasted Sandpiper

Size: 17–20 cm (7"–8"), wingspan to 40 cm (16")
Range: Alaska, northern Canada, central USA to South America; Russia

- prefer to run rather than fly if disturbed
- lift one wing up to flash white underneath to attract females; when they gather near he lifts both wings and struts around clicking his bill
- perform **courtship** behaviour in an arena area, or ‘lek’

Nest on the Arctic tundra.

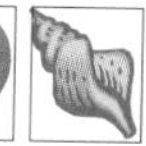

Least Sandpiper

Size: 12–15 cm (5"–6"), wingspan to 30 cm (12")
Range: Alaska, northern Canada, central USA to South America

- smallest North American sandpiper, sparrow sized
- in flight, they maintain a tight formation, showing alternate white and black as they turn
- flight speed 88 kmh (55 mph)
- lifespan up to 7 years

Nest in Yukon, Northwest Territories, Nunavut and northeastern Canada.

Pectoral Sandpiper

Size: 20–23 cm (8"–9"), wingspan to 40 cm (16")
Range: Alaska, northern Canada, central USA to South America; Russia

- named for two air sacs in their breast which are inflated during **courtship** and used to produce hollow booming sounds
- **migrate** 15,000 km (9,600 mi) from the Arctic to the tip of South America

Nest on the Arctic tundra.

Purple Sandpiper

Size: 20–23 cm (8"–9"), wingspan to 37 cm (15")
Range: Northern Canada, Atlantic coast of USA; Greenland, Iceland, Europe, Asia

- winter further north on the Atlantic coast than any other shorebird
- among the tamest of sandpipers, and can be approached closely

Nest on the Arctic tundra.

Rock Sandpiper

Size: 20–23 cm (8"–9")
Range: Alaska, Pacific Coast of Canada; Asia

- also called 'Aleutian sandpiper'
- camouflaged to match the dark wet rocks where they feed
- Pacific coast counterpart of the purple sandpiper

Nest on the Arctic tundra.

Semi-palmated Sandpiper

Size: 12–17 cm (5"–7"), wingspan to 32 cm (13")
Range: Alaska, northern Canada, Atlantic coast to South America

- possibly the most abundant of all shorebirds, with more than a million birds visiting the Bay of Fundy on their fall **migration**
- **migrate** 3,000 km (1,900 mi) in 80 hours
- flight speed 80 kmh (50 mph)
- lifespan up to 7 years

Nest in Yukon, Northwest Territories, Nunavut and northeastern Canada

Solitary Sandpiper

Size: 17–23 cm (7"–9"), wingspan to 42 cm (17")
Range: Canada, Atlantic coast to South America

Solitary Sandpiper

- nest in trees up to 12 m (40 ft) high in abandoned nests of other birds
- **migrate** alone instead of in flocks
- **precocial** young leave the nest after two days, jumping down to the ground

Nest Canada wide except for the Great Plains.

Spotted Sandpiper

Size: 17–20 cm (7"–8"), wingspan to 35 cm (14")
Range: Alaska, Canada, USA

- can swim and dive well, often escaping from raptors into the water
- females return to the nesting area first and fight with other females for nesting sites
- chicks can swim and dive to avoid danger, but prefer to lie motionless on the ground where they are very difficult to see
- flight speed 40 kmh (25 mph)
- lifespan up to 8 years

Nest Canada wide.

Stilt Sandpiper

Size: 15–23 cm (7"–9"), wingspan to 42 cm (17")
Range: Alaska, northern Canada, Atlantic coast to South America

- waders that feed in water up to their bellies
- nest site in the tundra is shaped by the bird rotating its breast against the soft terrain; older pairs often re-use previous years' sites

Nest on the Arctic tundra.

Upland Sandpiper

Size: 27–30 cm (11"–12"), wingspan to 50 cm (20")
Range: Alaska, central Canada and USA to South America

- almost half of their diet is crop destroying insects
- **migrate** 13,000 km (8,000 mi)
- lifespan up to 5 years

Nest in Alberta, and southern Saskatchewan to the Maritimes.

White-rumped Sandpiper

Size: 15–20 cm (6"–8"), wingspan to 40 cm (16")
Range: Northern and central Canada, central USA to South America

- **migrate** 15,000 km (9,000 mi) from the Arctic to South America
- immerse their entire head in the water to feed
- flight speed 80 kmh (50 mph)
- lifespan up to 5 years

Nest on the Arctic tundra.

The following four species are referred to as the Tattlers. Wary of human disturbance, they utter loud cries which warn all birds to flee, thus they 'tattle' on the hunters.

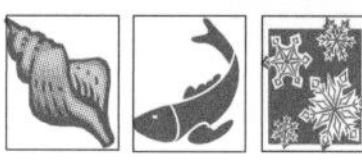

Wandering Tattler

Size: 23–25 cm (9"–10")
Range: Alaska, northern Canada, Pacific coast to South America

- **migrate** mostly over water
- named for their habit of wandering and have been found as far away as Japan, Australia and New Zealand
- submerge their entire head under the water when feeding

Nest in Yukon and northwestern British Columbia.

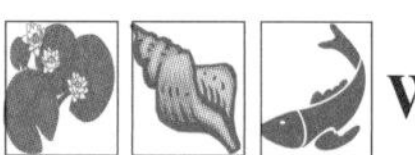

Willet

Size: 35–40 cm (14"–16"), wingspan to 77 cm (31")
Range: Central, coastal Canada and USA to Central America

- at the nest site, the male bows to the female before exchanging **incubation** duties with her
- population decimated by market hunters in the 1800's
- flight speed 75 kmh (47 mph)

Nest in southern Alberta, Saskatchewan and Manitoba.

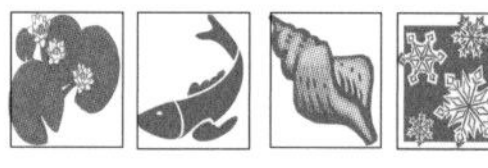

Lesser Yellowlegs

Size: 23–27 cm (9"–11"), wingspan to 52 cm (21")
Range: Alaska, Canada, USA to South America

- **migrate** 15,000 km (9,000 mi)
- flight speed 72 kmh (45 mph)

Nest in Yukon, Northwest Territories and northern British Columbia to Ontario.

Greater Yellowlegs

Size: 30–37 cm (12"–15"), wingspan to 65 cm (26")
Range: Alaska, Canada to South America

- swing their bill from side to side in the water while feeding
- do not probe into mud but pick their food off the surface
- nod their head as they walk
- flight speed 72 kmh (45 mph)

Nest across Canada except for the Great Plains.

These birds are well known for their habit of turning over stones, shells, clods of earth and seaweed with their bills, looking for food.

 **Black Turnstone**

Size: 20–23 cm (8"–9")
Range: Alaska, Pacific coast to Mexico

- characteristic winter bird of the Pacific coast
- aggressively defend their feeding areas
- also called 'rock plover'

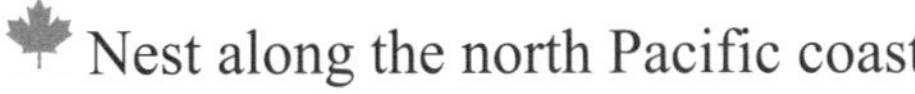
Nest along the north Pacific coast.

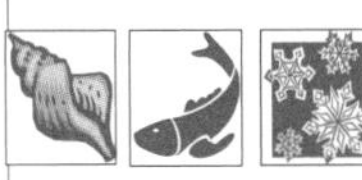 **Ruddy Turnstone**

Size: 17–23 cm (7"–9"), wingspan to 42 cm (17")
Range: Alaska, northern and coastal Canada, coastal USA to South America; Europe, Asia, Russia, Africa, India, Australia, New Zealand

- breeding males display head to head, with their tail spread out like a fan
- flight speed 64 kmh (40 mph)
- lifespan up to 13 years

Nest on the Arctic tundra.

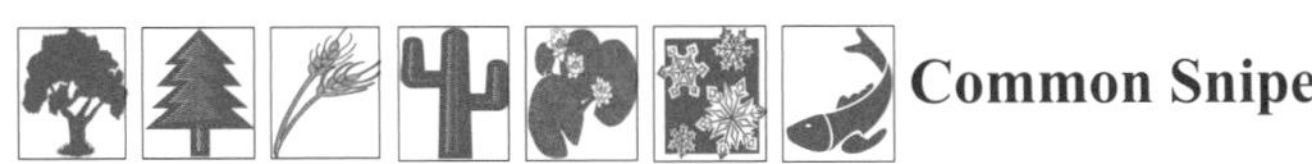 **Common Snipe**

Size: 25–27 cm (10"–11"), wingspan 50 cm (20")
Range: Alaska, Canada, USA to Central America; Europe, Russia, Iceland, Africa, India, Japan, Indonesia, Philippines

- the only snipe species native to North America
- spit up **pellets** of undigestible insect parts
- can swim and dive underwater, using their feet and wings for propulsion
- in **territorial** flights, the male spreads his outer tail feathers which vibrate during the dive, producing a hollow whistling sound called 'winnowing' that can be heard for 0.4 km (1/4 mi)
- flight is an erratic zig-zag when disturbed
- nearly hunted to extinction by market hunters
- feed by probing in the mud with their bill while pivoting around in a circle
- flight speed 100 kmh (62 mph)
- lifespan up to 6 years

Nest Canada wide.

Surfbird

Size: 20–23 cm (8"–9"), wingspan to 50 cm (20")
Range: Alaska, Pacific coast to South America

- named after their winter habit of foraging on coasts, feeding at the surfline and dodging the incoming waves
- insects make up the majority of their diet
- **migrate** from the Arctic, down the Pacific coast to South America, a trip of some 16,000 km (10,000 mi)

 Nest in Yukon.

American Woodcock

Size: 25–27 cm (10"–11"), wingspan to 45 cm (18")
Range: Eastern Canada and USA

- eyes are situated far up on their head so they can keep a lookout while feeding
- feed in dim light, so their eyes are large
- possibly the slowest fliers in the world, can fly at 8 kmh (5 mph) without stalling
- also called 'bogsucker', 'timber doodle' or 'night peck'
- live in woodlands where they can find earthworms in the moist soil
- eat their weight or more in earthworms in 24 hours
- feed by thumping their feet on moist ground to startle prey, then plunge bill in up to the nostrils
- perform a spectacular aerial **courtship** display, flying in ascending spirals up to 75 m (246 ft) then zigzagging to earth like a falling leaf
- lifespan up to 8 years

Nest from southern Manitoba to the Maritimes.

Did You Know...

A number of theories have been given for the ***migration*** *of birds. Among them are the avoidance of unfavourable climates, and the exploition of food supplies available for limited periods each year. Many species breed at high latitudes during the brief but insect rich Arctic summer, then fly to warmer climes in the fall.*

Seasonal ***migration*** *may have evolved as a means of increasing lifetime reproductive output. It provides the birds with areas that either are more productive or provide less competition than the wintering grounds. Daylight hours in spring and summer are longer at higher latitudes, resulting in more hours per day in which birds can gather food for their nestlings.*

World Species 53
Canadian Species 8

The Shearwater Family - Procellariidae

Characteristics
Shearwaters are heavy bodied, **migratory** seabirds related to albatrosses, although at 27–90 cm (11"–36") they are much smaller. Their dense, waterproof **plumage** is either all black, or black above and white below. These birds are commonly called tubenoses because of their unusual nostrils, which are enclosed in a horny tube on top of the bill. The bills are long, deeply grooved, and hooked at the tip for holding prey. The tail is short, and the wings are long, narrow and pointed which enables them to fly at high speeds. Their legs are short with webbed feet, and placed far back on the body for efficient swimming. Like all birds of the ocean, shearwaters have **salt-excreting glands.**

Behaviour
These birds are among the world's greatest avian travelers, spending the greater part of their lives on the ocean, coming ashore only to breed. Unlike most species, they drink seawater by suction rather than by tipping their heads back. Their flight is rapid, gliding, and usually close to the surface. Soaring inches above the ocean, hard banks to the side mean the tips of their wings 'shear' the water, hence the common name.

Shearwaters produce large amounts of a musky oil, rich in Vitamin A. This oil is discharged through the mouth in defense, during courtship, and to feed the young. It gives the birds and their nest sites an unpleasant odour.

Diet
These seabirds eat fish, zooplankton, cephalopods, **offal** taken both on and below the surface, and are completely marine in their feeding habits.

Reproduction
Shearwaters breed colonially in self-dug burrows, on offshore islands or cliff ledges which are visited only at night. Complex display flights are performed over the breeding colony while each bird produces their individual call. One large white egg is laid, and parents share **incubation** duties for 51–56 days. Both care for the young chicks, who are covered with long down, and fed a **regurgitated** mix of partially digested food and stomach oil which makes them very fat. They fly 45–100 days after hatching. Once the birds have left the nest, they have a very low mortality rate, and generally live 15 years or more. They do not breed until five years of age.

Family Status
These birds have been valued by man for centuries as a source of food. In Australasia, short-tailed shearwaters are known as mutton-birds, and taken as large chicks for their meat, valuable stomach oil and down feathers. One species in the south Atlantic has a breeding population of an estimated 4 million birds, and islanders annually take up to 20,000 chicks and eggs. Most shearwater species exist in millions of birds.

What is Canada's smallest bird?

(see page 97 for the answer)

Northern Fulmar

Size: 42–50 cm (17"–20"), wingspan 1 m (42")
Range: Alaska, northern and coastal Canada; Greenland, Europe

- fly very fast in long arcs up and down over the waves
- follow ships very closely, sometimes even within reach of the people on board
- can dive to 1.8 m (6 ft) below the surface, using their wings and feet for propulsion
- do not come to land until three or four years of age, and do not breed until they are seven to nine years old
- flight speed 80 kmh (50 mph)
- lifespan up to 34 years

Nest on Arctic islands.

Northern Fulmar

Buller's Shearwater

Size: 37–45 cm (15"–18")
Range: Pacific coast of Canada and USA; South America, New Zealand

- also called 'New Zealand shearwater'
- sometimes share their burrow with the tuatara, a large lizard found only in New Zealand

Nest on islands in Pacific Ocean.

Cory's Shearwater

Size: 40–45 cm (16"–18"), wingspan to 1.1 m (44")
Range: Atlantic coast of Canada and USA; the Azores, Canary Islands

- eat large squid and crustaceans taken at night from the surface of the ocean
- the only large shearwater to nest in the northern hemisphere

Nest on islands in the Atlantic Ocean.

Flesh-footed Shearwater

Size: 47–50 cm (19"–20")
Range: Pacific Coast of Canada and USA; Australia, New Zealand

- have two color phases: dark brown, and brown above with white below
- aquired the habit of diving for bait on fishing lines

Nest on islands in the Pacific Ocean.

Greater Shearwater

Size: 45–50 cm (18"–20"), wingspan to 1.2 m (48")
Range: Atlantic coast of Canada and USA; South Atlantic islands

- dive under the surface for fish, then rise back into the air to swallow it
- population is estimated at five million pairs

Nest on islands in the Atlantic Ocean.

Manx Shearwater

Size: 30–37 cm (12"–15"), wingspan to 82 cm (33")
Range: Atlantic coast of Canada and USA; Iceland, the Azores, Canary Islands

- birds of shallow coastal waters rather than open ocean, they are rarely found more than 16 km (10 mi) from the coast
- excellent swimmers and divers, they sometimes swim underwater using their wings and feet
- lifespan up to 12 years

Nest in Newfoundland and on islands in the Atlantic Ocean.

In about 60 days, when the Manx shearwater chick has shed most of its down and is well feathered, it is deserted by its parents. During this starvation period of 11–15 days, the chick remains in the burrow, coming to the surface only at night to exercise its wings. Finally it climbs to some elevated spot outside the burrow and launches into its first flight towards the ocean, 70–75 days after hatching.

Short-tailed Shearwater

Size: 32–40 cm (13"–16"), wingspan to 97 cm (39")
Range: Pacific coast of Canada and USA; Australia, Tasmania

- winter in north Pacific Ocean
- lifespan up to 30 years

Nest on islands in the Pacific Ocean.

Sooty Shearwater

Size: 47–50 cm (19"–20"), wingspan to 1 m (40")
Range: Coastal Canada, USA; South America, Australia, New Zealand

- the most common shearwater species, and one of the most abundant birds in the world
- **migrate** in large flocks of millions of birds

Nest on islands in the Pacific Ocean.

Sooty Shearwater

World Species 74
Canadian Species 2

The Shrike Family - Laniidae

Characteristics
Shrikes are medium sized, 20–25 cm (8"–10") perching birds with strongly hooked bills, strong legs, and feet with sharp claws. Throughout the family, **plumage** is boldly patterned, but the **New World** species are grey, black and white. They have large, thick heads, with a black band running through and behind the eyes. The only truly predatory songbirds, shrikes do not have talons but use their sharp claws for grasping. A tooth-like structure on the upper bill is used to bite the neck of their prey, severing the vertebrae.

Behaviour
Solitary birds of open country, shrikes are usually found sitting on exposed perches watching for prey. Both the feet and bill are used to manipulate prey, and some species impale the dead animals on thorns, stalks, fence barbs or stems, to be retrieved and eaten later. This resemblance to meat in a butcher shop has earned them the common name 'butcher birds.' They have a remarkable sense of location and do not seem to forget where they have hung their prey. Shrikes hunt only by day, and have excellent vision, comparable to that of the raptors.

Diet
Shrikes are **carnivorous,** bold, aggressive birds of prey who live on insects, rodents, small reptiles and small or nesting birds. They swoop down to catch prey or hop about on the ground to flush birds and insects, which are caught in the birds' feet when they fly. Mice are killed on the ground rather than picked up, as they might bite the feet of the bird.

Reproduction
Bulky cup-shaped nests are built in low trees or shrubs 2–6 m (8–20 ft) up, and two to nine greyish white eggs marked with brown are laid. Either just the female, or both parents, depending on the species, **incubate** the eggs 10–12 days. Both parents help feed the young, who are **brooded** when small. Chicks leave the nest 20–30 days after hatching.

Family Status
The shrike family is predominantly an **Old World** group centred in Africa. Of the two species found in Canada, one is on the endangered species list due to habitat loss and pesticide use.

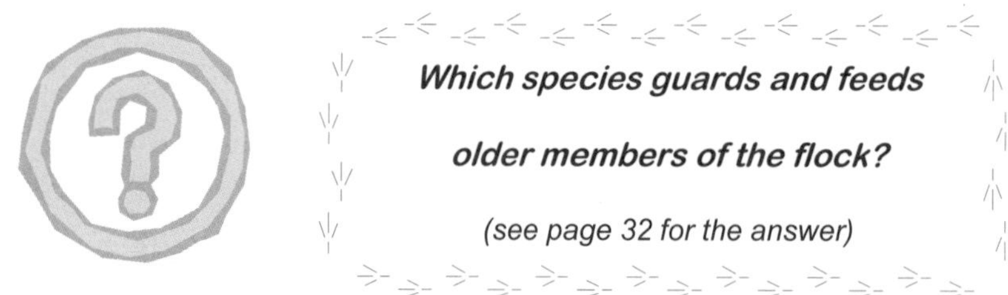

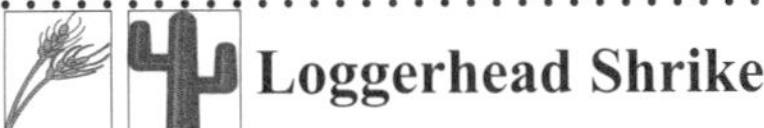

Loggerhead Shrike

Size: 20–25 cm (8"–10"), wingspan to 32 cm (13")
Range: Southern Canada, USA to Mexico

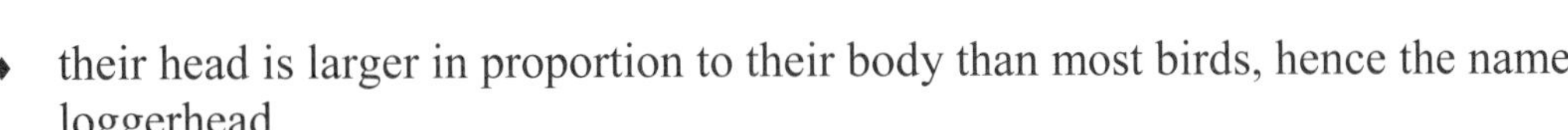

- their head is larger in proportion to their body than most birds, hence the name loggerhead
- the only shrike species living entirely in North America
- the impaling instinct appears in the young as early as 30–40 days after hatching
- 68% of their food in the summer is insects
- population is declining throughout their range
- flight speed 62 kmh (39 mph)
- lifespan up to 6 years

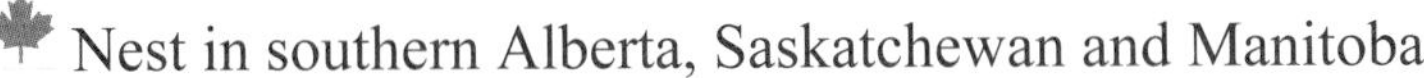

Nest in southern Alberta, Saskatchewan and Manitoba.

Northern Shrike

Northern Shrike

Size: 23–25 cm (9"–10"), wingspan to 40 cm (16")
Range: Alaska, Canada, USA; Europe, Asia, Russia, Africa, Arabia, India

- can recognize a mouse on the ground 84 m (240 ft) away, and one of its own kind at 380 m (1,250 ft)
- mimic the calls of other birds
- Latin name means '*watchful butcher*'
- disgorge **pellets** of fur, feathers and other indigestible bits
- flight speed 72 kmh (45 mph)
- lifespan up to 12 years

Nest in Yukon, Northwest Territories and northeastern Canada.

These birds have loud, harsh calls, and their name is derived from the Middle English word for 'shriek.'

World Species 111
Canadian Species 2

The Starling Family - Sturnidae

Characteristics

Now a familiar sight in North America, European starlings are not native to this continent. They were introduced in New York in the 1800's by a man who wished to introduce all the birds mentioned in Shakespeare's plays. They have been responsible for a sharp decline in native North American bird populations, as they deprive indigenous species of nesting sites.

Starlings are robust perching birds 17–25 cm (7"–10") long with dark iridescent **plumage**, strong bills and pointed wings. They walk with a waddling gait on their strong legs.

Behaviour

These **gregarious** birds always travel in large flocks, and are found in all habitats, but prefer open country, towns and cities. They are noisy, and chatter almost continually in flight or on the roost. Accomplished mimics, they often imitate the sounds of other birds as well as a variety of environmental noises.

Starlings are non-**migratory** over most of their range, and make small localized movements in winter.

Diet

Omnivorous birds, starlings eat insects, seeds, fruit and domestic scraps from garbage. They hold down food with one foot while pecking at it with their bill. In Europe, Asia and Africa they are regarded as agricultural pests who destroy food grain crops.

Reproduction

These birds are cavity nesters, using abandoned tree cavities or nest boxes. Two to eight blue green eggs are laid, and **incubated** 12–15 days by both sexes. The young are fed by both parents, and fly 21–27 days after hatching. The **plumage** of the juveniles is dull and gloss-less until they **moult** into their adult colouration.

Family Status

European starlings are members of the same family as oxpeckers and talking mynah birds. These birds have been introduced from their native Europe to Australia, Asia and the Pacific Islands as well as North America. It has been estimated there are more European starlings in the world than any other bird. Five species of starling are now extinct, as the tropical islands they lived on were invaded by rats and other predators.

With the population of European starlings numbering in the millions in Europe, the vast quantities of their droppings with its high uric acid content are eroding stone buildings and leaving a health hazard in many countries.

Unlike the rest of North America, Canada has two introduced species from the starling family. The crested mynah was introduced to British Columbia by bird fanciers originally from Asia.

Crested Mynah

Size: 23–25 cm (9"–10")
Range: Southwestern Canada, northwestern USA; Asia

- introduced in Vancouver, British Columbia in 1897 from their native China
- population declining due to the unfavourable climate; will completely die out in a very few years

Nest in southwestern British Columbia.

European Starling

European Starling

Size: 17–20 cm (7"–8"), wingspan to 37 cm (15")
Range: Alaska, Canada, USA, Mexico; Europe, Asia, Australia

- bill of the males is black in winter and yellow in summer
- the buff coloured, starry spots of fall **plumage** wear off during the winter, leaving glossy black feathers by spring
- 50% of their food is insects
- have two or three **clutches** per year
- flight speed 88 kmh (55 mph)
- lifespan up to 20 years

Nest Canada wide.

Did You Know...

*All adult birds **moult** their feathers at least once a year, some twice and a few three times. The main function of this process is to renew worn and faded plumage. Most birds shed wing and tail feathers, critical for flight, in one or two pairs at a time. This gradual process means they can always fly. Many **aquatic** or water birds, however, go through a process known as **eclipse moult**, where they lose all their flight feathers at the same time, and so are flightless until new ones grow in.*

*In raptors and vultures, only part of the wing feathers are renewed each time, with the rest being retained until the next **moult**. This is an adaptation for maintaining effective flight at all times.*

World Species 22
Canadian Species 3

The Storm Petrel Family - Hydrobatidae

Characteristics
Storm petrels are small, 12–25 cm (5"–10") oceanic birds related to albatrosses and shearwaters. The northern species have black or grey **plumage**, long wings, and forked tails with swooping flights. The southern members of the family are dark above and white below with short, rounded wings and square tails. The sexes look alike in all species. Their slender, hooked, bills have nostrils in a tube on top of the bill, and they have **salt-excreting glands.** Long, slender legs end in webbed feet.

Behaviour
These smallest of seabirds live all their lives at sea except for nesting. They hover close to the water surface when feeding, and some species hover to dangle their feet in the water to attract fish. Storm petrels are found throughout the larger oceans, feeding alone or in small, loose groups. Like other seabirds, storm petrels discharge a musky oil from the mouth and nostrils in self defense.

Diet
These birds live on fish and other small marine animals caught at sea. They also follow ships for the animal fats or oils thrown overboard.

Reproduction
Courtship involves complex aerial displays over huge colonies of thousands of birds. Storm petrels lay one white egg in a 0.6–0.9 m (2–3 ft) burrow, which is dug by both members of the pair. They nest on marine islands or inaccessible cliff ledges, and visit the site only at night, spending their days feeding at sea. The exceptionally long **incubation** of 35–49 days is shared by both parents, and both feed the chick **regurgitated** food and oil. The young chicks are hatched with their eyes closed and **fledge** at 8–10 weeks, from which point they fend for themselves out at sea. Storm petrels mate for life.

Family Status
Storm petrels have long been known to sailors as 'Mother Carey's chickens', as legend says she was a witch of the sea who was always followed by these birds. The common name storm petrel originated because their sudden appearance during windy weather seemed to sailors to be a bad omen presaging a storm.

Although storm petrels are one of the most abundant bird groups in the world, the Guadeloupe storm petrel has been extinct since 1911, due to predators introduced to its island nesting ground.

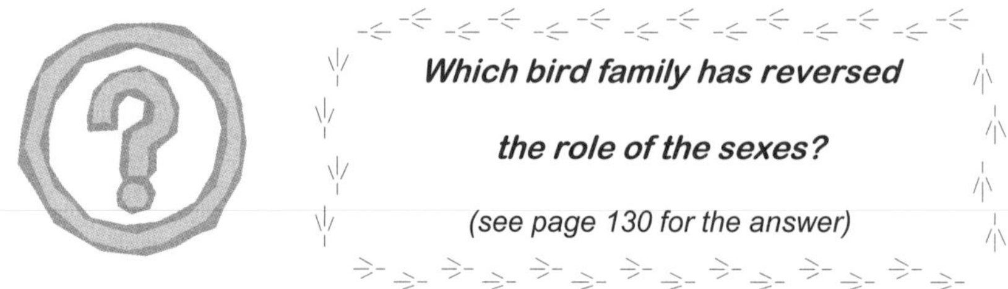

(see page 130 for the answer)

 **Fork-tailed Storm Petrel**

Size: 20–23 cm (8"–9"), wingspan to 45 cm (18")
Range: Alaska, Pacific coast of Canada and USA

- use the same nesting burrows year after year
- occasionally make shallow dives into the water for food

Nest on Pacific islands off the British Columbia coast.

 **Leach's Storm Petrel**

Size: 17–23 cm (7"–9"), wingspan to 47 cm (19")
Range: Alaska, coastal Canada and USA to South America

- seldom seen because they feed far out at sea and return to nesting burrows at night
- feed mainly on small shrimp and plankton plucked from the water surface
- not a ship follower
- lifespan up to 24 years

Nest on oceanic islands off British Columbia and the Maritimes.

 **Wilson's Storm Petrel**

Size: 15–17 cm (6"–7"), wingspan to 40 cm (16")
Range: Atlantic coast of Canada, USA; Atlantic, Pacific and Indian oceans worldwide

- rarely seen from the beaches except after storms
- a small seabird that flies back and forth over the water like a swallow
- often hover at the water surface with their feet gently touching the water
- nest in countless millions of birds
- thought by some to be the most abundant bird in the world

Nest on islands in the Atlantic Ocean.

There is one school of thought that says these birds are named after St. Peter, as their habit of dangling their feet in the water was compared to his walking on water. However, other experts say there is little to support this legend. The earliest English spelling of petrel was 'pitteral.'

World Species 79
Canadian Species 7

The Swallow Family - Hirundinidae

Characteristics

Swallows are small, 10–20 cm (4"–8") songbirds with long, pointed wings, and many species have forked tails. **Plumage** is dark, often with a glossy or metallic sheen, and the sexes look alike. Famed for capturing insects on the wing, they have several adaptations to an aerial life in addition to their pointed wings. Small feet are more suited to perching than walking, and their short, broad bills have wide **gapes** for catching insects. Many species also have **rictal bristles** at the base of the bill, thought to be an aid in catching flying insects.

Behaviour

All members of the swallow family are extremely **gregarious**, roosting and nesting together in large groups. They are accomplished fliers that capture insects by graceful twisting and turning with the mouth open, and spend more time in the air than any other songbird. Those in the **temperate** regions are among the earliest fall **migrants**, flying and feeding during the day and resting at night. These birds can often be seen sitting on perches, exposed branches or wires, and darting out to capture insects.

Diet

Swallows eat every possible flying insect species in the world.

Reproduction

Although most swallows are colony nesters, their nesting habits are highly variable. Species nest in tree cavities, sand bank burrows, bird boxes, saucer-shaped structures on rocks or buildings, or bottle-shaped structures of mud stuck to the side of a cave, cliff or building. Their broad bill acts as an efficient trowel for scooping up mud for their nests, and the female builds while the male brings her the materials. Three to eight white eggs are laid, and **incubated** 12 –17 days, sometimes by both parents but often just the female. The development period of the young is long, as the chicks must be able to fly very well on leaving the nest. Most chicks leave the nest 16–24 days after hatching.

Family Status

Swallows have a world-wide distribution except for the extreme latitudes. Their pleasant chirping noises, plus the fact that their return to **temperate** regions means spring has arrived has always given swallows a friendly place in people's minds.

Eastern cultures once used them medicinally to cure epilepsy, the bite of a mad dog and other illnesses.

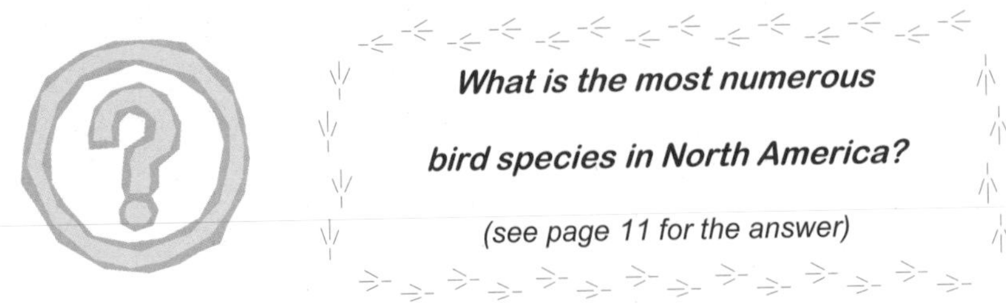

(see page 11 for the answer)

 **Purple Martin**

Size: 17–20 cm (7"–8"), wingspan to 40 cm (16")
Range: Eastern Canada, USA to South America

- the largest North American swallow
- Indian tribes used to put up hollow gourds to attract these insect-eating birds to their village
- flight speed 65 kmh (41 mph)
- lifespan up to 8 years

Nest in Alberta, Saskatchewan, Manitoba and southern Ontario through to the Maritimes.

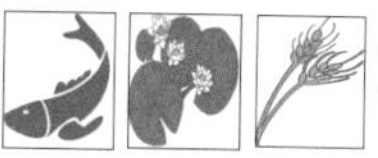 **Bank Swallow**

Size: 10–12 cm (4"–5"), wingspan to 27 cm (11")
Range: Alaska, Canada, USA to Central America; Eurasia

- the smallest North American swallow species
- summer wherever there are exposed sand or gravel banks beside water
- nest in self-dug burrows up to 1.2 m (4 ft)
- flight speed 50 kmh (31 mph)
- lifespan up to 8 years

Nest Canada wide.

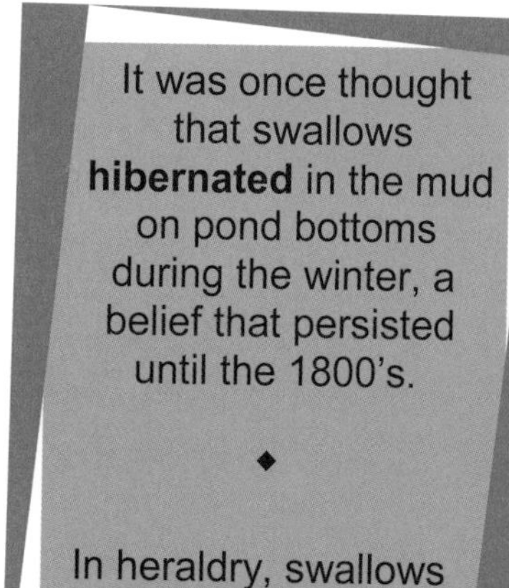

 **Barn Swallow**

Size: 12–17 cm (5"–7"), wingspan to 32 cm (13")
Range: Canada, USA to South America; Europe, Asia

- Canada's only swallow with a forked tail
- have been nesting on man's dwellings for 2,000 years
- drink and bathe in flight by skimming over the water
- flight speed 74 kmh (46 mph)
- lifespan up to 16 years

Nest Canada wide.

  **Cliff Swallow**

Size: 12–15 cm (5"–6"), wingspan to 30 cm (12")
Range: Canada, USA to South America

- bottle-shaped nests are built of mud, and always located near water
- two **clutches** per year
- flight speed 37 kmh (23 mph)
- lifespan up to 5 years

Nest Canada wide.

Cliff Swallow

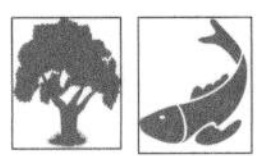 **Northern Rough-winged Swallow**

Size: 12–15 cm (5"–6"), wingspan to 30 cm (12")
Range: Southern Canada, USA to South America

- nest in self-dug burrows up to 70 cm (28") long
- name comes from the row of tiny barbs along the edge of the flight feathers
- not colony nesters

Nest in British Columbia, and southern Alberta through to Quebec.

    **Tree Swallow**

Size: 12–15 cm (5"–6"), wingspan to 32 cm (13")
Range: Alaska, Canada, USA to Central America

- in cold weather, they rely on berries and seeds if insects are scarce
- sometimes alight on beach or marshy shore to get insects from the ground
- prefer white feathers over those of other colours to line their nest
- defend a large **territory** and nest in isolated pairs or loose colonies
- flight speed 40 kmh (25 mph)
- lifespan up to 9 years

Tree Swallow

Nest Canada wide.

 **Violet-green Swallow**

Size: 12–15 cm (5"–6")
Range: Alaska, western Canada and USA to Central America

- often nest in man-made bird boxes
- flight speed 45 kmh (28 mph)

Nest in the Yukon, British Columbia and Alberta.

Legends about these birds abound: in Greece they were sacred to household gods; in Germany a swallow perching on a house foretold poverty; in Ireland and Scotland they were considered the devil's bird; in Asia they were thought to have brought fire to man; in Turkey the story was that these little birds brought the water to put out the fire in the Temple of Jerusalem; and in China they were considered lucky.

World Species 7
Canadian Species 3

The Swan Family - Cygninae

Characteristics

Swans are the largest and most graceful members of the waterfowl family, from 1.2–1.5 m (47"–62"), with wingspans to 2.4 m (8 ft). They resemble the geese, but are much larger and have longer necks. **Plumage** is generally white for the adults and grey for the young cygnets, and bills are yellow or black. The sexes look alike but the males, or cobs, are larger than the female pens. Swans have black legs ending in large webbed feet, which are placed well back on the body, making them awkward on land.

Behaviour

Swift, powerful swimmers, swans can dive if threatened and swim underwater. These birds can only land on water, as their great size requires a forgiving surface on which to alight. Their short legs do not allow a full downstroke of the wings, so they must run over the water surface for 4.5–6 m (15–20 ft) before rising into the air. Swans are most at home on the water, but will also sleep on land. **Gregarious** birds, they **migrate** in large flocks at higher altitudes than any other bird, and fly in either 'V' formations or long lines.

Diet

Their vegetarian diet consists of **aquatic** plants that can be reached by plunging the head and neck below the surface, or by tipping up.

Reproduction

Swans mate for life. The pair maintain a large **territory** and vigorously defend it from other swans, dogs, and even people. The nest is a large, bulky mound of sticks, plants and roots lined with down and feathers from the female's breast. The North American swans lay 2–13 creamy white eggs, **incubated** by the female while the male protects her and the nest site. **Delayed incubation** of 32–40 days starts when the last egg is laid so all chicks hatch at the same time. The downy, **precocial** young follow their parents to the water at 24–36 hours old, and fly 60–120 days after hatching. Young swans do not breed until their second or third year.

Family Status

Long considered symbols of beauty, dignity and immortality, swans figure strongly in song, story and mythology. They have been revered since 4,000 BC, as images carved into stone have been found dating from that period.

The trumpeter swan was almost exterminated in the 19th century due to overhunting for their skins, feathers and meat. Once placed on Canada's endangered species list, their population has since recovered.

Which species has the most limited breeding range of any North American bird?

(see page 186 for the answer)

Mute Swan

Size: 1.4–1.5 m (56"–62"), wingspan to 2.4 m (8 ft)
Range: Great Lakes region of Canada and USA; Eurasia, Africa, India, Korea

- not a native North American species, but were introduced to the Great Lakes area in the 1900's
- when swimming, they hold their neck in a graceful curve with bill pointing downwards, while native swans swim with neck straight and bill pointing out
- wingbeats make a singing sound in flight
- the male often takes the first hatched cygnet to water while the female **incubates** the others
- chicks will ride on the back of their parents or under their wings
- historic symbols of wealth and royalty in Europe; even today the ownership of these swans is controlled by The Crown, which has a Royal Swanherd to organize the annual roundup
- flight speed 88 kmh (55 mph)
- lifespan up to 40 years

Nest in southern Ontario.

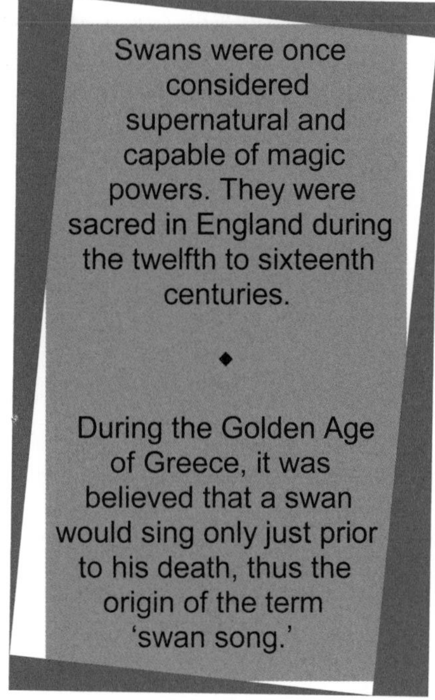

Trumpeter Swan

Size: 1.4–1.8 m (58"–72"), wingspan to 2.4 m (8 ft)
Range: Alaska, western Canada and USA

- Canada's heaviest native bird, and the largest swan in the world
- call is a deep, far reaching trumpeting sound
- between 1853 and 1877, the Hudson's Bay Company sold 17,761 trumpeter skins which were used for hats, powder puffs and down coverings
- one egg is laid every other day until the clutch is complete
- do not breed until their fifth year
- weigh 9–17 kg (20–38 lbs)
- lifespan up to 29 years

Nest in Yukon, Northwest Territories, and northern Alberta and British Columbia.

Tundra Swan

Size: 1.1–1.4 m (47"–58"), wingspan to 2.1 m (7 ft)
Range: Alaska, northern Canada, coastal USA

- formerly called 'whistling swan'
- adult **plumage** is not acquired until their second year
- fly at heights of 2.4 km (1.5 mi) in **migration**
- flight speed 72 kmh (45 mph)
- lifespan up to 19 years

Nest on the Arctic tundra.

World Species 80
Canadian Species 4

The Swift Family - Apodidae

Characteristics

Swifts are small to medium sized, 10–20 cm (4"–8") birds of remarkable flight speeds and maneuverability, closely related to hummingbirds. **Plumage** is generally drab shades of blackish to grey-brown with white markings. They are not songbirds, and their calls are short rasping or twittering notes.

Their anatomy is geared almost entirely towards flight. They have compact bodies, short necks, small bills with extremely large **gapes**, and very small legs and feet with strong, sharply pointed claws. They do not normally land on the ground, so their feet and legs are used only while at the nest, or when roosting. The long, pointed wings curve backward like **scimitars** and are thus adapted to high speed flight.

Behaviour

Swifts are the most aerial of birds, feeding, **courting**, collecting nest material, and even mating in the air. Drinking and bathing are done by swooping low over the water. These birds go into temporary dormancy during stormy weather when insects don't fly; the bodily functions nearly shut down so they need little food. Swifts will often locate high concentrations of insects, then fly back and forth among them with their wide mouth held open. They rest only by clinging to vertical surfaces.

Capable of the swiftest flight among small birds, swifts probably spend more hours in flight than any other land bird. To make the sharp turns in flight required to catch insects, one wing is beat more strongly than the other.

Diet

Aerial insects of all kinds are caught in flight.

Reproduction

Gregarious birds, swifts nest in large colonies. Nests are located in hollow trees, chimneys, caves, cliff holes or ledges under rock overhangs. Some species nest in total darkness, using **echolocation** clicks to find their way. Most nests are built of plant material, feathers and saliva, but some are built of saliva only. Both sexes **incubate** and feed the young **regurgitated** insects. Two to seven white eggs are laid and **incubated** 19–21 days. The young fly 20–30 days after hatching.

Family Status

Swifts have a world wide range, and are found wherever insects are plentiful. In parts of the Orient, the hardened saliva nests of cave-dwelling swiftlets are considered a delicacy when prepared as bird's nest soup, a tradition which is endangering these small birds.

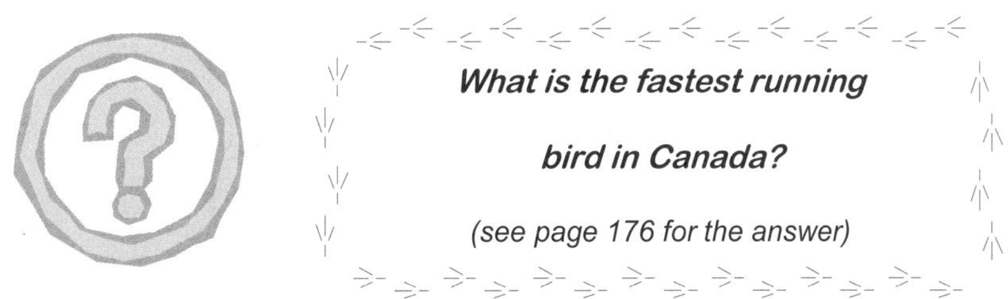

Black Swift

Black Swift

Size: 17–20 cm (7"–8"), wingspan to 37 cm (15")
Range: Alaska, western Canada and USA to Central America

- the largest swift species
- not often seen because they fly high over mountains and canyons
- come from a wide area to flock at the edge of storm clouds, feeding in the warm, insect laden air mass
- nests are made of moss and mud, and only one egg is laid

Nest in British Columbia, and near the continental divide in south

Chimney Swift

Size: 10–12 cm (4"–5"), wingspan to 32 cm (13")
Range: Eastern Canada and USA to South America

- when **migrating** flocks go to roost, they choose a large chimney or airshaft, and circle above it all flying in the same direction. The lowest birds start dropping into the opening, followed by others until it looks like a column of smoke going back into the chimney.
- flight speed 34 kmh (21 mph)
- lifespan up to 14 years

Nest from southern Manitoba through to the Maritimes.

The African palm swiftlet builds nests so small she cannot **incubate** her eggs. The nest is simply a pad of feathers on a broad leaf; she glues her eggs in place with saliva and **incubates** them by clinging to the sides of the nest. Once they hatch, the chicks anchor themselves in place with their own claws until they start to fly.

Vaux's Swift

Size: 10–12 cm (4"–5"), wingspan to 24 cm (11")
Range: Alaska, western Canada and USA to Central America

- smallest Canadian swift
- nest of twigs and needles is glued to the inside of a hollow tree with saliva
- western counterpart of chimney swift, with same behaviours

Nest in British Columbia.

White-throated Swift

Size: 15–17 cm (6"–7")
Range: Southwestern Canada, western USA to Central America

- nest on inaccessible cliff faces extremely difficult to reach by predators or man
- fly at more than 320 kmh (200 mph) and have been seen escaping from a peregrine falcon

Nest in southern British Columbia.

World Species 236
Canadian Species 2

The Tanager Family - Thraupidae

Characteristics
Tanagers are among the most brilliantly coloured and varied songbirds, with **plumages** of red, yellow, green, blue and black. They are 15–17 cm (6"–7") compactly built birds with short, thick bills which are notched or hooked at the tip. **Rictal bristles** are located around the bill. Their beaks are more slender than those of the closely related sparrows, but they do have the bony hump in the roof of their mouth, against which seeds can be crushed. Their closest relatives are the finches.

Although they are classed as songbirds, they are poor or weak singers and many have no song at all. The exception to this rule are the North American **migratory** species, who have pleasant songs.

Behaviour
All members of this family are strongly **arboreal,** living in trees and shrubs. They are **gregarious** outside of breeding season.

Diet
Tanagers eat insects of all kinds, spiders, seeds, berries and fruit.

Reproduction
Males mate with only one female, and the pair stays together all year. A characteristic form of behaviour occurs after pairing. Males make headlong, twisting pursuits of the female, ending in a melee as the birds tumble from branch to branch, or to the ground. Pairs are sometimes maintained for more than one season. Nests are shallow, open cups of plant material located in trees, bushes or tree cavities. Three to five whitish blue eggs are laid. The female **incubates** the eggs 13–14 days, but both parents tend the young. The young fly 9–11 days after hatching.

Family Status
Found only in the **New World**, most tanagers live in the tropics. A few species have colonized areas further north, and can be found as far as the treeline in the Northwest Territories.

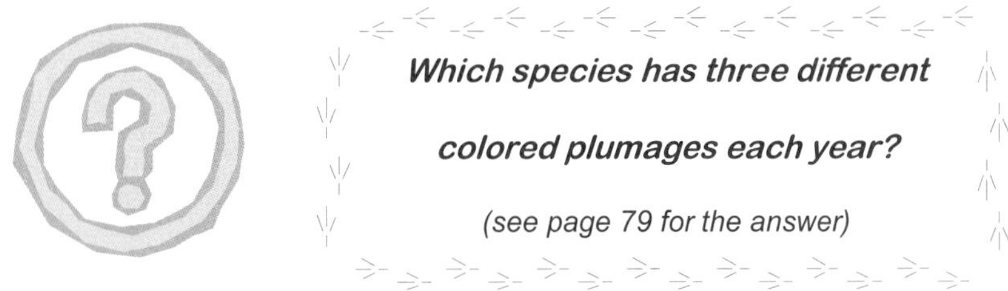

Scarlet Tanager

Size: 15–17 cm (6"–7"), wingspan to 30 cm (12")
Range: Eastern Canada and USA to South America

- **plumage** undergoes a seasonal change from red to yellow
- their nickname is 'red beebird' as they take bees and other flying insects
- the male is a ventriloquist, placing his song many metres away
- diet is mainly **carnivorous**: spiders, insects, worms, snails and slugs; also tear open wasps nests to eat larvae and pupae
- one bird was seen to eat 600 tent caterpillars in 15 minutes
- lifespan up to 10 years

Nest from southern Manitoba to the Maritimes.

The name tanager comes from the Tupi Indians, who called the birds *'tangaras.'*

Western Tanager

Size: 15–17 cm (6"–7"), wingspan to 30 cm (12")
Range: Alaska, western Canada and USA to Central America

- one of the most beautiful birds in the Rockies, with black, red and yellow **plumage**
- live in mountain forests up to 3,050 metres (10,000 ft)
- lifespan up to 15 years

Nest in Northwest Territories, British Columbia and Alberta.

Western Tanager

World Species 306
Canadian Species 12

The Thrush Family - Turidae

Characteristics
Thrushes are medium sized birds, 12–30 cm (5"–12"), known as the world's most exquisite songsters. Their soft **plumage** is highly variable, but usually browns, greys, blacks or blues predominate. They have moderate sized, slender bills, feet, legs and tail. Wings vary from short and rounded to long and pointed.

Behaviour
These are very **territorial** birds, and defend exclusive areas by aggressive posturing, fighting and song. They will often chase away birds much larger than themselves. Their song is rich and musical, and only the males sing.

Diet
Many members of this family feed on the ground, hopping about after insects, worms, spiders, mollusks and crustaceans. Berries, seeds, buds and fruit are also eaten.

Reproduction
The females build open, cup-shaped nests of plant matter, sometimes mixed with mud. Nests are located in trees, shrubs, among rocks or on the ground, depending on the species. Three to six bluish white eggs are **incubated** by the female 11–16 days. Egg colour is closely related to nesting sites; those that nest in holes are light blue, and those concealed in ground vegetation are blue with reddish spots. This relationship of egg colour to nest site reflects adaptations to easy visibility in dark holes, or camouflage from predators. Newly hatched young have fluffy dark down on the head and back, and feathers begin to grow within a week. Both parents feed and care for the young, who leave the nest 10–20 days after hatching. Chicks are fed even after **fledging**, and they beg for food with fluttering wings and high pitched calls.

Family Status
This family contains the nightingale, robin, solitaires, bluebirds and thrushes, and is found on all continents except Antarctica and New Zealand. They occupy a vast range of habitats from rain forests, deserts, and scrub grasslands to Arctic tundra.

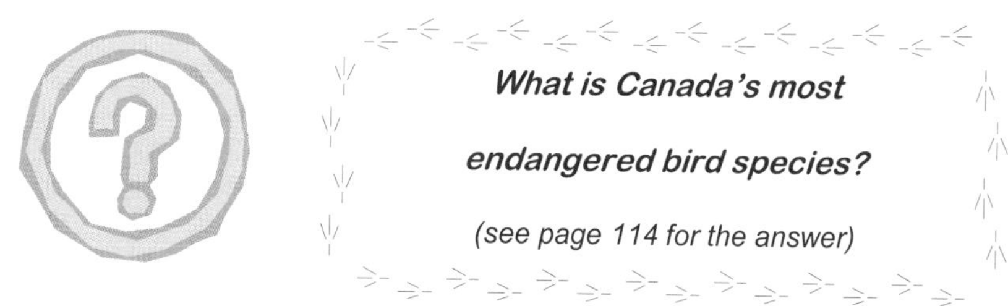

Bluebirds are the smallest members of the thrush family at 15–19 cm (6"–8") with wingspans up to 32 cm (13"). All species are of concern to conservationists, as their population is suffering from loss of habitat. They are the only members of the family to nest in cavities or bird houses, and are losing nest sites to the more aggressive European starlings and house sparrows. Bluebirds are native only to North America.

 **Eastern Bluebird** - Southeastern Canada, eastern USA to Central America

- eat mostly insects
- usually have two **clutches** per year
- one of the species most often victimized by the brown-headed cowbird
- state bird of New York and Missouri
- flight speed 27 kmh (17 mph)
- lifespan up to 6 years

Nest from southern Manitoba through to the Maritimes.

  **Mountain Bluebird** - Alaska, western Canada and USA to Mexico

- live from just below the timberline to 3,650 metres (12,000 ft)
- may hover over their hunting area looking for insects
- state bird of Idaho and Nevada
- flight speed (29 kmh)18 mph
- lifespan up to 4 years

Nest in the Yukon, British Columbia, Alberta and Saskatchewan.

Male bluebirds select a nest box site and fly in and out repeatedly, singing during the entire performance to attract a female.

 **Western Bluebird** - Southwestern Canada, western USA to Mexico

- differ from the eastern species by the males having a blue, rather than rust, coloured throat
- eat mostly insects
- in spring, small flocks break up into breeding pairs

Nest in southern British Columbia.

The Navajo considered these little birds sacred because their feathers are the colour of the sky. They were regarded as images of the rising sun, the supreme image of the creator.

Bluebirds are considered symbols of happiness, love, hope and harbingers of spring.

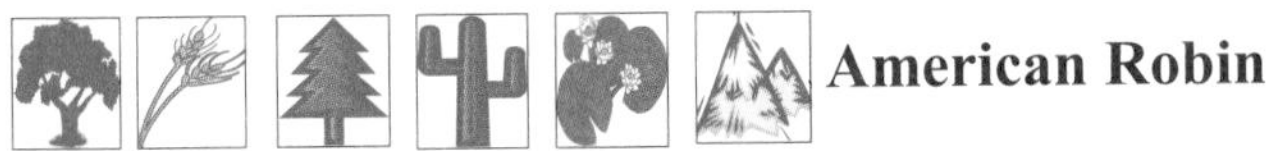

American Robin

Size: 23–27 cm (9"–11"), wingspan to 40 cm (16")
Range: Entire North American continent

- the largest Canadian thrush species
- also called 'Canada robin'
- noted for their dawn singing in April and May
- seem to listen for worms but actually hunt by sight
- sometimes get intoxicated from eating fermented fruit
- have two or three **clutches** per year
- highly susceptible to pesticide poisoning
- state bird of Connecticut, Michigan and Wisconsin
- flight speed 58 kmh (36 mph)
- lifespan up to 17 years

Nest Canada wide.

Legend says the robin received its red breast when it plucked a thorn from Christ's crown and the flowing blood turned its breast feathers red.

◆

In various cultures, robins were considered sacred, bad omens, or able to fortell the weather.

Townsend's Solitaire

Size: 20–23 cm (8"–9")
Range: Alaska, western Canada and USA to Mexico

- in the fall, large numbers may gather at fresh water
- usually seen singly or in pairs throughout the year
- the only solitaire species in Canada
- act like a flycatcher, darting out from perches to catch insects in midair
- nest on or near ground
- flight speed 32 kmh (20 mph)

Nest in British Columbia, Yukon and southwestern Alberta.

Bicknell's Thrush

Size: 15–20 cm (6"–8"), wingspan to 32 cm (13")
Range: Southeastern Canada, eastern USA to South America

Nest in southern Quebec and the Maritimes.

Grey-cheeked Thrush

Range: Alaska, Canada, northern USA to South America

Nest in Yukon, Northwest Territories, north eastern Canada.

- previously considered one species called the 'grey-cheeked thrush'
- **migrate** 13,000 km (8,000 mi)from Alaska to Peru
- sing up to 20 hours per day

Hermit Thrush

Size: 15–20 cm (6"–8")
Range: Alaska, Canada, USA to Central America

- have a habit of raising and lowering their tail repeatedly after alighting on the ground
- live up to 3,650 metres (12,000 ft) in the Rocky Mountains
- eat mostly ground dwelling insects
- nest on or near the ground
- state bird of Vermont
- lifespan up to 7 years

Nest Alaska, Yukon, Northwest Territories, across Canada except for the Great Plains.

Swainson's Thrush

Size: 15–20 cm (6"–8")
Range: Alaska, Canada, northern USA to South America

Swainson's Thrush

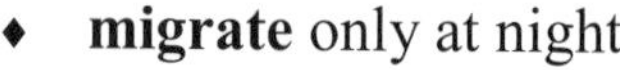

- **migrate** only at night
- males sing almost continually at night on their nesting grounds
- lifespan up to 3 years

Nest Alaska, Yukon, Northwest Territories, Canada except for the Great Plains.

Varied Thrush

Size: 23–25 cm (9"–10")
Range: Alaska, western Canada and USA

- summer in moist woodlands of Pacific coastal forests
- forage on the ground, usually hidden in shady retreats
- like mistletoe berries

Nest in Yukon, Northwest Territories, British Columbia and southwestern Alberta.

Wood Thrush

Size: 17–20 cm (7"–8"), wingspan 35 cm (14")
Range: Southeastern Canada, eastern USA to Central America

- when alarmed, they raise the feathers of the head like a crest
- also called 'bellbird'and 'swamp robin'
- have two broods per year
- official bird of the District of Columbia
- lifespan up to 8 years

Nest in southern Ontario, Quebec, Maritimes.

A group of thrushes is called a 'mutation,' as it was once thought that these birds lost their legs after they reached ten years and grew new ones.

 **Veery**

Size: 15–20 cm (6"–8")
Range: Southern Canada, USA to South America

- name comes from an imitation of their song
- nest on or near the ground
- use their bill to uncover food on forest floor, where they spend most of the day
- lifespan up to 9 years

Nest across southern Canada.

  **Northern Wheatear**

Size: 12–15 cm (5"–6")
Range: Alaska, northern Canada; Greenland, Iceland, Europe, Asia, India, Africa

- an **Old World** thrush species that arrived here prior to the last ice age
- do not **migrate** north and south, but from Alaska to east Asia
- nest in cavities, in or under rocks, or in abandoned burrows
- lifespan up to 7 years

Nest on the Arctic tundra.

Did You Know...

Birds' eggs come in a variety of colours, patterns and shapes. It is thought that originally all eggs were white, but natural selection favoured coloured and patterned eggs for the camouflage they provide. Certain birds that nest in protected tree cavities or ground burrows lay white eggs. Those that lay white eggs in open nests begin ***incubating*** *when the first egg is laid, thus hiding them from predators. Ground-nesting birds that lay white eggs cover them with plants, grasses or down when they leave the nest. Birds that lay coloured or patterned eggs greatly outnumber those that lay white ones; blue, green, brown, mauve, purplish or even deep red eggs are laid by various species.*

Eggs may be oval, round, conical or elliptical, depending on the species, but within each group of birds the eggs are alike. Owls and kingfishers lay round eggs; swallows and swifts lay elongate ones; and auks, murres and other cliff-nesting birds lay pear-shaped eggs. This shape is believed to be an adaptation to their nesting sites, as pear-shaped eggs roll around on their axis, and not off the cliff. The pear shape is also characteristic of birds that lay clutches of four eggs, such as plovers and sandpipers. Because of their shape, the eggs lie with their pointed ends almost touching in the centre of the nest, where they are more easily covered by the relatively small parent.

World Species 2
Canadian Species 1

The Wild Turkey Family - Meleagrididae

Characteristics

Turkeys are large, 91–122 cm (36"–48") powerful birds with strong legs that are spurred in the male. **Plumage** is generally dark with metallic reflections. The head and long neck are brightly coloured red or blue and white, and covered with warty protuberances. Males are larger than females, and may stand 1.2 metres (4 ft) tall. Both sexes have a tuftlike beard hanging from their chest, which may reach 30 cm (12") in older males. Their wings and tail are broad and rounded.

Behaviour

This is a **terrestrial** family, living in large flocks in woodlands and mixed open forest. They prefer to run rather than fly, and their flight is swift and powerful for short distances only. Turkeys flock together to roost in trees at night. Males are noted for their loud gobbling noise which attracts the females, or hens, during breeding season. They are non-**migratory** but wander extensively in search of food, and can survive several days without food during periods of heavy snow.

Diet

Turkeys scratch on the ground for seeds, nuts, fruit, corn, grains, insects, reptiles and amphibians. They are largely vegetarian, with only 15% of their food being animal matter.

Reproduction

The **courtship** display of the male consists of expanding his feathers, spreading his fan shaped tail, swelling his naked head ornaments, and drooping and rattling his wing quills while gobbling and strutting. Males mate with more than one female, and will fight to the death with nearby males. During breeding season, the male develops a thick mass of tissue on his breast which serves as a reserve of fat and oil, from which he draws sustenance to provide energy.

Nests are a slight depression in the ground concealed in vegetation. The nest building, **incubation** and care of the young are done entirely by the female, who may share a nest with other females. Ten to twelve creamy buff eggs are **incubated** 27–28 days. The **precocial** young spend their first night in the nest and begin following the female the next day. After two weeks the young birds can fly to low branches to roost, and they remain with the female until the following spring.

Family Status

Native only to the **New World**, turkeys are related to pheasants, quail and grouse.

 **Wild Turkey**

Size: 91–122 cm (36"–48"), wingpan to 1.4 m (5 ft)
Range: Southern Canada, central and eastern USA

- largest North American game bird, at 4–8 kg (9–16 lbs)
- fastest running bird in Canada, up to 31 kmh (50 mph)
- a large male may eat a pound of food at one meal
- flight speed 88 kmh (55 mph)
- lifespan up to 9 years

Nest from southern British Columbia to Manitoba.

In the 16th century, the King of Spain declared that every ship returning from The Americas bring five male and five female turkeys. Within 50 years, domesticated turkeys were common throughout Europe. Early North American settlers brought the birds with them from Europe, only to find the original turkey species already here.

World Species 38
Canadian Species 6

The Vireo Family - Vireonidae

Characteristics

Vireos are small to medium sized, 10–18 cm (4"–7") perching birds with short, strong legs and short necks. **Plumage** is in shades of green, yellow or grey with light undersides. The sexes are similar, and there are no seasonal changes in colouration. The bill is of medium length with a slightly hooked tip and a small notch. The nostrils and part of the forehead are partially covered with bristle-like feathers. Wings vary from short and rounded to long and pointed, depending on the species.

Behaviour

Arboreal birds, vireos are found in trees or dense shrubbery. Unlike many insect eaters, vireos move slowly and deliberately through the trees looking for insects. The males sing a rather loud, sprightly song of repeated phrases and warbles. A small breeding **territory** is defended with loud song and aggressive behaviour. Vireos in **temperate** regions **migrate** south during the winter, and are among the last birds to return in the spring.

Diet

Their diet is comprised of insects, which are picked from the foliage or the ground surface. Some berries are also eaten.

Reproduction

Vireos are famous for their hanging, cup-shaped nests which are built in the fork of a branch, and fastened by their rim. The nest is made of woven plant fibres and twigs, and located 0.6–18 m (2–60 ft) up. Two to five white eggs with dark markings are **incubated** 11–15 days by both parents in turn. The **altricial** young hatch completely naked, and leave the nest 10–15 days after hatching.

Family Status

This is one of the few bird species to have originated in North America, and they are found in the **New World** only. There are more species in North and Central America than South America.

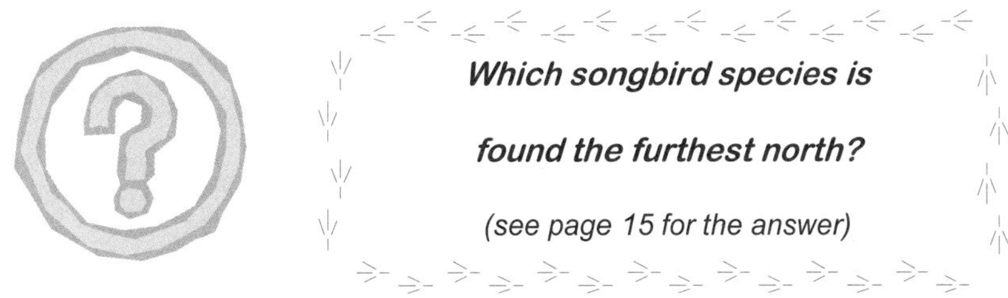

Vireos are shy, elusive singers with wingspans to 27 cm (11"). They occupy deciduous forests, open brushy woodlands, and forest edges.

Hutton's Vireo - Southwestern Canada, western USA to Central America

- song notes are repeated in a continuous series, up to 781 times in 11 minutes
- easily confused with the ruby-crowned kinglet in appearance, but not by behaviour
- almost fearless in defense of their nest

Nest in southern British Columbia.

Philadelphia Vireo - Canada, northeastern USA to Central America

- not common or abundant anywhere
- move about actively in trees when feeding, often hanging upside down from leaf clusters
- difficult to see, as they don't return to Canada until all the leaves are out in the spring
- tame and slow in movement during **migration**

Nest from Alberta to Manitoba.

Red-eyed Vireo - Canada, USA to South America

- Canada's most prolific singer, having been recorded with 22,197 songs in 10 hours
- sing throughout the hottest days of summer
- in **courtship** or when feeding young, the male may sway back and forth in front of the bird he is facing
- decorate the outside of the nest with bits of lichen to aid its camouflage
- once considered one of the most abundant birds of the deciduous forests, but their population is declining
- lifespan up to 10 years

Nest Canada wide.

Blue-headed Vireo

Nest from northern Alberta to the Maritimes.

Solitary Vireo

Cassin's Vireo

Nest in southern British Columbia.

Range: Canada, western USA to Central America and Cuba

- previously considered one species called 'solitary vireo'
- **courting** male fluffs out yellow flank feathers then bobs and bows to female, or follows her around singing low songs
- remarkably tame and fearless, an **incubating** bird may allow itself to be stroked on the nest

Warbling Vireo - Canada, USA to Central America

- males sing constantly, even when **incubating** and on the hottest days
- population is decreasing due to pesticides sprayed on trees
- lifespan up to 9 years

Nest in Yukon, Northwest Territories, and across Canada.

Warbling Vireo

Yellow-throated Vireo - Southeastern Canada, central USA to Central America

- uncommon over most of its range
- numbers are decreasing because of man's use of toxic chemicals on the trees

Nest in southern Saskatchewan, Manitoba and Ontario

Did You Know...

Hearing ranks next to sight in its importance to birds and their survival.

The ear openings of birds are hidden under feathers on the sides of the head. Birds are highly social animals, and depend on hearing for communication with others of their kind. Hearing also helps some birds locate prey species, and allows them to be alerted to dangers in their ***territory****.*

Although the hearing capability of birds has rarely been measured, some tests have shown their hearing to be more acute than that of man. Owls, parrots and pheasants have especially acute hearing, and most birds can locate the sources of a sound with remarkable accuracy.

During World War One, parrots kept in French fortresses and on the Eiffel Tower warned of the approach of airplanes too far away to be seen by humans. Geese, tree ducks and sheldrakes were often kept by primitive tribes as watchdogs, as these birds feed at night and are quick to respond to any unusual sound.

World Species 7
Canadian Species 1

The Vulture Family - Cathartidae

Characteristics

New World vultures are large, 57 cm to 1.3 m (23"–55") birds of prey with black **plumage** and naked heads and necks of red, orange or yellow. The feathers start on the lower neck and form a conspicuous ruff into which the head may be drawn. The sexes look alike. Vultures have very keen eyesight and it is thought they also have an excellent sense of smell. The wings are long and broad, the neck short. The bill is very thick, rounded and hooked at the tip, and the eyes are large.

Behaviour

Vultures are usually solitary, but may roost at night in small flocks. Powerful, graceful fliers, they usually soar in the air watching the ground below for carrion. They may be seen sitting on perches with wings fully outstretched and motionless.

Diet

These birds are carrion eaters, performing a useful sanitation service by removing dead animals. The woodland species may also eat fruit and other vegetable matter if food is scarce. Their bills and feet are not strong enough to open a carcass, so they must wait until the skin rots before eating.

Reproduction

Courtship of vultures consists of aerial displays of soaring and wheeling, preceded by dances between pairs. No nests are constructed, and one to three dull white eggs are laid on cave floors, in hollow trees, buildings, or on the ground. **Incubation** of 38–41 days is shared by both sexes, and the young are covered in down and fed **regurgitated** food by both parents. Chicks first fly 70–80 days after hatching. This is a very long lived family, with some zoo vultures living 50 years.

Family Status

This family includes the Californian, Andean and king vultures, as well as the smaller black and turkey vultures. The larger species are extremely endangered, while the smaller ones are not. The largest flying bird ever known was a **New World** vulture. It lived about 2 million years ago, and fossils have indicated a length of 7.5 m (25.5 ft) and a probable weight of 15 kg (33 lbs).

 **Turkey Vulture**

Size: 65–75 cm (26"–32"), wingspan to 1.8 m (72")
Range: Southern Canada, USA to South America

- their name comes from their red head which resembles that of the domestic turkey
- have the slowest wingbeat of any Canadian bird, at one beat per second
- have the largest olfactory system of all birds
- bask in the morning sun before taking flight
- may eat pumpkins if pressed for food
- adults may feign death if picked up or **regurgitate** foul smelling stomach contents
- **migrate** in flocks of hundreds of birds
- flight speed 55 kmh (34 mph)

Nest from southern British Columbia to Ontario.

World Species 3
Canadian Species 2

The Waxwing Family - Bombycillidae

Characteristics

Waxwings are 15–20 cm (6"–8") crested songbirds with soft, silky **plumage** in fawns and greys with white, black or yellow markings. Sexes look alike. The bill is short and slightly **downcurved,** hooked and notched at the tip with a broad **gape**. Short legs end in toes with long claws, and the wings are pointed. Although they are classed as songbirds, they do not sing.

Behaviour

Highly **gregarious,** waxwings travel in large flocks with a graceful, strong and undulating flight. They are mainly tree-dwelling birds, but occasionally feed on the ground. They are noted for their strange population fluctuations. Irregular breeding distribution and irruptive winter dispersals are thought to occur when low fruit yield coincides with high populations. Waxwings are nomadic, and do not hold **territories** outside the breeding season, when they defend the immediate area around the nest. They are unable to hold a larger **territory** because of their lack of song.

Diet

Waxwings eat small fruits, berries, flower petals, sap and insects.

Reproduction

The females build loose, bulky nests of twigs lined with rootlets, grass, pine needles and hair. Waxwings tend to nest later in the year than other birds, when berries are in good supply. Three to five pale blue eggs with dark markings are laid, and **incubated** 11–13 days. **Incubation** and feeding of the young are done by the female. Food is stored in her **crop** and **regurgitated** into the open mouths of the young. Chicks are fed insects because of their high protein value, as well as some berries.

Family Status

Waxwings are found in open deciduous and coniferous forests of sub-arctic and **temperate** North America. Their **Old World** counterpart, the Japanese waxwing, inhabits similar habitat in the Orient.

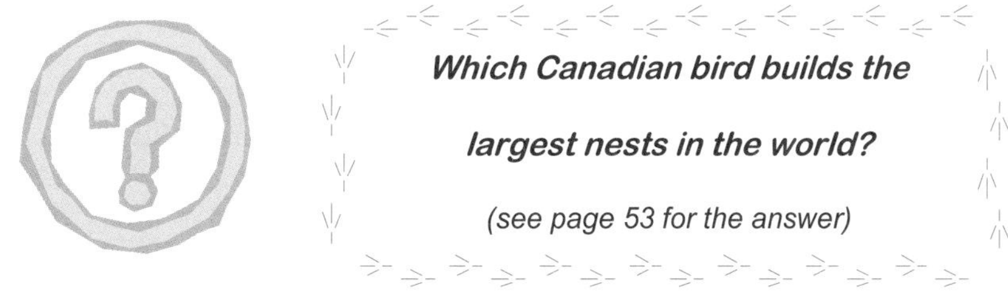

 **Bohemian Waxwing**

Size: 17–23 cm (7"–9"), wingspan to 35 cm (14")
Range: Alaska, western Canada and USA; Europe, Asia

- the largest waxwing species
- highly social, these birds travel in tight formations, descending en masse on fruit bearing trees
- in flight, the flock keeps up an incessant twittering

Nest in Yukon, Northwest Territories and northern British Columbia to Manitoba.

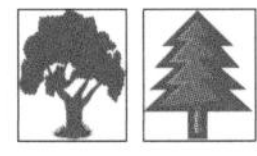 **Cedar Waxwing**

Size: 15–20 cm (6"–8"), wingspan to 30 cm (12")
Range: Alaska, Canada, USA to Central America

- may gorge on berries until they are unable to fly, and sometimes get drunk on over-ripe fruit
- in **courtship** the male hops toward a female with a berry in his beak; which she takes and hops away, then back, passing the berry back to the male
- berry-passing behaviour is also seen in a group of birds sitting in a row, and continues until one of them eats it
- flight speed 46 kmh (29 mph)
- lifespan up to 5 years

Nest across Canada.

These birds are named for the bright red, wax-like material that forms on the tips of the wing feathers. Scientists speculate that these waxy tips, elongated feather shafts, indicate a fit, adult breeding bird to other individuals.

World Species 260
Canadian Introduced Species 1

The Weaverbird Family - Ploceidae

Characteristics

A familiar sight around human habitations, the only member of this family in North America is the house sparrow. They are not native to this continent, but were introduced in the 1800's to several midwestern USA cities because they ate the caterpillar of the linden moth. Their occupation of the entire North American continent was accomplished in only 40 years. They have been responsible for a decline in native North American birds, as they deprive indigenous species of nesting sites.

House sparrows look like other members of the sparrow family, being small brown birds with grey and black markings. Males have a black throat patch, which indicates the age and seniority of the bird, and the largest patch in the flock has priority in feeding and breeding. The bill is short, conical and adapted to cracking seeds.

Behaviour

Noisy, boisterous and **gregarious** birds, they are dependent on man for the majority of their food. They are often found at bird feeders, where their vigorous scratching scatters all the food on the ground. They have no musical song, but merely a series of chips, clicks and cheeps.

Diet

House sparrows in North America eat bird food, seeds, insects and snails. In Europe, they are known as pests, eating food grains of wheat, barley and oats.

Reproduction

During **courtship**, a group of males will circle a female with wings drooped to the ground, or fight each other viciously for her favours. If they build their own nests, they are domed or covered, but house sparrows prefer to nest in man-made boxes, on buildings or in tree cavities. Three to seven eggs are laid in various combinations of white, green or blue. **Incubation** is done by the female for 11–14 days, and the young leave the nest around 17 days after hatching. Both parents feed the young, and **fledglings** beg for food with high pitched calls and shivering movements. House sparrows have two or three **clutches** per year.

Family Status

The Weaverbird family has their greatest numbers in Africa and Asia. Their population is thriving throughout the North American continent, and they do not **migrate.**

 **House Sparrow**

Size: 12–15 cm (5"–6"), wingspan to 25 cm (10")
Range: Canada, USA; Europe, Asia, Australia, Indonesia, North Africa

- year round resident in cities, towns and farm yards
- always found close to man
- flight speed 62 kmh (39 mph)
- lifespan up to 13 years

Nest Canada wide.

World Species 109
Canadian Species 37

The Wood Warbler Family - Parulidae

Characteristics
Wood warblers are small, 10–12 cm (4"–5") songbirds with **plumage** of predominantly yellow, with black, grey, white, red, blue or chestnut markings. Their bills are slender, and a close relationship exists between the bill structure and the manner of feeding. Slender pointed bills are used to probe in flowers and buds, flattened bills with **rictal bristles** are for aerial feeding, and short, stubby bills are for picking insects off foliage or the ground. Their legs are slender, and toes are long and slender.

Behaviour
Warblers are very active, flitting about continually in the leaves of trees, thickets, or on the ground. They always seem to be on the move, and are found in small flocks. Species living in the **temperate** areas **migrate** at night to warmer climates in the fall, where insects can still be found. On their return in the spring, males defend a **territory** against other males of the same species with song and visual displays. **Territory** size is variable, from 8–20 ha (0.3–8 acres).

Diet
All members of this family consume large quantities of insects, as well as spiders, berries and sap.

Reproduction
Warblers pair for a single season only. Most species nest in trees, vines or shrubs, but some use rock crevices, rock ledges, tree cavities or even the ground. Two to seven creamy white eggs with dark markings are laid. Females do all the nest building and the **incubation**, which lasts 10–15 days. Both parents feed the young, who are hatched with their eyes closed, and leave the nest 7–14 days after hatching. Adults often use an elaborate injury-feigning display to draw intruders from the nest.

Family Status
Wood warblers are found only in the western hemisphere, and are widely distributed throughout the **New World.** Population status varies from species to species, and some warblers are in imminent danger of extinction while others flourish.

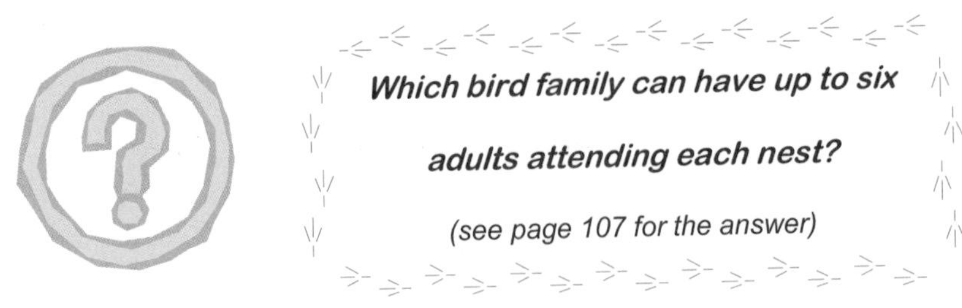

 **Yellow-breasted Chat**

Size: 15–17 cm (6"–7"), wingspan to 25 cm (10")
Range: South central Canada, USA to Central America

- the largest member of the wood warbler family
- excellent mimics of other bird songs
- their name refers to the constant babble produced by the male
- have the ability to hold food in their feet, which is unusual in this family

Nest in southern British Columbia, Alberta, Saskatchewan and Ontario.

 **Ovenbird**

Size: 12–15 cm (5"–6"), wingspan to 25 cm (10")
Range: Canada, eastern USA to South America

Ovenbirds are so named because it was thought their nests looked like miniature dome-shaped ovens.

- usually seen walking over the forest floor, scratching for insects in the leaf litter
- nest is built on the ground, an arch-shaped structure of grasses with a front opening
- lifespan up to 8 years

Nest in Northwest Territories, and from Alberta to the Maritimes.

 **Northern Parula**

Size: 10–12 cm (4"–5"), wingspan to 17 cm (7")
Range: Eastern Canada and USA to Central America

- nest is made in clumps of Spanish moss or old man's beard
- lifespan up to 4 years

Nest from southern Manitoba to the Maritimes.

 **American Redstart**

American Redstart

Size: 10–15 cm (4"–6")
Range: Canada, eastern USA to South America

- name refers to the patches of red on the outer sides of the tail; in Latin America they are called '*candelita*', meaning little candle or little flame
- act like a flycatcher, darting from perches to capture flying insects
- have **rictal bristles** about the mouth
- males do not acquire adult **plumage** until their second year
- lifespan up to 4 years

Nest across Canada.

Wood warblers are found in decidous and coniferous forests, brushy thickets and wooded swamps. They are listed here by their Canadian ranges.

Warblers found only in eastern Canada and eastern USA, migrating to Central and South America:

Black-throated Blue Warbler

- line their nest with horsehair, skunk fur, moss and porcupine quills
- female **broods** the young after they've hatched and both parents feed them

Nest from southern Ontario to the Maritimes.

Blue-winged Warbler

- cone-shaped nest is built on or close to the ground
- lifespan up to 5 years

Nest in southern Ontario.

Cerulean Warbler

- particularly sensitive to human disturbance
- nest decorated on the outside with moss, lichens and spider silk

Nest in southern Ontario.

Hooded Warbler

- seldom seen more than 6 m (15 ft) above the ground
- both sexes defend their **territory** of just under a hectare
- the **fledgling** family is divided into two, and each parent cares for half the **clutch**
- lifespan up to 11 years

Nest in southern Ontario.

Kirtland's Warbler

- have the most limited breeding range of any North American bird; nest only in an area 60 x 80 m (197 x 262 ft) in Michigan, and only in young pines that spring up after a fire
- parts of a bird sanctuary in Michigan are burned periodically to help establish a permanent breeding area for these birds

Nest in Michigan.

Warblers found only in eastern Canada and eastern USA *continued*

Pine Warbler

Pine Warbler

- usually tame and approachable
- lifespan up to 7 years

Nest from southern Manitoba to Quebec.

Prairie Warbler

- misnamed birds, as they do not live in prairies, but in open woods and overgrown pastures
- lifespan up to 10 years

Nest in southern Ontario.

Prothonotary Warbler

- named for their yellow hood which resembles those worn by papal notories of the Catholic church
- lifespan up to 5 years

Nest in southern Ontario.

Warblers found only east of the Rocky Mountains to the Atlantic coast, migrating to Central and South America:

Black-throated Green Warbler

- nest lined with mammal hair and feathers of other bird species
- range includes Greenland
- lifespan up to 6 years

Nest from Alberta to the Maritimes.

Blackburnian Warbler

- on nesting grounds, males like to sing while sitting atop of the highest spruce with fiery breast feathers gleaming in the sun

Nest from southern Saskatchewan to the Maritimes.

Canada Warbler

- received their name because they were first identified in Canada
- lifespan up to 7 years

Nest in northern Alberta, and southeastern Canada and the Maritimes.

Warblers found only east of the Rocky Mountains *continued*

Chestnut-sided Warbler

- nest is lined with cow and horse hair
- lifespan up to 5 years

Nest from southern Alberta through to the Maritimes.

Connecticut Warbler

- named for their place of discovery, but are seldom seen there
- walk, not hop, along branches picking up insects and spiders

Nest from central Alberta to central Ontario.

Golden-winged Warbler

- swing upside down from twigs when feeding
- lifespan up to 6 years

Nest in southern Manitoba and Ontario.

During winter in the tropics, some warblers are segregated by gender. The larger, older males of several species tend to live in swampy areas that have abundant insect prey. Younger males and females of the same species are more likely to be found in drier scrub forests where food is more difficult to find.

Mourning Warbler

- name comes from the pattern of black crepe-like markings on the throat, and the grey head, which are both symbols of sorrow

Nest from northern British Columbia and Alberta to southern Manitoba to the Maritimes.

Palm Warbler

- spend most of their time on the ground, constantly wagging their tale up and down
- misnamed birds, as they are seldom seen among palms
- lifespan up to 6 years

Nest in Northwest Territories, and northern Alberta through to the Maritimes.

Did You Know...

*Bird banders stretch fine nets, called mist nets, across openings in woods. Smaller birds are caught in these silken traps and are removed without injury for banding. The small, metal identifying band put on the leg helps scientists trace behaviour, **migration**, routes taken and destinations.*

Warblers found only in Alaska, western Canada and western USA, migrating to Central America:

Black-throated Grey Warbler

- their drab appearance is excellent camouflage in the blue-green-grey of junipers
- especially fond of oakworms and other green caterpillars

Nest in southern British Columbia.

MacGillivray's Warbler

- prefer cut-over or fire swept second growth forests
- call is sharper than those of other warblers

Nest in British Columbia and south western Alberta.

Townsend's Warbler

- forage in the upper canopy of coniferous forests
- at the height of the nesting season, the male sings in all weather

Nest in British Columbia, Yukon and south western Alberta.

Warblers found in every province and much of the USA, migrating to Central and South America:

Bay-breasted Warbler

- line their nests with rabbit hair
- adjust **clutch** size according to food supply

Nest in the Northwest Territories, and from Alberta through to the Maritimes.

Black and White Warbler

- unlike other warblers, their bill is slightly curved
- will line their nest with fine copper wire if it is available
- lifespan up to 11 years

Nest from Alberta to the Maritimes.

Blackpoll Warbler

Blackpoll Warbler

- one of the most abundant warblers
- in **migration**, fly non-stop from New England to Venezuela

Nest in Yukon, Northwest Territories and from northern British Columbia to the Maritimes.

Warblers found in every province and much of the USA *continued*

Cape May Warbler

- puncture grapes with their bill for the juice
- take sap from holes made by sapsuckers

Nest from Alberta to the Maritimes.

Magnolia Warbler

- named for the magnolia trees where the species was first identified
- lifespan up to 6 years

Nest across Canada.

Nashville Warbler

- named for the city where it was first identified, Nashville, Tennesee
- nest is lined with hairs from deer and moose

Nest from southern British Columbia to the Maritimes.

Orange-crowned Warbler

- nest is lined with fine grasses, deer and porcupine hair and feathers from other bird species
- lifespan up to 6 years

Nest across Canada.

Tennesee Warbler

- puncture grapes to get the juice
- eat berries of the poison ivy plant
- lifespan up to 4 years

Nest across Canada.

Many people think of warblers as local residents in Canada, but in reality, they are tropical birds that pay a brief visit to our country. Warblers that breed in North America spend just four months out of each year in the north. In the spring and fall, they **migrate**, reaching heights of 6.2 km (3.9 mi) and flying across the Gulf of Mexico to their winter homes in the West Indies, and Central and South America.

Yellow Warbler

- the only bird that appears all yellow from a distance
- have the greatest range of all wood warblers; nest from the Atlantic to the Pacific and from the Northwest Territories to Mexico
- when brown-headed cowbirds lay their eggs in the nest, female warbler builds a roof over all the eggs, including her own, and lays a new set
- lifespan up to 7 years

Nest Canada wide.

Warblers found in every province and much of the USA *continued*

Yellow-rumped Warbler

- one of the most numerous wood warblers
- nest is lined with feathers from other bird species
- one of the few warblers that can live a long time on fruit

Nest Canada wide.

Wilson's Warbler

Wilson's Warbler

- usually feed within 3 m (10 ft) of the ground
- sometimes nest in loose colonies

Nest Canada wide except for the Great Plains.

 **Louisiana Waterthrush**

Size: 12–15 cm (5"–6")
Range: Eastern Canada and USA to South America

- have bubblegum pink legs
- walk or run over stones, never hop
- nest always close to water

Nest in southern Ontario.

  **Northern Waterthrush**

Size: 12–15 cm (5"–6")
Range: Alaska, Canada, USA to South America

- bob their head and tail constantly, and walk rather than hop
- named for their preferred habitat of water edges and generally looking more like a thrush
- lifespan up to 6 years

Nest across Canada except for the Great Plains.

  **Common Yellowthroat**

Size: 10–12 cm (4"–5")
Range: Canada, USA to Central America

- male may breed with more than one female
- nests are attached to living tussocks of grass, reeds or cattails
- lifespan up to 7 years

Nest Canada wide.

World Species 200
Canadian Species 14

The Woodpecker Family - Picidae

Characteristics

Woodpeckers are **arboreal** birds who have adapted to life on tree trunks and branches more successfully than any other species. Sizes range from 15–30 cm (6"–22") and **plumage** is variable - greens, browns, greys, blacks and whites all marked with bars, spots or streaks of yellow, red, white or black. The sexes do not look alike. Living head-up and tail-down on vertical surfaces, they cling to trees with short legs ending in sharp, strong claws, two toes directed forward, one directed to the side and one below. Stiff central tail feathers support them against vertical surfaces. These tail feathers are so important to the bird they are **moulted** only after a new pair has grown in.

Their straight, hard, pointed bills are used as chisels to drill into wood, and for **drumming** during **courtship**. They grow continuously to prevent becoming worn out. The impact of drilling into hard wood is absorbed by a thick-walled skull and a narrow empty space between the brain membrane and brain itself. Their nostrils are covered with bristlelike feathers that protect them from wood dust raised when drilling. Their most remarkable feature is the long, extendible, wormlike tongue, which protrudes up to 6 cm (2") beyond the end of their bill when feeding. Some species have small barbs at the tip of the tongue which are coated with a sticky saliva; other species have sharp, horny tips for spearing larvae. Brush-tipped tongues are used for gathering sap.

Behaviour

Woodpeckers are normally solitary, or seen in mated pairs. Their undulating flight is strong but slow, and they do not fly for long distances. Most species are non-**migratory.** They do not form flocks because of possible competition for similar food in an area. They feed by moving up trunks, probing nooks and crannies. The insect-eating species rely on their hearing to locate movement in the tree bark. Sapsuckers drill a ring of small holes around living trees to make the sap ooze out.

Diet

Insects and their larvae, spiders, nuts, pine seeds, berries, fruit and tree sap are eaten by the various species. Some species store large quantities of nuts or acorns for future use.

Reproduction

Courtship varies among the species, with head swinging, slow flights, abortive mating and exchanges of low notes involved. Pairs often perform a duet of slow, rhythmic **drumming** or tapping. Both sexes excavate the nesting cavity, with some species nesting in dead trees, and others using living trees with decayed centers. They circle the nest with gashes that promote a heavy flow of resin, thus preventing attacks by predators. Nests are 15–45 cm (6"–18") deep with a larger egg chamber at the bottom which is bare except for a few wood chips. Two to ten dull white eggs are laid, and **incubated** 11–18 days by both parents, with the males sitting at night. The blind and naked young are fed by their parents—some bring insects to the nest and some feed by **regurgitation**. Chicks fly from the nest 21–35 days after hatching.

Family Status

Woodpeckers are found on all continents except Australia, Madagascar, Greenland, New Guinea and New Zealand. The ivory-billed woodpecker is one of the rarest birds in the world, as it is not known if they are extinct, or if a very small population still exists.

 **Northern Flicker**

Northern Flicker

Size: 30–35 cm (12"–14")
Range: Alaska, Canada, USA to Central America and Cuba

- consume more ants than any other Canadian bird
- spend more time on the ground than any other woodpecker
- tongue extends 8 cm (3") beyond their beak tip
- have about 132 common names
- hybridization between red and yellow-shafted flickers produces an orange-shafted form
- flight speed 37 kmh (23 mph)

Nest Canada wide.

 *Sapsuckers are named for their habit of drilling holes in the bark of a tree to get sap and insects from just under the surface.*

Red-breasted Sapsucker

Size: 20–23 cm (8"–9"), wingspan to 40 cm (16")
Range: Alaska, western Canada and USA

- take six to ten days to dig a nest hole
- lifespan up to 6 years

Nest in British Columbia.

Red-naped Sapsucker

Size: 15–23 cm (6"–9"), wingspan to 40 cm (16")
Range: Southwestern Canada, USA, Mexico

- entrance hole to the nest is about 3 cm (1 1/4"), and takes six to ten days to build
- interbreed with yellow-bellied at the eastern edge of their range, and red-breasted to the west

Nest in southern British Columbia and Alberta.

Williamson's Sapsucker

Size: 23–25 cm (9"–10")
Range: Southwestern Canada, western USA

- live only at higher elevations in mountain pine forests
- sexes are so unalike that the male and female were originally described as two separate species
- 86% of their animal diet is ants

Nest in southern British Columbia.

Sapsuckers *continued*

Yellow-bellied Sapsucker

Size: 20–23 cm (8"–9"), wingspan to 40 cm (16")
Range: Canada, USA, Central America

- drill square or round holes in over 275 species of tree
- young are fed a mixture of sap and insects
- lifespan up to 6 years

Nest across Canada.

Black-backed Woodpecker

Size: 20–25 cm (8"–10"), wingspan to 40 cm (16")
Range: Alaska, Canada, USA

- flake bark off dead conifers to get at grubs underneath
- lower edge of entrance hole is beveled by the birds to serve as a doorstep into the cavity

Nest across Canada except for the Great Plains.

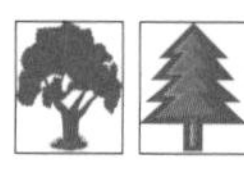

Downy Woodpecker

Size: 15–17 cm (6"–7"), wingspan to 30 cm (12")
Range: Alaska, Canada, USA

- smallest Canadian woodpecker species
- named for the soft, downy appearance of their **plumage**
- call may be heard 0.4 km (1/4 mi) away
- some pairs may stay together for up to four years
- in the fall, birds dig fresh holes in dead trees for winter roosting places
- lifespan up to 10 years

Nest Canada wide.

Downy Woodpecker

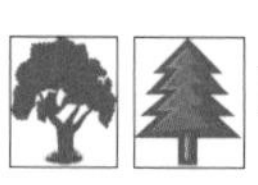

Hairy Woodpecker

Size: 20–25 cm (8"–10"), wingspan to 72 cm (17")
Range: Alaska, Canada, USA, Central America

- adults are highly sedentary and may stay on the same **territory** for life
- entrance hole to nest is 4–5 cm (1.5"–2")
- 75% of their food is insects
- name comes from the shaggy, rough appearance of plumage
- lifespan up to 14 years

Nest Canada wide.

 **Lewis' Woodpecker**

Size: 25–27 cm (10"–11"), wingspan to 52 cm (21")
Range: Southwestern Canada, western USA

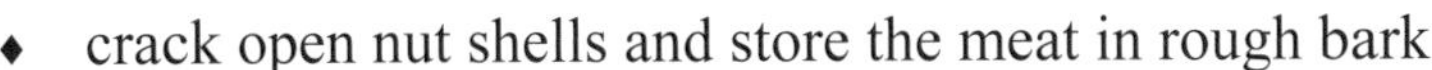

- crack open nut shells and store the meat in rough bark
- often pluck insects out of the air
- mate for life
- both sexes develop **brood patches**

Nest in southern British Columbia.

 **Pileated Woodpecker**

Size: 40–47 cm (16"–19"), wingspan to 75 cm (30")
Range: Canada, USA

- largest Canadian woodpecker
- nest may take 30 days to complete; entrance hole 9 cm (3.5")
- pairs occupy same area year after year
- dig and use several roosting cavities, entered about 30 minutes before sunset
- lifespan up to 13 years

Nest across Canada except for the Great Plains.

 **Red-bellied Woodpecker**

Size: 23–25 cm (9"–10"), wingspan to 45 cm (18")
Range: Southeastern Canada, eastern USA

- eat insects, sap, fruit, nuts, and the pulp and juice of oranges from the tree or the ground
- sometimes use the same nesting cavity each year
- lifespan up to 20 years; the record for any woodpecker

Nest from southern Ontario to the Maritimes.

 **Red-headed Woodpecker**

Size: 20–23 cm (8"–9"), wingspan to 45 cm (18")
Range: Southern and eastern Canada, central USA

- uncommon over most of their range due to the advance of European starlings
- dart into the air after flying insects
- also eat eggs or young of other birds
- Indian tribes regarded these birds as sacred, and used the bright red feathers as currency
- lifespan up to 10 years

Nest in southern Saskatchewan, Manitoba and Ontario.

 **Three-toed Woodpecker**

Size: 20–23 cm (8"–9"), wingspan to 37 cm (15")
Range: Alaska, Canada, USA; Europe, Asia, Korea, Japan

- tame, unsuspicious and less flighty than other woodpeckers
- prefer coniferous forests where they are burned, logged or swampy
- rarely move far from their home range

Nest across Canada except for the Great Plains.

 **White-headed Woodpecker**

Size: 20–23 cm (8"–9")
Range: Southwestern Canada, western USA

- the only Canadian woodpecker with a white head
- live largely on the seeds of the ponderosa pine
- frequently drink water

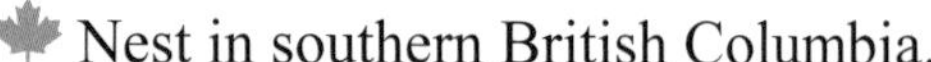

Nest in southern British Columbia.

Did You Know...

*The most important act that a bird performs is the **preening** of its feathers. They begin by grasping with their bill, one feather at the base and nibbling towards the tip to remove oil, dirt and parasites. Or they may just simply draw the feather through the partially clamped bill in one quick movement to smooth the **feather barbs** and remove dirt so they will lock together. This process also works fresh oil into the feathers from the **preen gland** located at the base of the tail.*

*Some birds help to **preen** each other's heads, usually paired birds at the nest site. Mutual **preening** is always concentrated on the head and neck, which a bird cannot reach with its own bill. These mutual caresses are thought to remove foreign objects from feathers, as well as reinforce pair bonds and reduce aggression.*

*One captive giant cowbird at a zoo in Texas frequently offered its head to people and solicited touching. Many responded by scratching the cowbird's head, and whenever people stopped, the bird displayed again to invite more **preening**. Caged parrots will often inch along the perch and bow their heads to people, in an invitation to scratch their heads.*

World Species 59
Canadian Species 7

The Wren Family - Troglodytidae

Characteristics
Wrens are small, 7–20 cm (3"–8") plump songbirds who scamper actively about with their tail cocked over their back. **Plumage** is many shades of brown, rufous or grey with black or white markings, and the sexes look alike. Short, rounded wings give them a rather weak flight, although it is quick and direct. Their bill is slender, sharp, pointed, somewhat curved and adapted for probing into crevices. Legs are strong with long claws.

Behaviour
Active, extremely quick, bustling birds, wrens are unobtrusive apart from their wonderful song, which is sung by both sexes. They have adapted to many different kinds of habitats and feed fairly close to the ground, moving through the undergrowth. Most species avoid coming out into the open. Wrens are solitary and extremely **territorial,** defending their area with song and physical encounters, even to the extent of destroying other birds' nests. Some species build roosting nests that are different from the nests used for egg laying.

Diet
Wrens are insect eaters, and also consume large quantities of spiders.

Reproduction
In some wren species, the male builds multiple nests for the female to choose from. He attracts her with his song, then leads her from nest to nest until she chooses one. Males mate with numerous females, and both parents feed the young. Marsh and sedge wrens weave globular nests with a side entrance, and many dummy nests. Other species nest in cavities, rock crevices or nest boxes. Three to ten white eggs with dark markings are laid, and **incubated** by the female only for 12–16 days. Young wrens leave the nest 11–19 days after hatching.

Family Status
Wrens are confined to the **New World**, except for the winter wren, which is called simply 'wren' in Europe. They are found in forests, desert, mountains, grasslands and gardens across the continent. Three species are classed as extinct, due to loss of habitat.

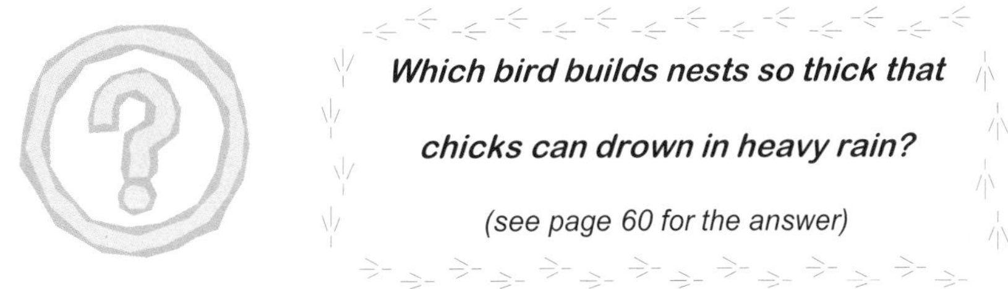

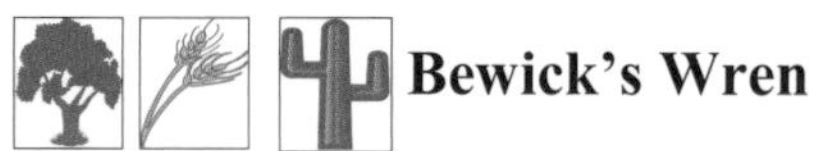

Bewick's Wren

Size: 12–15 cm (5"–6"), wingspan to 17 cm (7")
Range: Southwestern Canada, USA to Central America

- nest in almost any cavity: trees, knotholes, mailboxes, tin cans, cow skulls in pastures
- familiar back yard birds throughout their range
- name is pronounced like the car 'Buick'

Nest in southern British Columbia.

Carolina Wren

Size: 12–15 cm (5"–6"), wingspan to 20 cm (8")
Range: Southeastern Canada, eastern USA, Central America

- male occasionally stops feeding to sing in all kinds of weather throughout the year
- many songs are imitations of other birds
- non-**migratory**
- reported roosting in all kinds of cavities: old clothing, buildings, tin cans
- two **clutches** per year
- state bird of South Carolina
- lifespan up to 6 years

Nest from southern Ontario to the Maritimes.

House Wren

House Wren

Size: 10–12 cm (4"–5"), wingspan to 17 cm (7")
Range: Southern Canada, USA, Central and South America, West Indies

- the most common wren in Canada
- will destroy other birds' eggs to take over good nesting sites
- male defends **territory** of 0.1–1.4 ha (1/4–3 1/2 acre) by singing
- have nested in abandoned paper nests of hornets
- female inspects various nests built by the male, chooses one and lines it with grasses
- two or three **clutches** per season
- lifespan up to 7 years

Nest across southern Canada.

Marsh Wren

Size: 10–12 cm (4"–5"), wingspan to 17 cm (7")
Range: Southern Canada, coastal USA, Central America

- females build a nest of cattails and reeds lashed together with a side opening
- males build multiple dummy nests, and will destroy other birds' eggs and nests
- often perch sideways on reed stems
- male **courtship** display includes flying up to 4.5 m (15 ft) then fluttering gradually down

Nest in British Columbia, Alberta and Saskatchewan, and southern Manitoba to the Maritimes.

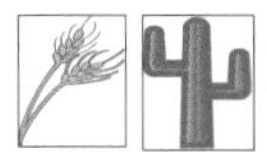

Rock Wren

Size: 12–15 cm (5"–6"), wingspan to 23 cm (9")
Range: Southwestern Canada, western USA to Central America

- name refers to their preferred habitat
- nest in ground squirrel burrows, cavities, rock crevices or buildings
- make a 20–25 cm (8"–10") path to the nest entrance with carefully laid pebbles

Nest in southern British Columbia, Alberta and Saskatchewan.

Sedge Wren

Size: 10–12 cm (4"–5"), wingspan to 15 cm (6")
Range: Southeastern Canada, eastern USA to Central America

- nest is a ball of woven plant material with a side opening, above mud or shallow water
- found in freshwater meadows where grasses grow with small scattered shrubs
- males build numerous dummy nests

Nest in British Columbia, Alberta and Saskatchewan, and southern Manitoba to the Maritimes.

Winter Wren

Size: 10–12 cm (4"–5"), wingspan to 15 cm (6")
Range: Alaska, Canada, eastern USA; Europe, Africa, Asia

- one of the smallest Canadian songbirds
- nest is lined with deer hair and feathers of other birds
- males build up to four dummy nests
- the only species of wren that has spread to the **Old World**
- conserve energy in winter by huddling together in a communal roost; as many as 30–40 birds have been found in a single hole
- their special roosting habits have enabled them to widely expand their range
- lifespan up to 5 years

> In Ireland, wrens were once thought to tell the future, and records predicting events based on wren behaviour have existed for centuries.

Nest across central Canada.

Migration - Why and How

Why do birds migrate? Many of the species seen in Canada in the summer months spend the winter in warmer climates. Why expend all that energy and face all the inherent dangers of flying thousands of miles twice a year?

At the end of each Ice Age, progressively more land appeared in the north. At the height of summer, birds that moved into these areas would have found a bonanza of food, longer daylight hours to feed and increased breeding space. But these birds would have also found that as winter approached, they had to retreat south. Present day migratory patterns have evolved over thousands of years of climatic change. Migrating birds use well established, food-rich paths along a north-south axis. In North America, there are four such flyways: Pacific, Central, Mississippi and Atlantic.

The need to undertake this journey is now instinctive, and millions of birds around the world fly north in the spring to breed. Internal changes trigger the urge to migrate. Reproductive organs begin to enlarge, and restlessness and perching towards the direction of departure precede migration. Despite a wealth of scientific experiments, it is still not known why birds select a particular breeding area. It is known, however, that once an area is established, it becomes a fixed destination and is used year after year. Decreases in autumn temperatures and light encourage eating to build up fat reserves; a small bird may lose nearly half its weight on the return journey.

Exactly how the birds find their way has puzzled people for centuries. We now know that they use a variety of tools, but full understanding still eludes us. Birds are thought to calculate the sun's arc relative to the horizon, using its height and direction to obtain a north-south axis. Nocturnal migrants may use the stars to navigate. A known sensitivity to changes in barometric pressure enables them to avoid bad weather and exploit tail winds. The ability to detect low frequency sound waves may help them hear things like breaking waves, while their own calls may be picked up as echoes off mountains. Other factors such as the magnetic field of the earth, or the moon, may also be used.

While the facts of migration may elude us, the dangers of it do not. Most songbirds migrate at night, when they may be struck by planes, automobiles or trains. They run into buildings, utility wires and high bridges. Radio and TV towers, and the steel cables that support them kill an estimated one million birds each year. Migrating birds have been found impaled on TV aerials, barbed wire fences and farming equipment. They become disoriented by the dazzling lights of airports, lighthouses and floodlit buildings.

It's worth noting that these circumstances account for more deaths each year than all other causes combined - and they're all man made.

The fact that these delicate, feathered creatures undertake these massive journeys continues to astound and amaze us. It is very sad to think that something as magical and mystical as bird migration has been turned against them by mans' intrusion into their world.

Threats to Birds—Past and Present

LOSS OF HABITAT
One half of the world's wetlands have been lost in the last century.

Logging and conversion have shrunk the world's forests by 50%, and 30% of the world's original forests have been converted to agriculture.

POISONS
Lead pellets from shotgun shells fall to the bottom of ponds, where they are ingested by waterfowl. Two to three percent of the waterfowl population is poisoned this way each year.

Strychnine and other poisons are mixed with grain to kill ground squirrels. This results in the death of the seed-eating birds who share the grain. The same poisons are put in carcasses of dead animals to kill predators such as coyotes, who share their food with raptors.

While the use of DDT has been banned in North America, it is still heavily used in the birds' wintering grounds in Central and South America.

INTRODUCED SPECIES
Entire species of island birds have been wiped out by introduced cats, rats, foxes, goats and pigs. They eat the plants that produce seeds as well as the eggs and young birds. Native species have no natural defenses against these new predators.

In North America, the house sparrow and the European starling invade the prime nesting sites of native birds, who are then forced to use marginally safe areas.

OVER-HUNTING
The passenger pigeon and the Eskimo curlew are but two examples of over-hunting. Once found in flocks that darkened the sky, millions of these birds were shot as they migrated across the plains. They are now extinct.

OIL SPILLS
Water birds caught in oil spills are weighted down by the oil, which coats their feathers. As they try to clean themselves by preening, the toxic oil is ingested and they quickly die.

FISHERMEN'S NETS
Diving birds such as gannets and members of the Auk family are trapped in fishermen's nets, where they suffocate and drown.

CAGED BIRD PET TRADE
The demand for exotic birds means poachers are wiping out entire populations. Roughly 2% of these birds live to their final destination, and once taken out of the wild they do not reproduce.

PLUME TRADE
The commercial trade in feathers for decorating hats and stuffing pillows, mattresses and sleeping bags endangered six bird families. It was outlawed in the early 1900's. Eider down is now collected spring and summer from the nests of the common eider duck in Iceland. The birds are protected and encouraged to nest. Only a part of the down is taken from each nest, with 35–40 nests needed to make 1/2 kg (1 lb) of down.

Birds by Another Name - Nouns of Assembly

Avocets	Recurvation
Birds	Assemblage, Aviary, Brace, Brood, Colony, Flight, Flock, Hoard, Host, Multitude, Party, Raft, Volery, Volley, Congregation
Bitterns	Blend, Sedge, Siege, Stand
Blackbirds	Scold, Team
Blue Jays	Herd, Singular, Sounder
Bobolinks	Chain
Buntings	Flock, Strut
Cardinals	Congregation, Radiance
Chickadees	Chatter, Commonality, Flutter
Chats	Parlance
Coots	Commotion, Covert, Fleet, Raft
Cormorants	Flight, Gulp, Vee
Cowbirds	Stealth
Cranes	Bugle, Flock, Herd, Sedge, Siege, Soar, Trumpet
Crows	Clan, Commotion, Conference, Hover, Murder, Nag
Curlews	Herd, Probe
Doves	Dole, Dule, Flight, Peck, Piteousness, Prettying, True Love
Ducks (diving)	Dopping, Dropping
Ducks (flying)	Flush, Plump, Team
Ducks (on water)	Paddling, Bunch, Fleet, Raft, Sail, Sore, Team, Badling
Ducks (on land)	Flight, Flock, Leash, Mob, Sail
Ducklings (on nest)	Clutch
Ducklings (off nest)	Clatch
Dunlins	Flight
Eagles	Convocation, Jubilee
Evening Grosbeaks	Quandary
Falcons	Cast, Strike
Finches	Charm, Company, Flight, Flock
Flycatchers	Zipper
Gannets	Dive, Ledge, Salt
Geese (on water)	Plump, Knot
Geese (on land)	Gaggle, Murder, Raft
Geese (flying)	Flock, Gaggle, Lag, Skein, Team, Vee
Goldfinches	Charm, Glister, Hoard, Rhythm, Trembling, Trimming
Goshawks	Flight
Grosbeaks	Rainbow
Grouse	Boom, Brace, Brood, Covey, Drumming, Lek, Pack
Guillemots	Bazaar, Loomery
Gulls	Colony, Galaxy, Scavenging, Recrudescence

Harriers	Glide, Heart, Quartering
Hawks	Cast, Couple, Flight, Kettle, Leash, Soar, Screw
Herons	Siege, Patience, Scattering
House Sparrows	Annoyance, Rash
Hummingbirds	Charm, Shimmer
Ibis	Crowd
Jaegers	Piracy
Jays	Band, Farce, Party
Killdeer	Feint
Kingbirds	Regency
Kingfishers	Watch
Knots	Cluster
Larks	Exaltation, Flight, Bevy
Loons	Asylum, Raft, Yodel
Magpies	Motley, Tiding, Tittering
Merlins	Leash
Mockingbirds	Mime
Murres	Bazaar
Nuthatches	Creep
Osprey	Eye
Owls	Parliament, Hoot, Interruption, Pedantry, Stare, Vigil
Partridges	Covey, Flock
Pelicans	Beaker, Pod, Pouch, Precision
Pheasants	Bouquet, Brace, Brood, Kit
Pigeons	Dropping, Flight, Flock, Statue, Stool
Pipits	Alacrity
Plovers	Congregation, Exaltation, Flight, Leash
Prairie Chickens	Covey, Flock, Swell
Ptarmigan	Camouflage, Covey
Puffins	Improbability, Preciousness
Quail	Bevy, Burst, Drift, Covey
Ravens	Unkindness, Croak, Gloom, Rant
Redstarts	Dart, Shot
Robins	Rotundity
Sanderlings	Retreat, Scramble
Sandpipers	Fling, Timestep
Seabirds	Wreck
Shearwaters	Cleavage

Snipe	Couple, Leash, Nocturne, Walk, Whisper, Winnow, Wisp, Zigzag
Snow Buntings	Squall, Wave
Snow Geese	Bank, Blizzard, Skein
Soras	Solitude, Sneak
Sparrows	Apology, Host, Quarrel, Tribe, Ubiquity
Starlings	Affliction, Chattering, Clutter, Crowd, Kitoch, Murmeration
Stilts	Teeter
Swallows	Flight, Gulp, Regularity, Sweep, Swirl, Swoop
Swans	Bevy, Game, Herd, Squadron, Tank, Team, Wedge, Whiteness
Teal (on water)	Bunch, Knob, Raft
Teal (rising from water)	Spring, Coil
Terns	Elegance
Thrashers	Scratch
Thrushes	Flute, Mutation, Speckle
Vireos	Cheer, Glean
Virginia Rails	Reel
Vultures	Coven, Wake
Warblers	Yellowing
Water Thrushes	Tinkle
Waxwings	Aristocracy
Widgeon	Bunch, Coil, Company, Flight, Knob, Trip, Wisp
Willets	Wish
Woodcocks	Covey, Fall, Flight, Plump, Probe
Woodpeckers	Bore, Descent, Drumming, Gatling
Wrens	Bubbling, Chime, Herd, Tinkling

Life Spans

The following life spans are based on banding returns, and are meant as a general guide, not a hard and fast rule for the species. New banding records could indicate different numbers, but this list gives an indication of how long members of each family may live.

Albatross Family
Black-footed (27)
Laysan (40)

Blackbird Family
Red-winged blackbird (14)
Common grackle (16)

Bunting & Sparrow Family
Dark-eyed junco (10)
Chipping sparrow (13)
Song sparrow (10)
Tree sparrow (9)
White-crowned sparrow (13)
White-throated sparrow (9)
Rufous-sided towhee (12)

Chickadee Family
Black-capped chickadee (12)
Tufted titmouse (12)

Crane Family
Sandhill crane (20)

Creeper Family
Brown creeper (5)

Crow & Raven Family
American crow (14)
Blue jay (15)
Grey jay (10)
Raven (29)

Dove Family
Rock dove (16)

Duck Family
Canvasback (19)
Ring-necked duck (10)
Common goldeneye (17)
Lesser scaup (20)
Mallard (29)

Eagle Family
Bald eagle (48)
Golden eagle (46)

Falcon Family
Prairie falcon (10)
American kestrel (17)

Finch Family
Indigo bunting (8)
Northern cardinal (28)
House finch (10)
Purple finch (12)
American goldfinch (8)
Black-headed grosbeak (25)
Evening grosbeak (13)
Pine grosbeak (8)
Rose-breasted grosbeak (24)
Redpolls (7)
Pine siskin (11)

Flycatcher Family
Least flycatcher (5)
Willow flycatcher (4)
Yellow-bellied flycatcher (4)
Great-crested flycatcher (11)
Western kingbird (7)
Eastern phoebe (9)
Wood peewee (7)

Goose Family
Canada goose (20)

Grouse Family
Ruffed grouse (7)
Sage grouse (7)
Sharp-tailed grouse (7)
White-tailed ptarmigan (15)

Gull & Tern Family
California gull (12)
Greater black-backed gull (19)
Herring gull (36)
Mew gull (24)
Ring-billed gull (20)
Glaucous gull (21)
Glaucous-winged gull (22)
Thayer's gull (36)
Black-legged kittiwake (15)
Arctic tern (34)
Black tern (17)
Caspian tern (26)
Roseate tern (9)

Hawk Family
Cooper's hawk (7)
Sharp-shinned hawk (12)
Northern goshawk (19)
Broad-winged hawk (7)
Ferruginous hawk (20)
Red-shouldered hawk (20)
Red-tailed hawk (29)
Swainson's hawk (9)
Northern harrier (16)

Heron Family
Great egret (22)
Snowy egret (16)
Black-crowned night-heron (21)
Great blue heron (21)

Hummingbird Family
Ruby-throated (5)

Ibis Family
White-faced ibis (14)

Jaeger Family
Parasitic jaeger (30)

Lark Family
Eurasian skylark (8)

Loon Family
Common loon (7)
Pacific loon (18)
Red-throated loon (23)

Mockingbird Family
Grey catbird (10)
Northern mockingbird (15)
Brown thrasher (12)

Nuthatch Family
Pygmy nuthatch (7)
Red-breasted nuthatch (7)
White-breasted nuthatch (9)

Osprey Family
Osprey (32)

Owl Family
Barn owl (17)
Barred owl (23)
Boreal owl (15)
Burrowing owl (11)
Great-horned owl (29)
Long-eared owl (27)
Northern saw-whet owl (17)
Screech owl (13)
Snowy owl (14)

Pelican Family
White pelican (34)

Partridge Family
Northern bobwhite quail (9)
California quail (9)
Ring-necked pheasant (8)

Pipit Family
American pipit (8)

Plover Family
Killdeer (6)
Piping plover (14)

Rail Family
American coot (9)
Common moorhen (6)

Sandpiper Family
Long-billed curlew (10)
Whimbrel (11)
Dunlin (14)
Red knot (13)
Least sandpiper (7)
Semi-palmated sandpiper (7)
Spotted sandpiper (8)
Upland sandpiper (5)
White-rumped sandpiper (5)
Ruddy turnstone (13)
Common snipe (6)
American woodcock (8)

Shearwater Family
Northern fulmar (34)
Manx shearwater (12)
Short-tailed shearwater (30)

Shrike Family
Loggerhead shrike (6)
Northern shrike (12)

Starling Family
European starling (20)

Storm Petrel Family
Leach' storm petrel (24)

Swallow Family
Purple martin (8)
Bank swallow (8)
Barn swallow (16)
Cliff swallow (5)
Tree swallow (9)

Swan Family
Mute swan (40)
Trumpeter swan (29)
Tundra swan (19)

Swift Family
Chimney swift (14)

Tanager Family
Scarlet tanager (10)
Western tanager (15)

Thrush Family
Eastern bluebird (6)
Mountain bluebird (4)
American robin (17)
Hermit thrush (7)
Swainson's thrush (3)
Wood thrush (8)
Veery (9)
Northern wheatear (7)

Wild Turkey Family
Wild turkey (9)

Vireo Family
Red-eyed vireo (10)
Warbling vireo (9)

Waxwing Family
Cedar waxwing (5)

Weaverbird Family
House sparrow (13)

Warbler Family
Yellow-breasted chat (8)
Ovenbird (8)
Northern parula (4)
American redstart (4)
Blue-winged warbler (5)
Hooded warbler (11)
Pine warbler (7)
Prairie warbler (10)
Prothonotary warbler (5)
Black-throated green (6)
Canada warbler (7)
Chestnut-sided warbler (5)
Golden-winged warbler (6)
Palm warbler (6)
Black & white warbler (11)
Magnolia warbler (6)
Orange-crowned (6)
Tennessee warbler (4)
Yellow warbler (7)
Louisiana waterthrush (3)
Northern waterthrush (6)
Common yellowthroat (7)

Woodpecker Family
Red-breasted sapsucker (6)
Yellow-breasted saps. (6)
Downy woodpecker (10)
Hairy woodpecker (14)
Pileated woodpecker (13)
Red-bellied woodpecker (20)
Red-headed woodpecker(10)

Wren Family
Carolina wren (7)
House wren (7)
Winter wren (5)

Canadian Birding on the Internet

Bird Studies Canada
http://www.bsc-eoc.org/bscmain.html

Birding in Canada
http://www.web-nat.com/bic/

Birds of North America
http://www.birdsofna.org

Canadian Bird Conservation Program
http://199.212.18.79/birds/mbirds.html

Canadian Bird Trends Database
http://199.212.18.79/birds/default.cfm

Cornell Lab of Ornithology - Project Feeder Watch
http://www.birds.cornell.edu

Ducks Unlimited Canada
http://www.ducks.ca

Fatal Light Awareness Program
http://www.flap.org/home2.htm

Important Bird Areas of Canada
http://www.ibacanada.com/

National Wildlife Research Centre - Bird Banding
http://www.cws-scf.ec.gc.ca/nwrc/bbo/birdband.htm

Partners In Flight - Canada
http://www.cws-scf.ec.gc.ca/canbird/pif/p_intro.htm

Peregrine Foundation
http://www.acs.ucalgary.ca/~tull/falcon/

The Wetlands Network
http://www.netcontrol.net/themata-b/bz32/

Conservation Websites

Canadian Nature Federation
http://www.cnf.ca/

Canadian Wildlife Federation
http://www.cwf-fcf.org/

Committee on the Status of Endangered Wildlife In Canada (COSEWIC)
http://www.cosewic.gc.ca/

Convention on International Trade in Endangered Species (CITES)
http://www.cws-scf.ec.gc.ca/cites/intro_e.html

The Ramsar Convention on Wetlands
http://www.ramsar.org/index.html

Trade in Traditional Medicine Using Endangered Species (TRAFFIC)
http://www.traffic.org/

Wild Animal and Plant Protection and Regulation of International and Interprovincial Trade Act (WAPPRIITA)
http://www.cites.ec.gc.ca/wappa/homepg.htm

World Conservation Union (IUCN)
http://iucn.org

World Wildlife Fund Canada
http://www.wwfcanada.org/

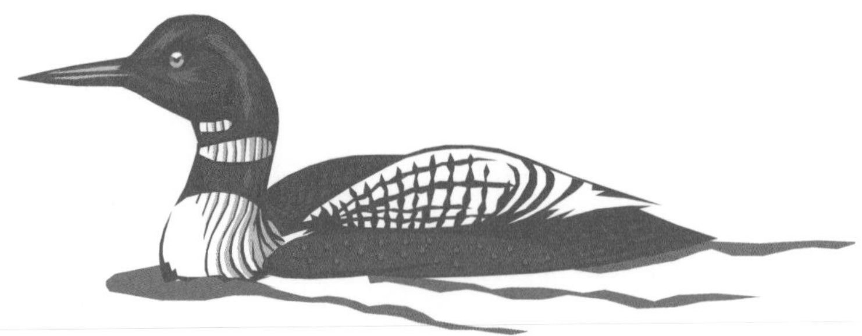

Canada's National Bird: Common Loon

Naturalist Clubs of Canada

If you would like to learn more about birds, animals and the natural wonders of our country, contact the naturalist group in your area. The following is just a partial list of Canadian Nature Federation affiliated groups.

BRITISH COLUMBIA

Burke Mountain Naturalists
(250) 936-4100

Central Okanogan Naturalists
(250) 769-6605

Federation of British Columbia Naturalists
(604) 737-3057

Oliver-Osoyoos Naturalists
(250) 376-9587

Prince George Naturalist Club
(250) 563-8032

Royal City Field Naturalists
(250) 521-2477

Vancouver Natural History Society
(604) 737-3074
jmccall@helix.net

Victoria Natural History Society
(250) 479-2054

YUKON

Yukon Conservation Society
(867) 668-5678

NORTHWEST TERRITORIES

Ecology North
(867) 873-6019
econorth@ssimicro.com

ALBERTA

Calgary Field Naturalists
(403) 285-8553
cfns@cadvision.com

Federation of Alberta Naturalists
(780) 427-8124
fan@connect.ab.ca

Grasslands Naturalists
(403) 529-6225

Peace Parkland Naturalists
(780) 539-6102

Red Deer River Naturalists
(403) 227-2944

SASKATCHEWAN

Nature Saskatchewan
(306) 780-9273
nature.sask@unibase.com

Regina Natural History Society
(306) 787-2807

Saskatoon Nature Society
(306) 373-2872
wmack@the.link.ca

MANITOBA

Manitoba Naturalists Society
(204) 943-9029
mns@escape.ca

Naturalist Clubs *continued*

ONTARIO

Federation of Ontario Naturalists
(416) 444-8419

Guelph Field Naturalists
(519) 836-7906
craig@cbn.on.ca

Hamilton Naturalists Club
(905) 648-8665

Huntsville Nature Club
(705) 636-7268

Huron Fringe Field Naturalists
(519) 524-6654

Kitchener-Waterloo Field Naturalists
(519) 893-6469

McIlwraith Field Naturalists
(519) 660-3535

Ottawa Field Naturalists Club
(613) 722-3050

Pembroke Area Field Naturalists
(613) 625-2610
cmichener@renc.igs.net

Presqu'ile Brighton Naturalists
(613) 475-3604

Richmond Hill Naturalists
(416) 731-8380
turkm@accessv.com

Sydenham Field Naturalists
(519) 627-5348

Thunder Bay Field Naturalists
(807) 626-0089
pskula@tbaytel.net

Toronto Field Naturalists
(416) 593-2656

QUEBEC

Catharine Trail Naturalist Club
(514) 695-7781
parkolas@sympatico.ca

Montreal Field Naturalist Club
(514) 695-7781

NEWFOUNDLAND

Humber Natural History Society
(709) 895-2564
nhs@nhs.nf.ca

NOVA SCOTIA

Annapolis Field Naturalist Society
(902) 532-5129
jpercyeauracom.com

Blomidon Naturalists Society
(902) 542-5983

Federation of Nova Scotia Naturalists
(902) 275-3361
nstn0308@fox.nstn.ca

Halifax Field Naturalists
(902) 455-8160
hfnexec@chebucto.ns.ca

NEW BRUNSWICK

New Brunswick Federation of Naturalists
(maryspt@nbnet.nb.ca)

Ford Alward Naturalist Association
(506) 246-5572

PRINCE EDWARD ISLAND

Natural History Society of PEI
(902) 658-2036

British Columbia

Provincial Bird: Steller's Jay

Lists of natural history clubs around the province can be obtained from:

Federation of BC Naturalists
425, 1367 West Broadway
Vancouver, BC V6H 4A9
Web site: http://www.members.zoom.com/fbcn/

Information on birding in BC can be obtained from:

British Columbia Field Ornithologists
Box 8059
Victoria, BC V8W 3R7
Web site: http://www.birding.bc.ca/bcfo/

Migratory Bird Sanctuaries

Christie Islet - 0.08 hectares
Esquimalt Lagoon - 130 hectares
George C Reifel - 648 hectares
Nechako River - 180 hectares
Shoal Harbour - 150 hectares
Vaseux Lake - 282 hectares
Victoria Harbour - 1,700 hectares

National Wildlife Areas

Alaksen - 299 hectares
Columbia - 1,001 hectares
Qualicum - 82 hectares
Vaseux-Bighorn - 792 hectares
Widgeon Valley - 125 hectares

For more information, contact:
Canadian Wildlife Service
Box 340, Delta BC V4K 3Y3
Telephone: (604) 946-9546

More BC Web Links

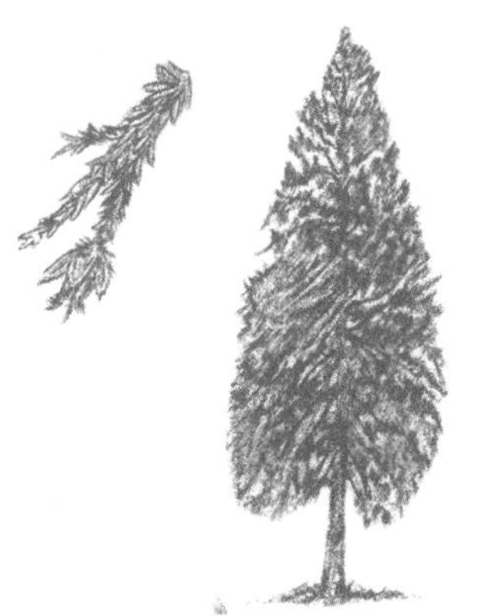

Provincial Tree: Western Red Cedar

Birding British Columbia
http://www.birding.bc

BC Bird Highlights
http://www.visionfoundation.org

Birding Festivals
http://www.island.net/~bfest

Wildlife Watch
http://www3.bc.sympatico.ca/driftwood/bcwwhome.htm

British Columbia

National Parks

Glacier & Mount Revelstoke National Parks
Box 350, Revelstoke, BC V0E 2S0
Telephone (250) 837-7500

Kootenay National Park
Box 220, Radium Hot Springs, BC V0A 1M0
Telephone (250) 347 - 9615

Yoho National Park
Box 99, Field, BC V0A 1G0
Telephone (250) 343-6324

Pacific Rim National Park
Box 280, Ucluelet, BC V0R 3A0
Telephone (250) 726-7721

Gwaii Haanas National Marine Conservation Area
Box 37, Queen Charlotte City, BC V0T 1S0
Telephone (250) 559-8818

Floral Emblem: Flowering Dogwood

For information on Provincial Parks in British Columbia, check the following website:

http://www.env.gov.bc.ca/bcparks/

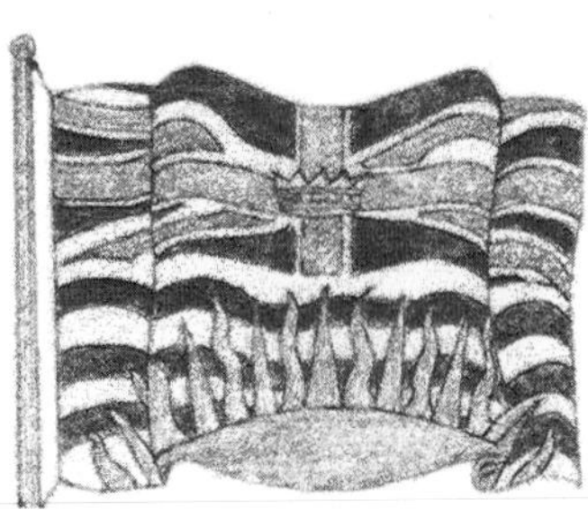

Provincial Flag

Alberta

Provincial Bird: Great Horned Owl

Migratory Bird Sanctuaries

Inglewood - 1,600 hectares
Red Deer - 130 hectares
Richardson Lake - 12,705 hectares
Saskatoon Lake - 1,135 hectares

National Wildlife Areas

Blue Quills - 98 hectares
Meanook - 214 hectares
Spiers Lake - 64 hectares

For more information, contact:
Canadian Wildlife Service
2nd floor, 4999 - 98 Ave
Edmonton, AB T6B 2X3
Telephone: (780) 468-8919

Lists of natural history clubs around the province can be obtained from:

Federation of Alberta Naturalists
Box 1472
Edmonton, AB T5J 2N5
Web site: http://www.connect.ab.ca/~fan/

Provincial Fish: Bull Trout

Provincial Tree: Lodgepole Pine

More Alberta Web Links

Wildlife Viewing Guide
http://www.gov.ab.ca/env/fw/view/index_java.html

Important Bird Areas (IBA)
http://www.bsc-eoc.org/Iba/albmain.html

Birding Hot Spots
http://www.camacdonald.com/birding/caalberta.htm

Alberta

National Parks

Banff National Park
Box 900, Banff, AB T0L 0C0
Telephone (403) 762-1550

Floral Emblem: Wild Rose

Elk Island National Park
Site 4, RR 1, Fort Saskatchewan, AB T8L 2N7
Telephone (780) 992-2950

Jasper National Park
Box 10, Jasper, AB T0E 1E0
Telephone (780) 852-6176

Waterton Lakes National Park
Waterton, AB T0K 2M0
Telephone (403) 859-2224

Wood Buffalo National Park
Box 750, Fort Smith, NWT X0E 0P0
Telephone (867) 872-7900

Provincial Mammal: Bighorn Sheep

For information on Provincial Parks in Alberta, check the following website:

http://www.gov.ab.ca/env/parks/

Provincial Flag

Saskatchewan

Provincial Bird: Sharp-tailed Grouse

For information on birding in Saskatchewan, contact:

Nature Saskatchewan
206, 1860 Lorne Street
Regina, SK S4P 2L7
Telephone (306) 780-9273
E-mail: nature.sask@unibase.com

National Parks

Grasslands National Park
Box 150, Val Marie, SK S0N 2T0
Telephone (306) 298-2257

Prince Albert National Park
Box 100, Waskesiu Lake, SK S0J 2Y0
Telephone (306) 663-4522

Migratory Bird Sanctuaries

Basin & Middle Lakes - 8,720 hectares
Duncairn Reservoir - 1,546 hectares
Indian Head - 32 hectares
Last Mountain Lake - 4,736 hectares
Lenore Lake - 8,830 hectares
Murray lake - 1,165 hectares
Neely Lake - 809 hectares
Old Wives Lake - 26,060 hectares
Opuntia Lake - 1,395 hectares
Redberry Lake - 6,395 hectares
Scent Grass Lake - 633 hectares
Sutherloand - 130 hectares
Upper Rousay Lake - 518 hectares
Val Marie Reservoir - 505 hectares
Wascana Lake - 104 hectares

National Wildlife Areas

Bradwell - 123 hectares
Last Mountain Lake - 15,602 hectares
Prairie - 2,949 hectares
Raven Island - 94 hectares
Stalwart - 1,460 hectares
St Denis - 361 hectares
Tway - 96 hectares
Webb - 427 hectares

For more information, contact:
Canadian Wildlife Service
2nd floor, 4999 - 98 Ave
Edmonton, AB T6B 2X3
Telephone: (780) 468-8919

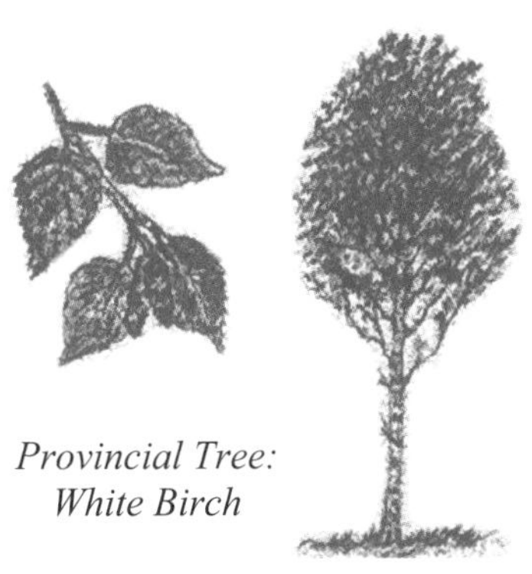

Provincial Tree: White Birch

Provincial Flag

Floral Emblem: Prairie Lily

Manitoba

Provincial Bird:
Great Grey Owl

Lists of natural history clubs around the province can be obtained from:

Manitoba Naturalists' Society
401, 63 Albert Street
Winnipeg, MB R3B 1G4
Website: http://www.wilds.mb.ca/mns

National Parks

Riding Mountain National Park
Wasagaming, MB R0J 2H0
Telephone 1-800-707-8480

Wapusk National Park
Box 127, Churchill, MB R0B 0E0
Telephone 1-888-748-2928

Migratory Bird Sanctuaries

None

National Wildlife Areas

Pope - 31 hectares
Rockwood - 32 hectares

For more information, contact:
Canadian Wildlife Service
2nd floor, 4999 - 98 Ave
Edmonton, AB T6B 2X3
Telephone: (780) 468-8919

Floral Emblem:
Pasque Flower

For information on Provincial Parks in Manitoba, check the following website:

http://www.gov.mb.ca/natres/parks/homepage.html

Provincial Tree:
White Spruce

Provincial Flag

Ontario

Provincial Bird: Common Loon

Lists of natural history clubs around the province can be obtained from:

Federation of Ontario Naturalists
355 Lesmill Road
Don Mills, ON M3B 2W8
Telephone (416) 444-8419

Information on birding in Ontario can be obtained from:

Ontario Field Ornithologists
Box 455, Stn R
Toronto, ON M4G 4E1
Website: http://www.interlog.com/!ofo

Migratory Bird Sanctuaries

Beckett Creek - 103 hectares
Chantry Island - 63 hectares
Eleanor Island - 0.6 hectares
Hanna Bay - 29,785 hectares
Mississippi Lake - 430 hectares
Moose River - 1,457 hectares
Pinafore Park - 430 hectares
Rideau - 800 hectares
St. Joseph's Island - 940 hectares
Upper Canada - 2,663 hectares

National Wildlife Areas

Big Creek - 773 hectares
Long Point - 3,250 hectares
Mohawk Island - 2 hectares
Prince Edward Point - 246 hectares
Scotch Bonnet Island - 0.8 hectares
St. Clair - 40 hectares
Wellers Bay - 40 hectares
Wye Marsh - 47 hectares

For more information, contact:
Canadian Wildlife Service
Box 490, Lambeth Station
London, ON N6P 1R1
Telephone (519) 472-6695

Provincial Tree:
Eastern White Pine

Ontario

National Parks

Bruce Peninsula National Park
Fathom Five National Marine Park
Box 189, Tobermory, ON N0H 2R0
Telephone (519) 596-2233

Georgian Bay Islands National Park
Box 28, Honey Harbour, ON P0E 1E0
Telephone (705) 756-2415

Point Pelee National Park
1118 Point Pelee Dr, R R # 1
Leamington, ON N8H 3V4
Telephone (519) 322-2365

Floral Emblem:
White Trillium

Pukaskwa National Park
Heron Bay, ON P0T 1R0
Telephone (807) 229-0801

St. Lawrence Islands National Park
2 County Road 5, RR # 3
Mallorytown, ON K0E 1R0
Telephone (613) 923-5261

For information on Provincial Parks in Ontario, check the following website:

http://www.ontarioparks.com/

Provincial Flag

Quebec

Provincial Bird: Snowy Owl

National Wildlife Areas

Baie de L'Isle Verte - 450 hectares
Cap Tourmente - 2,230 hectares
Iles de Contrecoeur - 22 hectares
Iles de l'estuaire - 72 hectares
Lac Saint Francois - 1,347 hectares
Pointe au Pere - 20 hectares
Pointe de l'Est - 684 hectares

For more information, contact:
Canadian Wildlife Service
1141 route de l'Eglise
CP 10 100
Sainte Foy, QC G1V 4H5
Telephone (418) 648-7225

Provincial Tree: Yellow Birch

Migratory Bird Sanctuaries

Baie des Loups - 4,000 hectares
Betchouane - 460 hectares
Bird Rocks - 600 hectares
Boatswain Bay - 17,900 hectares
Bonaventure Island - 1,340 hectares
Brador Bay - 500 hectares
Cap Saint Ignace - 130 hectares
Carillon Island - 500 hectares
Corossol Island - 7 hectares
Ile a la Brume - 4,450 hectares
Ile aux Basques - 1,000 hectares
Ile aux Fraises - 200 hectares
Ile aux Herons - 600 hectares
Ile Blance - 200 hectares
Ile Sainte Marie - 4,500 hectares
Ile Saint Ours - 300 hectares
Iles de la Paix - 1,100 hectares
Iles du Pot a l'eau-de-vie - 10 hectares
Iles Pelerins - 4 hectares
Kamouraska Islands - 37 hectares
L'Islet - 60 hectares
L'Isle Verte - 300 hectares
Montmagney - 160 hectares
Mont Saint Hilaire - 950 hectares
Nicolet - 2,850 hectares
Phillipsburg - 550 hectares
Saint Augustin - 5,530 hectares
Saint Omer - 60 hectares
Saint Vallier - 400 hectares
Senneville - 300 hectares
Trois Saumons - 200 hectares
Watshishou - 11,200 hectares

For more information, contact:
Canadian Wildlife Service
1141 route de l'Eglise
CP 10 100
Sainte Foy, QC G1V 4H5
Telephone (418) 648-7225

Quebec

National Parks

Forillon National Park
122 Gaspe Boulevard
Gaspe, QC G4X 1A9
Telephone (418) 368-5505

Floral Emblem:
White Garden Lily

La Mauricie National Park
Box 758
Shawinigan, QC G9N 6V9
Telephone (819) 538-3232

Mingan Archipelago
Box 1180
Havre-Saint-Pierre, QC G0G 1P0
Telephone (418) 538-3285

Saguenay-St Lawrence Marine Park
Box 220
Tadoussac, QC G0T 2A0
Telephone (418) 235-4703

For information on Provincial Parks in Quebec, check the following website:

http://www.sepaq.com/en/

Quebec Web Links

Birds of Quebec
http://www.ntic.qc.ca/~nellus/quebangl.html

Quebec Society for the Protection of Birds
http://www.minet.ca/~pqspb

Provincial Flag

New Brunswick

Provincial Bird:
Black-capped Chickadee

Lists of natural history clubs around the province can be obtained from:

New Brunswick Federation of Naturalists
277 Douglas Avenue
Saint John, NB E2K 1E5
Website: http://www3.nbnet.nb.ca/maryspt/NBFN.html

National Parks

Fundy National Park
Box 1001
Alma, NB E4H 1B4
Telephone (506) 887-6000

Kouchibouguac National Park
186, Route 117
Kouchibouguac National Park, NB E4X 2P1
Telephone (506) 876-2443

Provincial Tree:
Balsam Fir

Migratory Bird Sanctuaries

Grand Manan - 250 hectares
Machias Seal Island - 10 hectares

National Wildlife Areas

Cape Jourimain - 589 hectares
Portage Island - 439 hectares
Portobello Creek - 1,970 hectares
Shepody - 979 hectares
Tintamarre - 1,990 hectares

For more information, contact:
Canadian Wildlife Service
Box 1590
Sackville, NB E0A 3C0
Telephone (506) 364-5044

Floral Emblem:
Purple Violet

Provincial Flag

Nova Scotia

Provincial Bird: Osprey

More information on birding and natural areas in Nova Scotia can be obtained from:

Nova Scotia Bird Society
1747 Summer Street
Halifax, NS B3H 3A6
Website: http://www.chebucto.ns.ca/Recreation/NS-BirdSoc

National Parks

Cape Breton Highlands National Park
Ingonish Beach, NS B0C 1L0
Telephone (902) 224-3403

Kejimkujik National Park
Box 236
Maitland Bridge, NS B0T 1B0
Telephone (902) 682-2772

Provincial Tree: Red Cedar

Migratory Bird Sanctuaries

Amherst Point - 433 hectares
Big Glace Bay Lake - 240 hectares
Haley Lake - 100 hectares
Kentville - 200 hectares
Port Herbert - 350 hectares
Port Joli - 280 hectares
Sable Island - 2,350 hectares
Sable River - 260 hectares

National Wildlife Areas

Boot Island - 144 hectares
Chignecto - 1,020 hectares
Sea Wolf Island - 54 hectares
Sand Pond - 521 hectares
Wallace Bay - 585 hectares

For more information, contact:
Canadian Wildlife Service
Box 1590
Sackville, NB E0A 3C0
Telephone (506) 364-5044

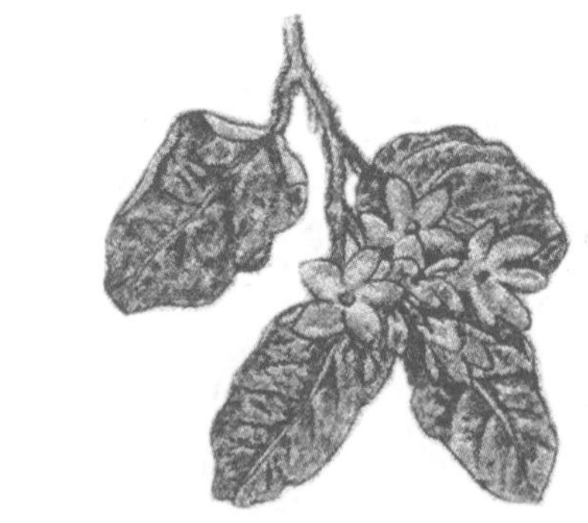

Floral Emblem: Trailing Arbutus

Provincial Flag

Prince Edward Island

Provincial Bird: Blue Jay

Migratory Bird Sanctuaries

Black Pond - 130 hectares

National Wildlife Areas

None

For more information, contact:
Canadian Wildlife Service
Box 1590
Sackville, NB E0A 3C0
Telephone (506) 364-5044

For information on birding in Prince Edward Island, contact:

Natural History Society of PEI
Box 2346
Charlottetown, PEI C1A 8C1

Floral Emblem: Lady's Slipper

National Parks

Prince Edward Island National Park
2 Palmers Lane
Charlottetown, PEI C1A 5V6
Telephone (902) 672-6350

For information on Provincial Parks in PEI, check the following website:

http://www.gov.pe.ca/visitorsguide/explore/parks/index.php3

Provincial Tree: Red Oak

Provincial Flag

Newfoundland

Provincial Bird: Common Puffin

For information on birding in Newfoundland and Labrador, contact:

Natural History Society of Newfoundland and Labrador
Box 1013
St. John's, NF A1C 5M3
Website: http://www.nhs.nf.ca

National Parks

Gros Morne National Park
Box 130
Rocky Harbour, NF A0K 4N0
Telephone (709) 458-2417

Terra Nova National Park
Glovertown, NF A0G 2L0
Telephone (709) 533-2801

Migratory Bird Sanctuaries

Ile aux Canes - 150 hectares
Shepherd Island - 16 hectares
Terra Nova - 870 hectares

National Wildlife Areas

None

For more information, contact:
Canadian Wildlife Service
Box 1590
Sackville, NB E0A 3C0
Telephone (506) 364-5044

Floral Emblem: Pitcher Plant

For information on Provincial Parks in Newfoundland, check the following website:

http://www.gov.nf.ca/Parks%26Reserves/provparks.htm

Provincial Tree: Black Spruce

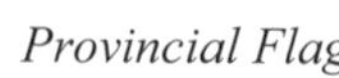

Provincial Flag

Yukon

Territorial Bird: Raven

Migratory Bird Sanctuaries

None

National Wildlife Areas

Nisutlin River Delta - 5,275 hectares

For more information, contact:
Canadian Wildlife Service
Box 340
Delta, BC V4K 3Y3
Telephone (604) 946-8546

For information on birding in the Yukon, contact:

Yukon Bird Club
Box 31054
Whitehorse, YK Y1A 5P7
Webpage: http://www.yukonweb.com/community/ybc

Floral Emblem: Fireweed

National Parks

Ivvaik National Park
Box 1840
Inuvik, NWT X0E 0T)
Telephone (867) 777-3248

Kluane National Park and Reserve
Box 5495
Haines Junction, YK Y0B 1L0
Telephone (867) 634-7250

Vuntut National Park
Box 19
Old Crow, YK Y0B 1N0
Telephone (867) 966-3622

For information on Yukon Territorial Parks, visit the following website:

http://www.yukonweb.com/notebook/tparks.html

Territorial Flag

Northwest Territories

Territorial Bird: Gyrfalcon

Migratory Bird Sanctuaries

Anderson River Delta - 108,300 hectares
Banks Island - 2,066,000 hectares
Cape Perry - 300 hectares
Kendall Island - 6,600 hectares

National Wildlife Areas

None

For more information, contact:
Canadian Wildlife Service
2nd Floor, 4999 - 98 Ave
Edmonton, AB T6B 2X4
Telephone (780) 468-8919

National Parks

Aulavik National Park
Box 29
Sachs Harbour, NWT X0E 0Z0
Telephone (867) 690-3904

Tuktut Nogait National Park
General Delivery
Paulatuk, NWT X0E 1N0

Nahanni National Park
Box 348
Fort Simpson, NWT X0E 0N0
Telephone (867) 695-3151

Wood Buffalo National Park
Box 750
Fort Smith, NWT X0E 0P0
Telephone (867) 872-7900

Floral Emblem: Mountain Avens

For information on Provincial Parks in the Northwest Territories, check the following website:

http://www.gov.nt.ca/RWED/pt/index.htm

Territorial Fish: Arctic Grayling

Territorial Tree: Jack Pine

Territorial Flag

Nunavut

On April 1, 1999, the Canadian north was split into two territories, with Nunavut taking the eastern part of the Northwest Territories. At the time of this writing, the government of Nunavut had yet to decide upon their territorial symbols.

National Parks

Auyuittuq National Park
Box 353
Pangnirtung, NT X0A 0R0
Telephone (867) 473-8828

Quttinirpaaq (Ellesmere Island) National Park
Box 353
Pangnirtung, NT X0A 0R0
Telephone (867) 473-8828

Sirmilik National Park
Box 353
Pangnirtung, NT X0A 0R0
Telephone (867) 473-8828

Migratory Bird Sanctuaries

Akimiski Island - 336,700 hectares
Bylot Island - 1,087,800 hectares
Cape Dorset - 25,900 hectares
Dewey Soper - 81,600 hectares
East Bay - 11,600 hectares
Harry Gibbons - 148,900 hectares
McConnell River - 32,900 hectares
Prince Leopold Island - 50,400 hectares
Queen Maud Gulf - 6,278,200 hectares
Seymour Island - 800 hectares

National Wildlife Areas

Nirjutiqavvik - 178,000 hectares
Polar Bear Pass - 262,400 hectares

For more information, contact:
Canadian Wildlife Service
2nd Floor, 4999 - 98 Ave
Edmonton, AB T6B 2X4
Telephone (780) 468-8919

For information on the territorial parks of Nunavut, check the following website:

http://www.nunatour.nt.ca/parks.html

Territorial Flag

Glossary

Allopreening	preening of the feathers of one bird by another
Altricial	chicks that are blind and helpless at birth
Anting	term for birds putting ants among their feathers to rid themselves of parasites
Aquatic	living or growing in water
Arboreal	tree-dwelling
Brood (s)	parent sitting on young birds to keep them warm and protected after they hatch
Brood parasite	a bird which lays its eggs in the nest of other species
Brood patch	an area on the stomach where the down feathers drop off and resulting bare patch becomes swollen and richly supplied with blood vessels, which warm the incubating eggs
Brooded	parents providing warmth and shelter to their chicks after they have left the nest
Cache (s)	a hidden store or hiding place
Cached	food that has been hidden for future consumption
Caching	the act of moving food to a hiding place
Carnivorous	a diet consisting exclusively of animal flesh
Circumpolar	the Arctic area of North America and Asia
Clutch (es)	total number of eggs laid for a single nesting
Conical	shaped like a cone; rising from a circular base and tapering to a point
Court (s)	males trying to win or attract a female
Courtship	behaviour carried out to attract a female for breeding
Crop	a thin walled extension of the esophagus used to store food
Decurved bills	bills that are slightly curved downwards
Delayed incubation	a process that doesn't start until all or nearly all the eggs have been laid
Depth perception	the ability to judge how deep or far away an object is
Diurnal	active during the day
Doldrums	region of light winds and calm areas around the equator
Downcurved bill	bills curved downwards
Drumming	sounds made by wings or bills that resemble the rolling notes of a drum
Dump nester (s)	birds that lay their eggs in the nests of other birds
Echolocation	detection of an object by means of reflected sound
Eclipse moult	process where all flight feathers are lost at once, leaving the bird unable to fly
Extirpated	no longer found in a particular area
Feather barbs	webs alongside the main feather shaft which overlap and interlock
Feather comb	toothed middle claw used for scratching and removing parasites
Fledge (ed)	time when young birds leave the nest and still depend on their parents for food
Fledglings	young birds that have just left the nest
Flight feathers	main wing feathers or stiff tail feathers used when steering in flight
Gape (s)	to open the mouth wide
Gaping	the act of opening the mouth wide, usually to catch insects in flight

Garrulous	talkative, prattling
Gizzard (s)	muscular part of the stomach where food is broken into smaller particles before digesting
Gregarious	living in groups with a social organization
Grit	course sand or pebbles swallowed to help grind up food
Gular pouch	large distensible pouch below the lower mandible, used in catching and storing fish
Hibernate (tion)	strategy for surviving winter temperatures by reducing the metabolic rate to a minimum, entering a deep sleep, and surviving on stored food
Holarctic	the circumpolar, bio-geographic region comprised of North America, Europe and Asia
Hypothermia	when the body temperature drops below normal
Imprint	a form of learning that only occurs early in an animal's life
Incubate (s) (ed)	to provide warmth and protection to eggs by sitting on them until they hatch
Incubating (tion)	the action of a parent bird sitting on its eggs and applying body heat
Incubators	birds who are sitting on egg clutches
Invertebrates	animals with no backbone
Mandible (s)	upper and lower parts of the bill
Migrant, migrators	birds that migrate to different geographical areas
Migrate (ed)	to move from one geographical area to another
Migrating (tions)	the act of moving from one place to another, usually twice a year
Migratory	species that make periodic journeys from one area to another
Monogamous	mating of a male with only one female
Moult	the periodic shedding of feathers; the process by which feathers are renewed
New World	North, Central and South America
Nictitating membrane	a membrane attached to the corner of eye, providing additional protection
Nocturnal	active at night
Offal	parts cut out in preparing a carcass, i.e.. cleaning of fish
Old World	Europe, Asia, Africa
Omnivorous	a diet of plants and animals
Parasitic	dependent on others for growth or living
Parasitize (s)	behaviour of a parasite; animals living on, in or using of another for support
Pectoral muscles	large muscles of the chest
Pellets	small, compacted balls of indigestible animal matter
Peripheral vision	the ability to see to the side without moving the head
Plumage (s)	feathers on a bird
Plume trade	commercial trade in feathers once used to make hats, pillows, mattresses etc
Polygamous	mating of male with several females
Powder down	feathers that appear as a powdery substance which produce a fine, waxy powder
Precocial	chicks born with their eyes open and able to stand and walk immediately

Preen gland	gland located near the tail which secretes an oily substance
Preening	grooming behaviour performed by the cleaning and oiling of feathers
Primary feathers	outer flight feathers on the wing
Rapacious	greedy or grasping; subsisting on prey taken by violence
Regurgitate (ed)	to cast up incompletely or partially digested food to be re-ingested
Regurgitation	the act of casting up partially digested food
Rictal bristles	stiff, modified feathers which aid the capture of insects in flight
Salt-excreting	glands in the nostrils which get rid of excess salt to prevent dehydration
Scimitars	short, curved swords which are broadest at the pointed end
Secondary feathers	inner flight feathers located on the trailing edge of the wing
Temperate	geographical areas with moderate temperatures
Terrestrial	ground dwelling
Territorial	pertaining to a territory; behaviour of actively patrolling and defending their home area
Territory (ies)	an area occupied by individuals or breeding pairs which is defended against intruders
Thermals	rising currents of warm air found over land masses
Tubular nostrils	paired tubes along the ridge of the bill, through which air is carried back to the nostrils and then to the lungs
Upcurved bills	bills are bent slightly upwards

Resources Used

Alderton, David - Nature Facts, 1992, Bramley Books, 108 p

Attenborough, Sir David - Life of Birds, 1998, BBC Books, 320 p

Bateman, Graham Editor - All the World's Animals: Songbirds, 1985, Torstar Books, 160 p

Day, David - Encyclopedia of Vanished Species, 1989, Mclaren Publishing Hong Kong, 288 p
Discovery Connection - Birds: An Explore Your World Handbook, 1999, Discovery Communications, 192 p

Godfrey, W. Earl - The Birds of Canada, 1986, National Museum of Natural Sciences, 595 p

Martin, Laura C - The Folklore of Birds, 1993, 280 p

McGillvray, Bruce & Semenchuk, Glen - Field Guide to Alberta Birds, 1998, Federation of Alberta Naturalists, 350 p

National Geographic Society - Field Guide to Birds of North America, 1999, National Geographic Society, 480 p

Perrins, Dr. C & Harrison, Dr. C.J.O - Birds of North America: Their Life, Their Ways, 1979, Reader's Digest Books, 416 p

Peterson, Roger Tory - Field Guide to Eastern Birds, 1990, Houghton Mifflin Company, 384 p

Peterson, Roger Tory - Field Guide to Western Birds, 1990, Houghton Mifflin Company, 432 p

Robbins, Chandler S. - Golden Field Guide to Birds of North America, 1983, Golden Press, 360 p

Savage, Candice - The Wonder of Canadian Birds, 1985, Western Producer Prairie Books, 211 p

Smith, Susan M. - The Black –capped Chickadee: Behaviour, Ecology and Natural History, 1991, Cornell University Press, 304 p

Stokes, Donald & Lillian - Guide to Bird Behaviour, Vol I 1983, Vol III 1989, Little, Brown & Company, 397 p

Stokes, Donald & Lillian - Field Guide to Birds of North America, 1996, Little, Brown & Company, 519 p

Terres, John K - Encyclopedia of North American Birds, 1991, Audubon Society Press: 1109 p

Weidensaul, Scott - North American Birds of Prey, 1989, W.H. Smith Publishers, 96 p

Index

-D-

-E-

-H-

-I-

-J-

-K-

-L-

-M-

-N-

-O-

-P-

-Q-

-R-

-S-

-T-

-V-

-W-

-Y-